ENGLISH TOPOGRAPHIC TERMS
IN FLORIDA

ENGLISH TOPOGRAPHIC TERMS

IN FLORIDA

1563-1874

BY

Edwin Wallace McMullen, (Jr.)

Here is the old land of America
And in this sea-girt nook, the infant steps
First foot-prints of that Genius giant-grown
That daunts the nations with his power today.
  —RALPH WALDO EMERSON

UNIVERSITY OF FLORIDA PRESS
Gainesville
1953

To the Memory of My Father

ACKNOWLEDGMENTS

I AM INDEBTED TO THE LATE PROFESSOR HARRY MORGAN AYRES FOR having suggested this subject to me, and also for reading part of the text and making invaluable recommendations regarding the project as a whole. Among the great number of friendly people who have taken an interest in this undertaking from its inception and supplied me with many bibliographical leads, I wish to thank especially Professor A. J. Hanna, of Rollins College; Professor Norman E. Eliason, of the University of North Carolina; Dean H. E. Spivey, of the University of Kentucky; and Miss Hazel L. Bowman, formerly of the University of Florida. For their interest in my search for the origin of the term *Everglades* I am very grateful to Dr. M. M. Mathews, Dictionary Editor of the University of Chicago Press; Professor Alton C. Morris, of the University of Florida; Marjory Stoneman Douglas, author of *The Everglades: River of Grass;* and particularly Mrs. Alberta Johnson, formerly Corresponding Secretary and Librarian of the Florida Historical Society. I wish to extend my gratitude to my wife, Marian Hoper McMullen, for assisting materially in the enormous mechanical task which a work of this nature entails. For reading the text and making helpful suggestions I wish to thank Professors W. Cabell Greet and Elliott V. K. Dobbie. For his helpful counsel and many suggestions I am most grateful to Professor Allen Walker Read, under whose direction this study has been brought to a conclusion.

EDWIN WALLACE McMULLEN, JR.

CONTENTS

INTRODUCTION

I. *The Purpose of This Research*

A COMPREHENSIVE HISTORICAL TREATMENT OF AMERICAN ENGLISH MUST include a consideration of topographic terms. Within recent years linguists have begun to take notice of the topographical element in the enormous quantity of literature produced by the early European adventurers in America who wrote descriptions of the new land. Recognizing the significance of this portion of our vocabulary, the editors of the *Dictionary of American English on Historical Principles* discuss this particular group of words in each of the four volumes.[1] Moreover, in his treatise on Lewis and Clark, E. H. Criswell gives a thorough discussion of both the nature of the terrain covered by the expedition and the terms used to describe the topographic features which were observed.[2] Yet, with the exception of Dr. G. D. McJimsey's dissertation on Virginia expressions,[3] references to this class of terms have hitherto been of an incidental nature.[4] It is the purpose of this study to extend the investigation of topographical substantives initiated by Dr. McJimsey into the territory comprehended by the present confines of Florida. Also, the material for this survey is limited to books written in English pertaining to this area from 1563 to 1874, inclusive.

The results of this research are recorded in two parts; namely, an introduction and a glossary. The latter comprises the definition and illustration of each term, while the former purports to answer the following questions: What portion of the Floridian topographical vocabulary has been borrowed from the Indian, French, or Spanish

[1]Sir William A. Craigie and James R. Hulbert, editors, *A Dictionary of American English on Historical Principles* (Chicago: University of Chicago Press, 1938-1944), "Prefatory Notes" to vols. I, pp. vii, ix, x; II, p. v; III, p. v; IV, p. v.

[2]E. H. Criswell, *Lewis and Clark: Linguistic Pioneers*, University of Missouri Studies, XV, No. 2 (Columbia, Mo., April, 1940), pp. xli-xlv.

[3]George D. McJimsey, *Topographic Terms in Virginia*, in *American Speech* Reprints and Monographs, No. 3 (New York: Columbia University Press, 1940).

[4]Such as the remarks found in H. L. Mencken, *The American Language*, fourth edition, revised (New York: Alfred A. Knopf, 1937), p. 115; *idem, Supplement II* (New York: Knopf, 1948), pp. 573-74; and G. H. McKnight, *English Words and Their Background* (New York: D. Appleton Co., 1923), p. 27.

inhabitants of the state? What British dialectal forms have been preserved in the topographic literature of this area? Which topographic terms now obsolete in British speech were in use in Florida prior to 1875? What changes in meaning occurred in the transplanting of such words from England? Which terms included in this study can be classified as Americanisms, Southernisms, or Floridian localisms? How were the new terms formed? Finally, what significant facts come to light when Floridian topographic terms are analyzed on the basis of related features?

II. *Definition of the Problem*

In order to restrict the scope of inquiry, it was necessary to modify Dr. McJimsey's definition of a topographic term as "merely a word or phrase applied to a group of topographic features which possess essentially the same characteristics" (*op. cit.*, p. 3). The present work is limited to the study of words applied to those topographical features which exist in their purely natural state, as contrasted with the alterations artificially produced by man. The redefinition, then, is as follows: A topographic term is an expression which designates a natural characteristic or feature of the surface of the earth. Thus, such a term as *old field*, which refers to an area apparently at one time cultivated and later abandoned by the Indians, has been excluded (in this connection, consider terms like *old land, old town*); but a word like *bridge*, in the sense of a natural limestone formation over a subterranean stream, has been accepted as a logical member of this body of terms. A further reduction of the problem would be to subdivide all (natural) topographic terms into those which denote either (1) a visible object having a characteristic shape (*e.g., hill, sink*), or (2) an area or place which is distinguished in some way from the surrounding terrain—usually by the type of soil or growth (such as *sand hill* or *palm hammock*).

One method of defining a problem is to discuss what has been eliminated; therefore, certain groups of topographic terms which have not been included in this work will be taken up here. In the first place, the more concrete and specific terms have been utilized, to the almost total exclusion of the general. For example, it has been felt that such expressions as *district, environs, part, quarter, region, territory, vicinage,* and *vicinity* belong more properly in a study of words having a broad inter-pretation. A similar vagueness accounts for the discarding of *border, boundary, edge, end, frontier, margin, verge, elevation, eminence, height, top, hunting ground, stamping ground,* and *stamping place.* Features which are temporary, such as *ebb tide, flood, flood tide, fresh, freshet, tide, high tide, low tide, high water, low water, high-water mark, low-water mark, inundation, surf* (line of foamy water caused by breaking of the sea), *swell* (rising of a river), and *wave* fall within the same rough category.

Another group of indefinite terms which have been omitted are the collocations formed with *-side,* such as *bankside, bayside, branch side, creekside, hillside, marsh side, meadow side, pond side, riverside, run side, seaside, South Side, swamp side,* and *waterside.* Expressions relat-ing to either land as property or residence, or the cultivation of land, have also been left out: namely, *cleared ground, cleared land, dividend, improvement, lot, plot, seat, settlement, common, ungranted land, field, new ground,* and *new land.*

The following terms constitute another class which are often given a topographical interpretation, but which have not been included be-cause they are seldom used without a qualifying phrase: *angle* (of island), *back* (of tract), *base* (of hill), *belt* (of land), *body* (of land or water), *bottom* (inmost part of bay), *bottom* (of hill), *brim* (of Everglades), *brow* (of hill), *clump* (of trees), *cluster* (of trees), *crest* (of hill), *curve* (of lake), *dip* (of rock), *doubling* (of river), *entrance* (of gulf or river), *entry* (into lake), *flow* (of river), *foot* (of hill), *line* (of trees), *nest* (of sand hills), *network* (of islands), *orifice* (of sink-ing river), *outcropping* (of limestone), *outline* (of coast), *patch* (of swamp, grass, or coral rocks), *path* (of stream), *piece* (of land), *piece* (of water), *range* (of country, hills, etc.), *recess* (of stream), *rib* (of thickets), *rim* (of pines and palmettos), *sheet* (of water), *skirt* (of hammock, island, land, or woods), *slip* (of land), *spot* (of land), *strip* (of land), *thread* (of water), *top* (of hill or ridge), and *train* (of islands).

Since *acclivity, affluent, ascent, confluence, conflux, declivity, defile, descent,* and *flexure* belong on a more formal level, they, too, have not been included in this study. Certain other terms given a topographical application by Florida authors but which have been rejected as too technical or literary—i.e., too far removed from the folk speech—are as follows: *aisle* (of river), *alluvion, alluvium, aperture, artery* (river), *batture* (water), *communication, connection, contraction* (of channel), *disemboguement, disemboguing, embankment, embouchure, embranchment, issue* (of water), *juncture, ocean* (of vegetation), *tunnel* (of foliage), and *vortex.*

Even though this work does not involve topographical adjectives, it may be well to call attention to the modifying elements in the following: *barren country, barren lands, bluff river* ("We found the river bluff on this shore, but apparently low on the other"—1823 STCS 30),[5] *coastwise rivers, fallow country, fenny pond, fordable stream, Forked Creek, glady land, glady pond, hilly country, hilly lands, inland lakes* (inland bays, lakes, and waters), *marshy land, pondy country, scrubby land, thickety branches, wooded land, wooded point,* and *woody ground.* Also, topographical characteristics are indicated in *piney ground, Piny Point, reedy ground, reedy swamp, Sandy Key, sandy land, Sandy-point, shoal bar, shoal water,* and *Stony River;* but in each case it was felt that the first component was merely adjectival.

Furthermore, certain verbs are used to depict activities ascribed to topographic features; *e.g., bend*—and the common phrases, *assume a bend, make a bend,* or *take a bend—, branch out, disembogue, drain, engulph, meander, peninsulate* (the hill "is nearly peninsulated by a marsh"—1821 F 74), *shoal,* and the phrase *takes its rise.*

III. *Brief Résumé of Geographical and Geological Facts Pertaining to Florida*

Florida, the most southerly state of the United States, is bordered on the north by Alabama and Georgia, on the east by the Atlantic Ocean, on the south by the Straits of Florida, which separate it from Cuba, and by the Gulf of Mexico, and on the west by the Gulf and by Alabama. The state has the longest coastline of any in the Union, consisting of 472 miles on the Atlantic and 674 miles on the Gulf coast. Actually, the tidal shore line—including the Ten Thousand Islands, and all bays, estuaries, and other tidal reaches—extends 3,751 statute miles from the northern boundary on the Atlantic to the western boundary on the Gulf.[6] The total area of the state is 58,560 square miles, of which 4,298 are water surface.[7]

Although the average elevation above sea level is lower than that of any other state except Louisiana, the terrain of Florida is not so monotonous as might be expected. Geographically, the state may be divided into four sections: (1) the east-coast region, which borders the Atlantic and extends from Fernandina to Key West; (2) the lake or central-ridge district; (3) the west-coast area; and (4) the panhandle of west Florida. The east coast is a part of the Atlantic coastal plain. Inland from the coast, a triangular area of pine and palmetto flatwoods reaches from the Georgia border to a point between the Everglades and the Atlantic on the southern tip of the peninsula. The western coastline is less regular than the eastern, being indented by a number of bays and harbors, the largest of which are Charlotte Harbor, Tampa Bay and Pensacola Bay. Much of the west coast and almost all of the east coast are separated from the sea by a line of sand reefs and narrow islands which enclose shallow and narrow bodies of water—such as Indian River and Lake Worth—called rivers, lakes, lagoons, bays, and harbors. The Ten Thousand Islands, which are located along the lower Gulf coast, form a group of mangrove-covered islets divided, and often submerged, by rapid tidal channels as yet uncharted. The northwestern portion of the state is topographically similar to southeastern Alabama, being a rolling, hilly country stretching along the northern shore of the Gulf.

The central ridge extends north and south and forms a divide which separates the streams of the east coast from those of the west. The highest elevation of this plateau above sea level is about 300 feet. The central region is remarkable for its large number of lakes, there being approximately 30,000 between Gainesville and Lake Okeechobee. These lakes consist largely of sink holes or depressions caused by solution of the limestone element in the soil. Many of the lakes are connected by subterranean channels, and a change in the surface of one lake is often accompanied by a change in the surface of another. Lake Okeechobee, 720 square miles in area, is, according to the Federal Writers' Project (op. cit., p. 11), "the second largest body of fresh

[6]Federal Writers' Project of the Works Progress Administration for the State of Florida, *Florida: A Guide to the Southernmost State* (New York: Oxford University Press, 1939), p. 10.
[7]*Encyclopaedia Britannica* (Chicago: Encyclopaedia Brittanica, Inc., 1946).

water lying wholly within the United States." North of Lake Okee-chobee are the Kissimmee Prairies, which comprise the largest cattle ranges in the state.

The chief feature of the southern portion of the state is the Ever-glades, which until 1842 was an unexplored, mysterious region known only to the Seminole Indian. The 'Glades is an extremely level expanse of country, approximately 2,860,000 acres in area, where the natural drainage is so poor that water stands on the surface the greater part of the year. According to geologists, this enormous basin—which is now mostly covered with tall grasses and sedges, the most common being a tawny saw grass—was once an open sea. As is stated in the Federal Writers' Project volume on Florida (*op. cit.*, p. 15) the peninsula "ex-tended at one time only to the lower rim of Lake Okeechobee, but far to the south of that point another formation emerged from the up-building of live coral on submerged oolitic rock. Gradually wind and waves rolled up barriers along the Atlantic and Gulf coasts, extending the peninsula toward the coral reefs and eventually forming dunes that shut out the sea. The enclosed area, rank with marine plant-life, became a fresh-water basin, and its decaying vegetation through the centuries turned into the peatlands that now comprise the Everglades."

Within the state there are many swamps, the largest of which are the Big Cypress Swamp, adjoining the Everglades on the west, and the Okefenokee Swamp, extending from Georgia into the northeastern part of Florida.

Most of Florida has a foundation of limestone, and where the crust is broken sinks or potholes from one to hundreds of acres in size occur. Many lakes, surface streams, and the tremendous Florida springs can be explained as breaks in the limestone. Underground watercourses frequently cause the earth's surface to cave in, exposing streams such as the one at Falmouth Spring, the Santa Fe and Alapaha rivers, and Bear Creek, which disappear only to reappear miles beyond. The springs often feed into lakes, and lake systems in turn become the sources of rivers, Lake George being the principal source of the St. Johns, and Lake Kissimmee of the Kissimmee.

According to G. T. Rude, of the United States Coast and Geodetic Survey, there is an oceanic spring nine miles southeast of St. Augustine, about two and one-quarter miles off the coast.[8] This spring has a swirl

---

[8]Gilbert Thomas Rude, "St. Augustine and Its Oceanic Spring," *Bulletin of the Geographical Society of Philadelphia*, XXIII (July, 1925), 85-91.

visible a mile away and so powerful that a boat is thrown out of it. In choppy weather there is a very noticeable "slick" (an oily surface on the sea) and the ocean breakers roll back from it as from a shoal or reef. The odor of the water at this place, which under certain conditions can be detected two miles away, resembles that of the sulphur springs of Florida. As the author of the report[9] quoted by Mr. Rude comments, "The ocean bed in the vicinity of the spring is comparatively level and about 55 [sic] deep, composed of fine gray sand. The spring emerges from a hole only about 25 feet in diameter and 125 feet deep, or 69 feet below the bed.... To the northeast of the center of this spring, the hole is enlarged to a diameter of about 300 feet...."[10]

With regard to the geological history of the state, the WPA guidebook (op. cit., p. 14) observes: "The far-reaching Floridian Plateau includes not only the State but an even greater surrounding area that lies less than fifty fathoms beneath the Atlantic Ocean and the Gulf of Mexico. Primarily an offspring of the sea and bearing the marks of its marine parentage, the plateau was built up largely during the most recent of the five geologic eras; it is the youngest part of the United States, a land infant but 45,000,000 years old."

Growing coral reefs, found nowhere else in the United States, lie in clear shallow waters for two hundred miles along the southern tip of the peninsula. However, the peninsula itself is not a great coral reef; actually, less than one per cent of its structure is coral.

There are seven principal types of land in Florida which support vegetation, namely, the flatwoods, scrublands, swamps, savannas, salt marshes, hammocks or hardwood forests, and high pinelands. The five most common trees in the state are (the half dozen varieties of) oak, pine, cypress, palm, and mangrove. Northern Florida has the longleaf and other pines, cypresses, magnolias, bays, gums, and oaks. But much of the native vegetation of southern Florida (which is below what is called the frost line) occurs nowhere else in the United States; it is there that the cypresses, mangroves (called land builders, their aerial roots collecting quantities of earth and debris), ferns, lianas, aerial plants, and decorative palms flourish.

[9]Written by Lt. A. M. Sobieralski of the U.S. Coast and Geodetic Survey.
[10]Rude, op. cit., p. 91.

IV. *The History of Florida*

Since the story of Florida embracing "four centuries under five flags" is far too complicated to be adequately dealt with here, the following remarks will be limited to those events which had some bearing on English and American literature prior to 1875. The first historical undertaking in this part of the New World to become linked with the literature of England was the 1539-1540 expedition of Fernando de Soto, the account of which was translated by Richard Hakluyt in 1609 under the title of *Virginia Richly Valued.*

However, it is with the story of the founding of St. Augustine—which is the oldest European settlement within the bounds of the original United States, preceding the successful establishment of the English at Jamestown by forty-two years—that English literary history has its first connection with the Florida region. In 1562 Jean Ribaut, with a band of French Huguenots, landed first near St. Augustine and then at the mouth of the St. Johns River, which he called the River of May. A narrative of this voyage appeared in London entitled *The VVhole and true discouerye of Terra Florida . . . Written in French by Captaine Ribauld* "And nowe newly set forthe in Englishe the xxx. of May. 1563." In 1564 René de Laudonnière, with another party of Huguenots, established Fort Caroline at the mouth of the St. Johns; but the colony did not prosper, and in 1565 Laudonnière was about to return to France when (on August 28) he was reinforced by Ribaut and approximately three hundred Frenchmen. On the same day that Ribaut landed, a Spanish expedition arrived in the Bay of St. Augustine, whose commander, Pedro Menéndez de Avilés, killed almost the entire garrison at Fort Caroline, and later executed Ribaut and his followers when they became shipwrecked near Matanzas inlet. Menéndez then founded St. Augustine and established Fort San Mateo (Fort Caroline). In the spring of 1568 Dominique de Gourgues, a friend of Ribaut, avenged the latter's death by capturing this fort and executing the Spanish garrison; however, he did not attack St. Augustine.

In 1629-1630, Charles I of England gave one of his ministers, Sir Robert Heath, a patent to the region between Albemarle Sound and the St. Johns River in Florida (lat. 36° to 31° N.).[11] Heath made no

---

[11]The present geographical limitations of Florida are 24° 30′ and 31° N., and 79° 48′ and 87° 38′ W. (*Encyclopaedia Britannica*).

use of this grant; and in 1663, Charles II of England made another proprietary grant of the Heath territory. To this area the new proprietors, the Earl of Clarendon and seven others, gave the name Carolina. In 1665, their grant was enlarged and extended south to latitude 29° N. and westward to the Pacific, so that Georgia and the northern half of the East Florida peninsula were included.

When the English colonies of the Carolinas and Georgia were founded, there was constant friction between the British and the inhabitants of Florida. In 1702 a force from South Carolina captured and burned St. Augustine but, being unable to reduce the fort, withdrew at the approach of Spanish reinforcements. In 1740 General James Edward Oglethorpe, governor of Georgia, made an unsuccessful attack upon St. Augustine.

By the treaty of Paris in 1763 Florida was ceded to England and the provinces of East Florida and West Florida were formed. The boundaries of West Florida were 31° N. (in 1767 the northern line was made 32° 28'), the Mississippi River on the west, and the Chattahoochee and Apalachicola rivers on the east. A period of prosperity now set in. Civil government was organized and immigration began. In 1769 Andrew Turnbull, an Englishman, brought over a band of about 1,500 Minorcans—said to be the largest colony ever transported in one body to British America—whom he engaged (until their desertion to St. Augustine in 1776) in the cultivation of indigo at New Smyrna. In the last three years of British occupation the government spent $580,000 on the two provinces; consequently, the people of Florida were for the most part loyal to Great Britain during the War of American Independence.

By the Treaty of Paris in 1783 Florida reverted to Spain; and, since no religious liberty was offered, many of the British inhabitants left East and West Florida. In 1795 Spain and the United States settled the northern boundary of Florida at 31° N.

Around 1812 the American government asked the Spanish authorities of East Florida to permit an American occupation of the country in order that it might not be seized by Great Britain and made a base of military operations. When this request was refused, the Americans seized Fernandina in the spring of 1812, an action later repudiated by the American government. American sympathizers attempted to organize a government at St. Marys, and a petty civil war began between the Americans, who called themselves "Patriots," and the Indians, who were encouraged by the Spanish. In 1814 British troops landed at Pensacola to begin operations against the United States. In retaliation General Andrew Jackson captured the town, but a few days later withdrew to New Orleans. The British then built a fort on the Apalachicola River (called the Negro Fort, which was destroyed by the Americans under General Clinch in 1816), and from there directed expeditions of Indians and runaway Negroes against American settlements long after the conclusion of peace in 1814. In 1818 General Jackson, believing that the Spanish were inciting the Seminole Indians to attack the Americans, again captured Pensacola. By the treaty of 1819 Spain ceded East and West Florida to the United States; the treaty was ratified in 1821 when the United States took formal possession.

Immediately after the cession of Florida to the United States, pressure was brought to remove the Seminole Indians and open the country to settlement. At first the Indians merely consented, by the Treaty of Fort Moultrie in 1823, to live within certain limits. However, bloody incidents developed as the population increased; and a new demand was made to have the Indians removed. By treaties made at Payne's Landing in 1832 and Fort Gibson in 1833 the Indian chiefs agreed to exchange their Florida lands for equal territory in the western part of the United States. Nevertheless, the efforts of the United States to enforce the treaty brought on another Seminole War (1835-1842), which resulted in the removal of all but a few hundred Seminoles whose descendants still live in southern Florida. All in all, there were three so-called Seminole Wars (1817-1818; 1835-1842; and 1855-1858). In 1858 most of the Florida Indians were moved to Indian Territory.

In 1845 Florida became a state of the American Union. On January 10, 1861, Florida seceded and joined the Confederate States of America. The important coast towns were readily captured by Union forces; but an invasion of the interior in 1864 failed, the Union forces being repulsed in a battle at Olustee on February 21, 1864.

On July 4, 1868, Florida assumed a full civil government; moreover, in the same year the State Bureau of Immigration was established. From that date to the present no serious obstacle to the spread of population and general development of the state has occurred. By 1875 the pioneer stages of Florida's history were practically at an end.

V. *Source Material*

Since the pioneering phase of the development of the state terminated approximately with 1875, this treatment has been limited to material appearing before that date. In that year one of the railway companies commissioned Sidney Lanier to write a guidebook of Florida, and the appeal to tourists was begun on a scale that has steadily increased until the present time. Therefore, it is within the literature of exploration and pioneer observation that most of the source material of this subject falls.

With the exception of one definitive manuscript—De Brahm's *History of the Three Provinces* ... (1773), a scrutiny of which was considered essential to this project—no unpublished material has been utilized. In general, magazine articles and newspapers have also been excluded, outside of the 1871-1874 series of articles printed in the *New York Sun* and bound together by the New York Public Library in one *Scrapbook*, and the more recent publication of early items in *Tequesta* and the *Florida Historical Quarterly*.

Prior to the cession to the United States in 1821—except for the British occupation (1763-1783)—topographic records in English pertaining to this area are very sketchy. Exceptions to this statement do occur, but the significant writers number only five, namely, Mark Catesby's *The Natural History of Carolina, Florida and the Bahama Islands*, the first volume of which appeared in 1731, and the second in 1743; William Bartram's *Travels through North and South Carolina, Georgia, East and West Florida*, 1791 (Bartram gathered his material around 1774, when he visited the Indian town of Cuscowilla in the Alachua region; in 1773 De Brahm lists him among the residents of East Florida as a planter and draughtsman who had left the Province; Bartram's *Travels* exerted the greatest literary influence of any of the Florida books before 1875, making a lasting impression on Coleridge); George Gauld's *Observations on the Florida Kays* [sic], *Reef and Gulf*, 1796 (the author spent nearly twenty years—1764-1781—surveying the coast and keys); the *Journal* of Andrew Ellicott, 1803, who surveyed the Florida-Georgia boundary; and Captain Hugh Young's "Topographical Memoir on East and West Florida with Itineraries ..." (published in the *Florida Historical Quarterly*), which was written early in 1818, as General Andrew Jackson wrote Secretary of War Calhoun on May 5 of that year, referring to this work. (Young set down what he could observe on the march and obtained much information from one long-time resident in the country—probably a certain William Hambly.)

With regard to the early writings in this field, no one person is so significant as Richard Hakluyt. The 1563 translation of Ribaut's first voyage preceded Hakluyt's own translation in 1587 of the Laudonnière collection of all four Huguenot voyages to Florida, but all of this material was re-published in *The Principall Navigations*, 1589, and in 1600 (Volume III). The 1569 *true declaration of the troublesome voyadge of M. John Haukins to the west Indies* and the 1589 *Summarie and True Discorse of Sir Frances Drakes West Indian Voage* (begun by Walter Bigges)—both works being written in English—were also reprinted in the *Principal Navigations*. Moreover, in 1609 Hakluyt brought out another one of his translations, this one being his version of De Soto's partial exploration of Florida entitled *Virginia Richly Valued*.

Seventeenth-century reports in English on Florida are meager in number and information. The grants of Charles I in 1629-1630 and of Charles II in 1663 provided a legal basis for further activity on the part of the English in this area. Among the publications appearing in the first part of the century are both the *Microcosmos* (1621) and the 1652 enlarged edition of the same book entitled *Cosmographie* by Peter Heylin; the (1625) *Purchas his Pilgrimes* of Samuel Purchas (who re-translated the Hakluyt rendition of Herrera's "Description of the West Indies" because the latter "contained too much of the Spanish garble"); and the *Historia Mundi: or Mercator's Atlas* of Ivdocvs Hondy, which was "Englished by W. S." and appeared in 1635—all of these works yielded a little material. A few topographic references to Florida are contained in *The World Surveyed* (1660), by Vincent Le Blanc (translated by F[rancis] B[rooke]); *A Relation of a Discovery lately made on the Coast of Florida* (1664) by William Hilton; *A Brief Description of the Province of Carolina on the Coasts of Floreda* (1666); *The Discoveries of John Lederer* (1672), by John Lederer (translated "out of Latine" by Sir William Talbot); *Carolina; or a Description of the Present State of That Country, etc.* (1682); and *The Present State of Carolina* (1682), by "R. F."

With the exception of the two volumes by Catesby which have already been mentioned, all of the early eighteenth-century works up to 1745 belong to a series of items mostly of pamphlet size pertaining to the contest between the inhabitants of Florida and the Carolinas for the intervening territory. The invasions and raids on both sides were not very successful, but the failure of the British to destroy the fort at St. Augustine produced literary articles both in defense of and in opposition to the policies of Governor Moore, who campaigned in 1702, and Governor Oglethorpe, whose first invasion occurred in 1740. To this classification belong the following: John Archdale, *A New Description of That Fertile and Pleasant Province of Carolina*, 1707; John Oldmixon's remarks on Florida in *The History of Carolina*, 1708, and *The British Empire in America*, 1708; Pat. Tailfer, *et al.*, *A True and Historical Narrative of the Colony of Georgia*, 1741; *A Geographical and Historical Description of the Principal Objects of the Present War in the West-Indies . . . and San Agustin*, 1741; *The Report of the Committee of both Houses . . . in the late expedition against St. Augustine*, 1742; *An Impartial Account of the Late Expedition against St. Augustine*, 1742; George Cadogan, *The Spanish Hireling Detected*, 1743; *A Full Reply to Lt. Cadogan's Spanish Hireling*, 1743; and Edward Kimber, *A Relation, or Journal of a Late Expedition to the Gates of St. Augustine*, 1744. Further incidental remarks given in Thomas Osborne's *A Collection of Voyages and Travels*, 1745, and Thomas Jefferys' *A Description of the Spanish Islands*, 1762, indicate the fact that England was keeping a wary eye trained on the Florida territory. According to Brinton, who wrote in 1859 (see below, pages 16-17), this same Jefferys, who was Geographer to His Majesty, edited both the 1763 volume by Roberts and the 1766 *Journal* of John Bartram.

After 1763, the writers of minor importance fall into two groups: (1) those from whom only a small amount of material could be gleaned, and (2) those whose authority or originality there is some reason to doubt. The following belong to the first category: Thomas Hutchins, *An Historical Narrative and Topographical Description of Louisiana, and West-Florida*, 1784; John Pope, *A Tour through the Southern and Western Territories of the United States . . . and the Floridas*, 1792; *Niles Weekly Register* (Volumes III, 1803, and VIII, 1815); John Melish, *A Military and Topographical Atlas of the United States; Including the British Possessions & Florida*, 1813; Captain James Barr, *A Correct and Authentic Narrative of the Indian War in Florida*, 1836; M. M. Cohen, *Notices of Florida and the Campaigns*, 1836; William Cullen Bryant, *Letters of a Traveller*, 1850; Charles Lanman, *Adventures in the Wilds of the United States*, 1856; and Ledyard Bill, *A Winter in Florida*, 1870.

Although it is not always possible to place authors definitely within the second category mentioned above, an effort has been made to distinguish the questionable writers from the thoroughly reliable. The 1763 Treaty had hardly been concluded when William Roberts, a professional writer, brought out his *Account of the First Discovery and Natural History of Florida*. This volume includes seven or eight pages of an eye-witness account by a certain Thomas Robinson, and also a geographical description by T. Jefferys. Roberts (who had never seen Florida) states that he drew upon two principal sources: (1) captured original Spanish and French charts, and (2) information supplied by navigators. Though the book contains some inaccuracies, it is nonetheless the most informative English work on Florida to appear up to 1763. Among the several writers who apparently copied from William Stork's *Description of East Florida* (first published 1769) was John H. Wynne, *A General History of the British Empire in America* (1770). Although the circumstantial evidence—such as the name of the commanding officer at Fort St. Marks—sounds convincing in the *Naufrage et Avantures de M. Pierre Viaud* (translated into English in 1771 as *The Shipwreck and Adventures of Monsieur Pierre Viaud*), some of the incidents related therein seem farfetched. For some of his comments on Florida Jedidiah Morse drew directly from Roberts (at least in the former's *Geography Made Easy*, 1784) and William Bartram (in *The American Gazetteer*, 1797). According to Brinton (mentioned above), William Darby (*Memoir on the geography and Natural and Civil History of Florida*, 1821) was an engineer from Maryland who probably never set foot in Florida. James Grant Forbes (*Sketches, Historical and Topographical, of the Floridas*, 1821) drew very freely from Romans (who wrote in 1775, and is discussed below on pages 15-16) and Stork, and possibly from the *Journal* of Ellicott (1803; even though he sometimes acknowledges his indebtedness to Romans, the total result of his efforts is spoken of by Brinton as a wretched compilation of old works. Historically the works of John T. Sprague (*The Origin, Progress, and Conclusion of the Florida War*, 1848) and George R. Fairbanks (*The History and Antiquities of the City of St. Augustine, Florida*, 1858) are very sound; but since the greater part of their material is quoted directly—in the instance of the former—from official documents such as the *American State Papers* (discussed below) or —in the instance of the latter—from early accounts such as those of Ribaut and Roberts, very little original substance remains in their volumes which is suitable for the present purpose. Both of the publications issued by the Florida Lands and Immigration Commissioners (J. S. Adams, *Florida: Its Climate, Soil, and Productions*, 1869; and Dennis Eagan, *Sixth Annual Report*, 1864) copy voluminously from Byrne's *Letters on the Climate, Soils, and Productions of Florida*, 1851 (see below, page 16).

With regard to the literature of major importance to this research, four principal collections of brief items stand out, namely, the *American State Papers* and other publications of Congress; volume two of Wilbur Henry Siebert's *Loyalists in East Florida, 1774 to 1785*, which contains the *Records of Their Claims for Losses of Property in the Province*, most of which were originally taken from the "Memorial Book. 3. 1786" of Audit Office, Loyalist Series, Volume III, in the Public Records Office in London; the *Florida Historical Quarterly;* and *Tequesta* (Journal of the Historical Association of Southern Florida). The United States governmental publications contain a vast quantity of rich material ranging from the 1663 land grant given by Charles II to the Earl of Clarendon, to the multifarious official records of claims, titles, military and naval affairs, the lengthy and complicated Indian relations, and even the secret plans for a blockade of the "basin of St. Augustine" in 1778. Practically every volume of the *Florida Historical Quarterly* yielded valuable material in the form of early letters and journals. The fifth issue of *Tequesta* included the account of the first recorded crossing of the Everglades by Preble in 1842.

The first native of America to write about Florida was John Bartram, whose *Journal* was first printed with William Stork's *Description of East Florida* in 1769. Although Bartram's notes are not organized, they are usable and invaluable. Bartram's son, William, who accompanied his father to Florida as a lad, and later returned to the region in 1773, is discussed on page 11. Stork is considered the historian of British East Florida, and his material is so accurate that numerous other writers quoted or copied from him later on.

The recognized authority for the geography of the western coast of Florida was George Gauld (already mentioned on page 11); and the corresponding expert for the eastern coast was his superior, John Gerard William De Brahm, who was Royal Surveyor General of the Southern District of North America, and whose extensive unpublished manuscript on East Florida was completed in 1773.

Another subordinate of De Brahm was Captain Bernard Romans (A

Concise Natural History of East and West Florida, 1775), whose work was very thorough. For the purposes of this study Romans is an excellent source; but it is said that his charges against Turnbull's management of the indigo plantations at New Smyrna were exaggerated.

The next two significant works are William Hayne Simmons' *Notices of East Florida,* 1822, and Charles Blacker Vignoles' *Observations Upon the Floridas,* 1823. Although the British Vignoles appears to be as accurate as any of the other early surveyors, he may have drawn occasionally upon Stork or, possibly, Romans.

In 1823 Simmons was chosen to survey the site of the capital of the newly acquired territory in conjunction with Colonel John Lee Williams, who is without doubt the most exhaustive and authoritative writer on the natural features of Florida within the scope of this study. The *Journals* of both men narrating their selection of Tallahassee remained unpublished until 1908, when they were printed in the *Florida Historical Quarterly.* The other works by Williams are *A View of West Florida* (1827) and *The Territory of Florida* (1837). Excepting the Everglades region, the author had an intimate knowledge of both East and West Florida. According to what Brinton says on page 70 of his *Notes on the Floridian Peninsula,* 1859, Williams came to Florida in 1820; and in the opinion of the former, the 1837 edition was the most complete work that had ever been published on the territory of Florida. Brinton just missed seeing Williams alive by one day; however, he says that while alive Williams had been held in very high moral esteem, and that during the bitterest of the Indian fighting he had lived within the Seminole territory without being molested. On page 71 of the *Notes* Brinton quotes a trader as saying of Williams that he was "too good for these parts." Although the works produced by Williams cannot be considered literature, yet his ability to describe with accuracy what he observed is second to none among the Floridian authors.

The best-written of the several firsthand accounts of the Second Seminole War is the anonymous *A Sketch of the Seminole War and Sketches during a Campaign,* 1836. Another work of the first rank is the *Letters on the Climate, Soils, and Productions of Florida* of Dr. Bernard M. Byrne, 1851, who served seven years in the peninsula of Florida.

The works of three authors complete the survey of important works on this subject. In his *Notes on the Floridian Peninsula* (1859) Daniel Garrison Brinton proves without doubt that he is the best literary critic among the writers on Florida before 1875; and his *Guide-Book of Florida* ... (1869) was found very useful for the present purpose. In 1871 Dr. J. M. Hawks edited *The Florida Gazetteer,* which is the first work of its kind pertaining to the state. The final significant publication consists of a series of articles printed in the *New York Sun* from 1871 to 1874, most of them written by a reporter named Ziska. The articles, which are the result of firsthand observation, depict frontier life in Florida very vividly.

VI. *Difficulties Presented by the Source Material*

The greatest single difficulty encountered in dealing with Florida records before 1875 is the paucity of indigenous literature. Some of the authors whose works are utilized in this study were American. However, the fact that apparently none of the writers was a native Floridian is undoubtedly due to the unfavorable conditions under which English-speaking people in the territory had to live; namely, the Spanish occupation, the Seminole uprisings, and the confusion of the Civil War and Reconstruction period.

Prior to 1766 all those who wrote on Florida were (1) visitors whose stay was brief, (2) translators, or (3) authors repeating what others had written. After 1766 the literary output consisted of the works of both Americans who came from other parts of the country, and British authors resident in the state before 1784. Nevertheless one compensating fact regarding the writers of British East Florida is (as Charles L. Mowat points out in the *Florida Historical Quarterly,* XX, 345) that the small community located there contained a greater number of original minds than its size or infancy entitled it to. This statement holds true especially with regard to Stork, De Brahm, Romans, the elder Bartram, and the later writers, Gauld and William Bartram, who had been associated with the locality during the British period. Thus, a good deal of the material both of that time (and after 1821) is the work of men (such as Williams) who—if they had not always lived in Florida—at least had an intimate knowledge of the physical features of the state.

While probably most of the literature written about Florida contains some information of a topographic nature, searching through much of it proved to be very unrewarding. Both the material of an incidental nature (such as Sarah Allen's *Narrative of the Shipwreck ... of Mrs. Sarah Allen ...*, 1816, or the anonymous *A Winter from Home*, 1852) and better-known works which may be excellent for other purposes (e.g., *The History of the American Indians* by James Adair, 1775) have been sampled, but found either to yield very little or to contain a high degree of repetition. Accordingly, the major effort has been concentrated on locating those writers who provided detailed descriptions of the local topography.

VII. *Analysis of Terms*

The apparently inexhaustible variety of topographic terms is impressive. Beginning with the simple forms, such as *river, swamp, channel, ridge*, and *marsh*, one finds that not only are these words given several meanings (some of them very intricate and detailed in application) but also many of the same terms frequently combine with other words to form compounds some of which in turn are complex—e.g., *backbone ridge, back-water swamp, cabbage-tree hummock, clear-water pond, fresh-water marshland, fresh-water tide-swamp, hardwood land, mangrove-swamp land, pine-barren land, river-swamp land, salt-water marsh, ship channel, sugar-cane land, tide-river swamp, tidewater channel*, and *turpentine land*. The primary reason for this multiplicity of terms is that topographic terms overlap, yet remain distinct from, expressions used in a number of allied fields, including agriculture, geology, geography, hydrography, botany, zoology, navigation, surveying, toponymy, and topography in the artificial or cultural sense (*e.g.*, a *canal* which has been artificially constructed).

Although it has been difficult to draw the line in some cases, an attempt has been made to include in the glossary only terms which specifically refer—or at least cannot be said conclusively not to refer—to those features of the Florida terrain which exist in their natural, untampered state (or did so at the time their usage was recorded). Thus, *mulatto soil* or *cane patch* more properly belong in a treatise on soils and their cultivation; while *mulatto land* or *cane swamp*, which describe a type of land previous to or regardless of cultivation, are therefore included in the present study.

McJimsey has already distinguished between place names and topographic terms (*op. cit.*, pp. 3, 25-26) on the basis of degree of spec-

ificity, to which James B. McMillan[12] adds the principle of invaria-
bility of form. Nevertheless, those place names which are topographic
possess a concrete quality lacking in many other names: *e.g.*, compare
Jacksonville with its earlier designation, *Cowford*. In this work the
present writer has included place names consisting partially or totally
of topographic elements, regardless of whether they were substantives
or substantive phrases, common or proper names.

Although it has not been possible to rule out all general terms, those
which have been retained have been utilized only in restricted or specific senses. Thus, *ground* (definite portion of the earth's surface) and
land (ground or soil) have been entered in the glossary only when
preceded by specifying terms indicating the nature of the soil. Also,
country has been included only in the sense of (1) a region associated
with a particular place or river, or (2) an unsettled district. *Continent,
ocean,* and *sea* have been strictly limited to specific references to local
areas; and *tract* has been used (in collocations) because of the frequency with which it is associated with *land*. One other term, *range*
and its compounds, has been treated in its more restricted meaning of
an area affording pasturage for cattle, rather than in the broader sense
of an extent of country.

In addition, the following words which usually appear with qualifying phrases are recognized by the DAE, OED, and NID as having
common topographic meanings and therefore have been made a part
of this survey: *arm* (of land, or sea); *bed* (of river, or rocks); *bend*
(of river, coast, or swamp); *bottom* (of sea, or river); *chops* (of channel); *cod* (of bay—inmost recess of a bay); *course* (of river); *head*
(of river, or land); *mouth* (of river, or gulf); *neck* (of land, or pond);
point (of land); *rise* (of land); *shelf* (of land, or rocks); *slope* (of
country); *source* (of river); *spit* (of land); *tongue* (of land); and
turning (of river).

With regard to the hyphenation of compounds in the glossary, the
following arbitrary system has been observed: (1) forms listed in the
DAE, OED, or NID have been followed here; (2) forms hyphenated
in the illustrated quotations have (usually) been hyphenated in the entry
headings (and in the introduction as well); and (3) compounds used
attributively have been uniformly hyphenated (in order to distinguish

[12]"Observations on American Place-name Grammar," *American Speech*, XXIV
(December, 1949), 243.

the modifying element), such as *fan-palmetto barren, fresh-water tide-swamp,* and *tide-river swamp.*

The spelling of the quoted text is usually retained whenever information is bracketed in the illustrations: *e.g.,* under the term *arm* (*of land*), the 1874 quotation begins, "[The traveller] . . . ," in which the British spelling has been preserved.

Finally, throughout the analysis which follows, certain terms believed to be mere attributive constructions rather than actual compounds have been mentioned. Except in the glossary, these terms are always labeled as attributives by the abbreviated form, "(attrib.)," which follows the term; *e.g., cape land* (attrib.). However, these forms are listed in the glossary under their first components. This entire group of terms is discussed below under "The Limitation of Topographic Terms."

(A)   Analysis on the Basis of Usage:
British English vs. American English in Florida

Despite the fact that the percentage of British sources for the literature of Florida is probably higher than that of the other Atlantic states, an analysis of these records has revealed a significant body of American peculiarities of speech. In order to illustrate American usage as opposed to British, the terms in the glossary will be discussed below in the following order: (1) Borrowings from Spanish, French, and American Indian; (2) Dialectal, Archaic, Poetic, Rare, and Obsolete Terms; (3) Terms Whose Meanings Have Been Extended; (4) Terms Whose Meanings Have Been Limited: (a) Elliptical and Nautical Terms; (b) Terms Preceded by a Qualifying Term; (c) Attributive Collocations Not Accepted as Compounds; (d) Collocations Formed with Coordinating Attributives; (5) Neologisms: (a) Americanisms; (b) Southernisms; (c) Localisms—New Compounds: New Compounds Consisting of Noun Plus Noun; New Compounds Consisting of a Noun Preceded by a Compound; New Compounds Included for Semantic Reasons; and (6) Quotations Which Antedate the DAE and the OED.

(1)   *Terms Borrowed from Spanish, French, and American Indian*

The greatest number of loan words used in Florida came from the Spanish, the earliest examples of which were mainly Spanish adaptations of Indian terms picked up through contacts with the West Indian natives. *Cay(o)*, *kay(o)*, originally a Taino (? or French) word, was still in use in Florida in 1854; but the form *key* appears as far back as 1742. The same word occurs in combination as *cedar key*, *fresh-water key*, *mangrove key*, *sand kay*, and *sand key*. *Savanna*, another Taino word, was applied by the Spaniards to the saturated flat grasslands which are sometimes thinly covered with cypress and pine trees. One writer distinguishes between the savannas of East and West Florida, characterizing the latter as open areas consisting of high ground and occasional hillocks. The *savanna* collocations are as follows: *cypress savanna*, *grass savanna*, *hammock savanna*, *pineland savanna* (attrib.), *pine savanna*, *savanna branch* (attrib.), *savanna country* (attrib.), *savanna ground* (attrib.), *savanna land*, *savanna plain* (attrib.), *savanna swamp* (attrib.), *saw-grass savanna*, and *wet savanna*. Spanish *mangle* was also taken from the Taino and later compounded with an English word to form the haplologic *mangrove*, which occurs in collocative form as *mangrove forest*, *mangrove island*, *mangrove islet*, *mangrove key*, *mangrove land*, *mangrove swamp*, and *mangrove-swamp land*. With the first Spanish explorers must have come *laguna* (fresh-water lake), which in its later form, *lagoon*, was used to denote an area of salt water separated from the sea by sand dunes; however, two additional meanings of *lagoon* (bay, inlet; shallow fresh-water pond connected with a river) appear to have developed in America. The combined forms of *lagoon* are *head lagoon* (attrib.), *lagoon bank* (attrib.), and *salt lagoon*. Although *palmetto* (occurring here as the first component of compounds), like *key*, was anticipated in English use, it may have been borrowed independently here. The DAE comments that the "spelling *palmetto* may be of American origin." The compounds formed with this term are *palmetto flat*, *palmetto ground*, *palmetto hammock*, *palmetto jungle*, *palmetto land*, *fan-palmetto barren*, *saw-palmetto flat*, and *saw-palmetto land*. There is insufficient evidence to state with certainty that *malpass* is another form of *malpais* (bad lands). According to the OED the obsolete form *indico*, in *indigo land*, may have come from the Spanish. The first element in *alligator hole* was surely imported by the first seekers of the Fountain of Youth, but was not recorded before the attributive component in *coquina land* 1837.

The only American Indian term transmitted to the Florida region through the French is *bayou*, which originally was a Choctaw word. However, a number of other direct borrowings were the result of the contacts of Florida pioneers with French settlers in the Louisiana territory; *e.g., levee, portage, rapid,* and *prairie,* which combined frequently with other terms, as in *grass prairie, morning-glory prairie, prairie country, open prairie, prairie land,* and *wet prairie.*

The Indian tongues contributed very little directly to the topographic vocabulary of Florida. The only examples in these records are the first components of *hickory hill, hickory land, ?titi thicket,*[13] and *tupelo swamp.*

(2) Dialectal, Archaic, Poetic, Rare, and Obsolete British Terms

Although there is a fair proportion of dialectal material in the Floridian topographical vocabulary occurring before the last quarter of the nineteenth century, distinguishing this element positively and accounting for its presence is very difficult. At any rate, the following terms, and attributive elements of the collocations into which some of the words enter, are claimed by the EDD as probably having their origin in the British dialects: *?Adia* (the term *Ade* is applied by navigators of the Severn to reaches where there are eddies in a river, as Swinny Ade, near Coalport); *back water* (still water in a field during a river flood), in *back-water swamp; bight, bite* (bay, projection in a river); *bottom* (low-lying land, valley, ravine; freq. in pl.), in *cane bottom, river bottom, river-bottom land, second bottom; brake* (copse, thicket; rough land covered with furze), in *canebrake, reed-brake; brink* (bank of river); *clift* (cliff), in *oyster clift; cockle* (cockleshell: fossil bivalve, or snail shell), in *cockle bank, cockle bluff; country* (particular district; region); *dale* (river valley between ranges of hills); *dell* (little dale, narrow valley); *dismal* ("low spirits," EDD), in *dismal swamp; drowned* (flooded), in *drowned land; elbow* (bend in stream); *fast* (solid, firm), in *fast ground, fast land; field* (unenclosed arable land, as opposed to pasture), in *?oakfield, plain field* (attrib.); *flag* (general term for sword grass and other waterside plants), in *flag-grass pond; flat* (smooth, level place); *fresh water* (spring water as distinguished from rain water), in *fresh-water spring; gall* (barren spot in a field, through which springs of water constantly ooze up—this sense is close

---

[13]A question mark preceding a term indicates that there is some reasonable basis for including the expression in the group under discussion, but the evidence for so doing is inconclusive.

to the Romans, 1775, definition of *bay-galls* as watercourses—also, wet, spongy land; gen. in pl.), in *bay-gall, cypress gall; gap* (opening or pass amongst hills); *ground* (rocky sea bottom; bottom of a channel); *gully* (narrow brook or stream); *gut* (narrow channel or stream); *gutter* (channel or narrow watercourse); *head* (source or spring of a river or stream), in *head branch, head spring, headstream, head-water(s); hummock* (rising ground, a hillock or mound of earth), in *hummock land; knap* (small hill, hillock); *knob* (low, roundish hill); *knoll, knowl* (small hill), in *cabbage knoll, grass knoll, pine knoll; lawn* (open space in a forest; ?obs. except in place names); *level* (a plain, open flat ground), in *pine level; low country* (low-lying districts as distinguished from hill country); *lowland* (low-lying land as opposed to hill country); *march, marish* (marsh), in *marish ground, march land; marsh* (meadow); *meadow* (low, boggy grassland), in *meadow ground, meadowland; nook* (recess); *open* (opening); *pool* (small lake); *quicksand* (sand so mixed with water as to render it fluid); *run* (small channel; stream, brook—"chiefly U.S. and *north. dial.,*" OED—quoted by DAE); *sink* (place where superabundant water stagnates in the ground); *sobbed* (wet, saturated with moisture—EDD gives "sobby land"), in *sobbed land; sour* (cold, wet, unfertile; boggy, swampy), in *sour ground, sour land; strand* (seacoast, beach, shore); *strong* (rich, not clayey), in *strong land; swale, swail* (slight dip or depression in the surface of the ground); *tank* (pond); *waste* (piece of uncultivated land); *water* (river, stream, brook; also, lake); *well* (surface spring; pond); *wild* (a weald).

Because the scope of this project does not extend beyond 1874, it is difficult to determine whether or not all the terms in the glossary are still a part of the living language in America. However, according to the DAE, OED, or NID, the following terms and forms either appear to have died out in British usage, or are classed as archaic, poetic, or rare: *bank* (seacoast, shore); *barre; beach,* in *beech* (tree) *hammock; bite; ?breaker; brink* (bank); *channel* (small stream); *coast* (river-bank; borderland; region); *continent* (as distinguished from islands and peninsulas); *cut* (inlet: prob. obs. in England); *dale; desert* (wild, uninhabited region); *field* (open land, plain); *firm land* (dry land; also, mainland, continent, as opposed to an island); *forest* (waste, wilderness); *fountain* (spring; source of stream); *fresh marsh* (fresh-water marsh); *fresh river; ground* (sea bottom); *?gulf shore; haulover* (DAE); *hill* (mountain); *hold* (ellipt. for holding ground); *ile; indico* *land* (v. *indigo land*); *knowl;* ?*lake* (pond); *main; marish* (marsh); *marish ground; medow;* (both elements of) *medowe grounde; mount* (hill); *pass* (ford, ferry—"now rare," OED); (phr.) *reef of rocks; rippling* (ripple); *river of* ("now somewhat rare," OED: last date: 1817— here, 1873); *rode* (road); *sand* (the shore); *sea-bank* (shore); *seaside; shoar; streit* (occurs once [1652]; form not recorded in OED); ?*strand* (the NID does not agree with the OED that this term is "now poet., arch. or dial."); *stream* (appended to a river name—"now only poet.," OED); *upland; well* (spring forming pool or stream); *water-stream* ("now rare," OED); *wild* ("now mostly rhet. or poet.," DAE).

(3) The Extension of Topographic Terms

The necessity of applying a term to an object whose form resembles that denoted by the original word accounts for the extension of a number of topographic nouns. For example, the term *bank* (sloping margin of a watercourse) is also used to denote the slanting ground surrounding a lake or pond, or that adjacent to a swamp; furthermore, the term is given its usual interpretation once to include both the alluvion and land between high and low water mark, and the shoals and sand-bars sometimes covered by water. Moreover, the meaning of *coast* is extended to include both the islands belonging to the coastal region and the adjacent waters. *Seacoast* is also used in the sense of *coastal waters*, and *shore* is applied to the waters along a shore. The British interpretation of *watershed* as a water parting or narrow elevated tract of ground between two drainage areas has probably been given an American extension of meaning when it is used to denote the whole gathering ground of a river system. Two additional meanings have been discovered for *ridge*, namely: (1) a sand-bar or shoal (from the sense of a line or reef of rocks), and (2) a range or chain of islands (from range of hills). Other examples of the same type of development of meaning are as follows: *bar* (dry sand-bar; also, key or island); *bay* (dilation in river); *bend* (indentation in coastline); *branch* (lagoon; bay which forms part of a larger bay); *cape* (the keys called the Martyrs; also, the shoal of a cape); *cod* (recess of bay); *course* (line or direction of chain of islands, the coast, a cave, a reef); *cove* (creek; meadowland adjoining a cove or inlet); *creek* (tributary brook); *cut* (inlet); *dam* (natural barrier temporarily closing an inlet); *gulf* (both seas on each side of the Florida peninsula); *island* (clump of trees in a prairie: extended to apply to a cypress pond); *junction* (union of a river with a bay, and a bay with the Gulf of Mexico); *lake* (expanded part of a river; creek; river); *nook* (small bay); *orchard* (wild-orange grove); *plain* (drift of vegetation; a floating island); and *prong* (bay which is an arm or branch of another bay).

(4) The Limitation of Topographic Terms

Though limitation of meaning may be achieved in a number of ways, one of the commonest methods is illustrated by collocative formations. Perhaps the largest group of compounds in the glossary is that which has as its first element some type of vegetation, such as the following:

cabbage-bluff, cabbage grove, cabbage hammock, cabbage knoll, cabbage land, cabbage pond, cabbage swamp, cabbage-tree hummock, cabbage-tree island, cabbage-tree land, cypress bog, cypress-branch, cypress gall, cypress grove, cypress hammock, cypress island, cypress pond, cypress savanna, cypress sink, cypress swamp, grass knoll, grass lake, grassland, grass marsh, grass meadow, grass plain, grass point, grass pond, grass prairie, grass savanna, live-oak grove, live-oak hammock, live-oak hummock, live-oak land, live-oak swamp, live-oak thicket, mangrove forest, mangrove island, mangrove islet, mangrove key, mangrove land, mangrove swamp, oakfield, oak grove, oak hammock, oak hill, oak-land, oak ridge, oak scrub, oak swamp, oak thicket, oak upland, oak wilderness, palmetto flat, palmetto ground, palmetto hammock, palmetto jungle, palmetto land, palmetto scrub, palmetto swamp;

and the twenty-three *pine* compounds (*q.v.*).

The most prolific of the combining forms is the term *land,* which occurs in the following compounds:

back land, bay land, bitter land, bluff land, bottom land, branch land, cabbage land, cabbage-tree land, cane land, cape land (attrib.), clear land, coastland, coquina land, cornland, cotton land, cypress-swamp land (attrib.), drowned land, farming land, fast land, firm land, flatland, forest land, fresh marshland, fresh-water marshland, grassland, grazing land, hammock land, hardwood land, headland, hickory land, high-hammock land, highland, hummock land, indigo land, intervale land, limestone land, live-oak land, lowland, mainland, mangrove land, mangrove-swamp land, marl land, marshland, meadowland, mixed land, mulatto land, oak-land, orange land, palmetto land, pasture land, peach land, pineland, pine-barren land, planting land, prairie land, red land, red-clay land, rice land, river-bottom land (attrib.), river-land, river-swamp land, rolling land, rush land, savanna land, saw-palmetto land, scrubland, sobbed land, sour land, strong land, sugar-cane land, sugar land, swamp land, tideland, timbered land, timber-land, turpentine land, upland, upland hill (attrib.), waste land, wet land, wild land, woodland.

Another general term which is restricted by attributive elements is *country:*

back country, coast country, cove country (attrib.), desert country (attrib.), farming country, grazing country, lake country, limestone country, low country, marsh country (attrib.), open country, pine country, pine-barren country (attrib.), pine-wood(s) country (attrib.), pond country (attrib.), prairie country, rolling country, savanna country (attrib.), sea-shore country (attrib.), sweet-water country, timbered country, waving country, wild country, wilderness country (attrib.).

Ground in the sense of *land* or *soil* combines to form the following:

fast ground, firm ground, grazing-ground, low ground, marsh ground, meadow ground, palmetto ground, pasture-ground (for birds), prairie ground (attrib.), rising ground, savanna ground (attrib.), scrub ground (attrib.), sour ground, summit ground (attrib.).

Another common term with a high frequency of combination is *water(s):*

back water, back-water swamp, dead water, ebb water (attrib.), eddy water, fresh water, gulf water (attrib.), headwater, lake water (attrib.), marsh water (attrib.), pond water (attrib.), river water (attrib.), salt water, salt-water marsh, salt-water river, sea-water, sweet-water country, tidewater, tidewater channel, tributary water (attrib.).

Another form of limitation, the restriction of basic sense, is illustrated in the interpretation of *divide* as a dividing ridge, *channel* (water-course) as the principal branch of a river, *field* as a *floating field* (q.v.), *head* (projecting point of rock or sand bank) as a submerged rock or reef, *interval* as a gap or opening in rocks or reef, and *garden* as a natural grove (possibly a literary use).

Some of the importations were given topographic meanings in America for the first time; *e.g., bridge* (*natural bridge—q.v.*), *forks, opening, outwatering* (place of exit of a stream into the sea), *sink hole, slide* (steep river-bank down which animals slide), and *spine* (ridge).

A number of terms in the glossary are compounds, both elements of which were created from old topographic terms. The following expressions (from which the compounds formed with *country, ground* in the sense of land or soil, *land,* and *water,* have been excluded) illustrate this type of combination:

backbone ridge, bay shore, coast-ridge, creek branch, desert island, gulf coast, gulf shore, gulf stream, hammock island, island swamp, lake country, marsh island, ocean-river, pasture range, river-bank, river bottom, river channel, river swamp, sea-bank, sea-beach, seaboard, seacoast, sea island, seaport, sea-sand hill, sea-shore, seaside, sea-water, shoal water, spring branch, spring creek, springhead, thicket-wood(s), tide-river swamp, tidewater, tidewater channel, watercourse, water run, water-stream.

The one example in these records of a portmanteau word after the manner of Lewis Carroll's *slithy* is *swammock*. This blend-word is formed by the contamination of *swamp* and *hammock*.

Another peculiarity of usage is illustrated by two possible individualisms: *seaport* (when applied to an inland river port) is listed by the DAE as perhaps an individualism; and (running) *water(s)* (*q.v.*) are classified by De Brahm (1773) in a way which appears to be arbitrary.

Other examples of limitation of meaning occur in certain compounds descriptive of typical natural features of Florida, such as:

alligator hole, bay head (swamp), coral bank, coral reef, double-land, high-hammock land, lime grove, loblolly-bay swamp, myrtle swamp, myrtle thicket, open grove, open wood(s), oyster bar, oyster reef, sand beach, sand hill, sand key, sand point, saw-palmetto land, shell beach, sulphur spring, turtle hole, wet glade, wet savanna, and wrecking ground.

(a) ELLIPTICAL AND NAUTICAL TERMS

A narrowing of meaning is also illustrated by the following elliptical terms: *barrens* (pine barrens); *bridge* (natural bridge); *cypress* (cypress swamp); *field* (floating field); *fresh lake* (fresh-water lake); *fresh marsh; fresh marshland; fresh pond; fresh river; fresh spring;*

gulf (Gulf of Florida); *hammock* (hammock land); *high hammock* (high-hammock land); *hold* (holding ground); *interval* (interval land); *island* (floating island); *main* (mainland); *out shore* (outside shore); *prairie* (prairie land); *stream* (Gulf Stream: called the Stream, the stream of the Gulf of Florida, or the Florida stream); and *Swamp* (swamp land).

The only nautical terms in the glossary are *cod* (recess of bay), *double land, ground* (sea bottom), *middle ground* (sea bottom), and *rip-rap.*

(b)   TERMS PRECEDED BY A QUALIFYING TERM

A good number of terms are preceded by a qualifying term and thus given a more concrete topographic interpretation. Because the evidence does not justify the acceptance of the following terms as compounds, they are included under the head components:

(1) ground: barren ground, broken ground, thickety ground, stony or rock ground, lowish or middle ground, middling ground, declining ground, marshy ground, pebbly ground, sandy ground(s), bad ground(s), solid ground, dry ground;

(2) hammock: back hammock, black hammock, grey and black hammock, detached hammock, dry hammock, inferior hammock, light and heavy hammock, wet hammock, wild hammock;

(3) inlet: dry inlet (an inlet sometimes free of water; an inlet usually separated from the sea by a narrow sand-bar; poss. the sand-bar itself);

(4) land: arable land, barren land, broken or waving land, floating land, light land, middling land (hammock land), natural land, open land, overflowed land, plantable land, rich *vs.* poor land, strong land, thin land, uncleared or wooded land;

(5) marsh: clear marsh, green marsh, high marsh, low marsh;

(6) river (Note the river called both "White" and "Black."): main river, open river;

(7) shore: iron-bound shore (a rock-bound shore), main shore (the shore of the mainland as opposed to that of an island);

(8) spring: aperient spring, chalybeate spring, main spring, medicinal spring, stinking spring;

(9) stream: main stream, subterannean [*sic*] stream, tributary stream, underground stream, winding stream;

(10) swamp: bare swamp, Boggy swamp, hard swamp, head swamp, isolated swamp, rushy swamp, woody swamp.

("Bare swamp" is difficult to explain: Since swamps are distinguished from marshes by being timbered, a bare swamp can hardly be one which lacks vegetation; however, it may be that the author is referring to swamp land which has been cleared, but which is still called swamp. Also, the "isolated swamps," which are the sources of small streams, are specified as "cypress swamps, cypress ponds, and bay-galls.")

(c) ATTRIBUTIVE COLLOCATIONS NOT ACCEPTED AS COMPOUNDS

Again, because of a lack of evidence, it was felt that one group of terms had not yet become crystallized into compounds. Some of the terms given below appear only in the form of place names, but they illustrate what is probably the final step in the formation of compounds. Those terms, then, which are listed in the glossary (under the head terms) as attributive formations but which as yet lack proof of being used as compounds are as follows:

basin spring, bay-gall branch, bay-gall swamp, bluff island, bluff point, bluff shore, branch creek, Cabbage-swamp tract, cape land, claybank creek, cove country, cove swamp, Cowford ferry, creek bayou, creek island, creek lake, creek swamp, cypress-swamp land, desert beach, desert coast, desert country, desert plain, desert waste, elbow creek, Ever-Glade Morass, fresh-water basin, fresh-water well, gulf water, hammock forest, hammock ridge, Haulover Creek, Haulover isthmus, head lagoon, head lake, lagoon bank, lake branch, lake creek, lake shore, lake water(s), marsh bend, marsh country, marsh flat, marsh point, marsh water, meadow valley, natural-bridge creek, pine-barren country, Pine-Barren creek, Pine-Barren spring, pine-barren swamp, pineland pond, pineland savanna, pineland swell, pine-wood(s) coun- try, pine-wood plain, plain field, pond branch, pond country, pond creek, pond water, prairie ground, river marsh, river morass, river water, river-bottom land, sand-hill peak, sand-hill pond, savanna branch, savanna country, savanna ground, savanna plain, savanna swamp, scrub ground, scrub hammock, sea-shore country, sea-shore tract, shoal bank, shoal cape, shoal river, shore ridge, sulphur-spring run, summit ground, summit pass, swamp branch, swamp island, swamp run, tributary stream, tributary water, upland hill, waste plain, waste pond, water passage, wilderness country.

(d) COLLOCATIONS FORMED WITH COORDINATING ATTRIBUTIVES

One other body of terms remains to be considered at this point. Some topographic collocations appear to consist of coordinating rather than simple attributives, and seem to be used to designate areas composed of more than one characteristic feature; *e.g., pine and palmetto land,* or land on which both cabbage palmettos and pine trees grow. Because this type of phrase is not included in any dictionary (with the sole exception of the adjectival *oak-and-hickory* which is given in the DAE), the entire group of terms has been excluded from the glossary itself. However, the following compounds are offered here by way of illustrating another type of limitation. Since these expressions are practically self-defining, no definitions—other than the one DAE citation just mentioned—have been given below.

ASH AND MAPLE SWAMP.
1783 in SIEBERT II. 289 [Schedule of Denys Rolle: Quality of Land] Ash & Maple Swamp, [etc.].

CABBAGE AND OAK HAMMOCK.
1773 MS. 273 In Savah. Ground-Cabage and Oak Hammok near—.

CABBAGE AND OAK SWAMP.
1773 MS. 285 C. [cabbage] & O. [oak] swamp . . . on high Pe. [pine] Ld. [land] Gum: Cabb. [cabbage] & Oak Swp [sic] [swamp]—very big and near.

CYPRESS AND BAY SWAMP.
1765 B 7 Savannahs and ponds . . . are interspersed generally in the pine-lands in most part of the southern provinces, together with the cypress and bay-swamps.

CYPRESS AND BAY THICKET.
1818 Y 147 Nine and three-quarters miles to Slippery Log Creek through a country with great sameness of character—flat, low and wet with occasional cypress and bay thicket on either side.

IN AND OUTLET.
1773 MS. 320 Keppel *In & Outlet in Lat:* 25° 35′ 16″. [Poss. on the analogy of the phr. *in and out;* the ref. is prob. to both an inlet and outlet. *Cf.* OUT AND INLET.]
1823 V 120-21 East from *old Matacombe* is the south point of *Matanza reef* and *Spencer in and outlet.*

OAK AND CABBAGE POND.
1773 MS. 284 A big oak & Cab: Pond near.

OAK AND GUM SWAMP.
1773 MS. 284 Rivut. [rivulet] runs in Do. [ditto] Pond—forms a fine oak & gum swp . . . oak & Gum swp. close.

OAK AND HICKORY COUNTRY.

1818 Y 24   In the oak and hickory country, the hills are neither so high nor so steep as the sand-hills.

OAK AND HICKORY HILL.

1818 Y 24   The distinguishing features of the two kinds of hills are—the oak and hickory, with a thick undergrowth of the one—and the predominance of pine, without undergrowth on the other.

OAK AND HICKORY LAND.   Land having a native growth of oaks and hickories upon it. DAE 1735 under *oak-and-hickory*. Prob. Southern.

1773 MS. 266   In Oak & Hickery Land.

1784 GME 97   Then commences a fine high, pine country, intermixed with oak and hickory land.

1787 in SIEBERT II. 204   One hundred and seventy five acres of rich Oak and Hiccary Land, fit for Indigo, Cotton, Tobacco, Indian Corn, etc.

1812 FHQ IX. 71   Our route . . . lay through some Oak and Hickory land and along the top of a ridge of hills.

1812 F 125   Vast quantities of live oak and hickory lands in this district.

1823 FHQ XIV. 94   There is also a district extending from east to west along the Georgia line . . . of first rate oak and hickory lands.

1823 V 74   The extent, from the waters of the Santaffy in the direction of the ridge, and extending on each side, including the Alachua territory, down to the head of Spirito Santo bay . . . is a beautiful undulating fertile country, containing large bodies of hammock and oak and hickory land.

1851 BYRNE 14   [A] great part of which is first rate land of the different denominations of high hammock, oak and hickory, rich prairie, and pine.

1869 FICSP 33   The first-rate pine, oak and hickory lands are found in pretty extensive bodies in many parts of the State.

OAK AND HICKORY SCRUB.

1823 V 44   The northern sand bluff [has] . . . a luxuriant under brush of oak and hickory scrub.

OAK AND PINE BLUFF(S).

1766 B 20-21   We rowed several very crooked courses by some oak and pine bluffs 5 or 6 foot high.

OAK AND PINE HILL.

1773 MS. 279   On Oak & Pine hill—no good Timber.

OUT AND INLET, OUT OR INLET.

1773 MS. 340   Hawke Channel has eight Out-and-Inlets, safe Communications from the Florida Stream, through the Reefs and Shoals of no less than eighteen feet water . . . Beside these Out or Inlets, are three Passages through the Martyr Islands into Richmond Bay. [Poss. an analogy of the phr. *out and in*. Prob. the meaning intended here is a passage which serves as both inlet and outlet. *Cf.* IN AND OUTLET.]

PALMETTO AND PINE LAND(S).

1766 B 10-11   There is little difference in their height for scores of miles, unless near the palmetto and pine-lands.

PASTURE AND PINE LAND.

1787 in SIEBERT II. 204-05   One thousand ... Acres of Pasture and Pine land ... 1450 Acres of rich Pasture & Pine Land ... On this Pine Land, there might be about 72,000 Pine Trees ... the whole cloathed with a constant verdure from succeeding Crops of most excellent Grass for rearing and feeding Horses & Cattle.

PINE AND OAK LAND.

1773 MS. 274   In hilly pine & oak Land.

PINE AND PALMETTO LAND.

1818 Y 41   The St. Mark heads fifteen miles N.N.E. from the Fort in a large grassy pond surrounded by low poor pine and palmetto land.

PINE AND SAW-PALMETTO PLANE.

1825 GADSDEN 130   The last seven miles pine and saw-palmetto planes.

SHELL AND SAND BLUFF.

1836 SSW 275   The eastern side of the St. John's is distinguished from the western by these shell and sand bluffs.

----

(5)   Neologisms

(a)   AMERICANISMS

A large percentage of the terms in the glossary are Americanisms. In many cases there is positive dictionary evidence not only that the expressions were either coined or given new meanings in the New World, but also that they are used throughout either the entire United States, or a great portion of it. The following are listed in the DAE as Americanisms, or (in a few cases) are given only in the CD or NID:

anchorage ground; ash swamp; back country; back land; back swamp; barren(s); bayou; bluff; bluff land; bottom land; brake (canebrake); branch; carrying place; cattle range; ?causeway (raised way across marsh or water—NID); cedar swamp; clay bluff; ?coastland; country (associated with a spec. place or river); cove (meadowland adjoining a cove; inlet); creek (tributary brook); crossing; crossing place; cutoff (bayou, or connecting stream); delta (as associated with American rivers: here, with ref. to either the Apalachicola or Suwannee River); dismal swamp; divide (watershed); dividing ridge; drain (small stream or branch); drowned land; dry creek; falls (pl. with sing. sense); farming land; flat (tract of elevated level land); flatwoods; floating island; fork(s) (all three senses); fresh river; fresh-water river; grass plain; grass prairie; hammock; hardwood land; haulover; head branch; hole (small bay; inlet or creek); hummock ("often with special reference to Florida"—DAE); interval (interval land); intervale land; island (piece of ground rising from a level track; also, grove or clump of trees in a prairie); lagoon (bay, inlet, sound; also, shallow, fresh-water pond or lake us. connecting with a lake or river); ?limestone sink (NID only); ?malpass (?malpais—bad lands); maple swamp; mud shoal; natural bridge (in Florida a limestone formation covering a subterranean stream: this "bridge" formation is not always obvious); oakland; oak ridge; old river; open (opening; a natural clearing); open prairie; ?outlet (stream flowing out of lake, etc.—NID); oyster reef (CD); ?oyster rock (NID); pasture range; peach land; peat bed (CD); pine bluff; pineland; pine plain, pine plane; point (tapering woodland extending into prairie; also, peak or elevation above a stream); portage; prairie (also, ellipt. for *prairie land*); prairie country; prairie land; raft; range; rapid; ?reed-marsh (one DAE q.: Western); ripple; rippling; river (Some American authors preserve the British custom of preceding the word *river* with the proper name, but the contrary practice is also illustrated here.); river bottom; river-land; rolling country; rolling land; salt creek; salt pond; sand barren; sand bluff; scrubland; seaboard (the coastline; also, esp. the Atlantic coast); ?sedge island; shell bank; ship channel; sink (sink hole); sink hole; slew; slough; slue; ?spine (ridge: first quot. in OED is American); spring branch; spring creek; swale; swamp land; swash (corresponds to British swatch); ?swell (of ground: without qualifying phrase—"the absol. use is specially American," OED—DAE); timbered country; timbered land; timberland; ?turpentine land (OED); valley (with ref. to specific rivers); ?watershed (no British examples in the OED); wet prairie; wet swamp; wild land.

(b) SOUTHERNISMS

Some Americanisms, such as *palmetto ground*, *palmetto swamp*, *pine-barren land*, and *pine savanna* appear to be used only in the Southeastern Atlantic states. Terms appearing in none of the dictionaries but listed in McJimsey and therefore assumed to be Southernisms are *cedar island*, *fresh pond*, *marsh* (meadow), *oak swamp*, *oystershell bank*, *ridge* (divide), and *salt-water river*. Moreover, those terms whose usage is unrecorded outside the Southern states are as follows: alligator hole; bay-gall; bay shore; bay swamp; ?cane bottom; canebrake; cane land; cane swamp; cotton land; ?cut-off; ?cypress gall; cypress pond; cypress swamp; fresh pond; fresh spring; fresh-water brook; ?fresh-water creek; ?fresh-water marsh; fresh-water pond; freshwater run; ?glade (everglade); Glade (name of particular area of the everglade sort); gum swamp (swamp or area in a large swamp in which the black-gum or sour-gum or any other species of Nyssa is the dominant tree; poss. the same as tupelo swamp); ?hammock land; hard marsh (a marsh the basis of which is a marly clay and whose soil is too solid for water to disunite its particles); hickory land; hole (small pond); hummock land; inland swamp; islet (grove or clump of trees in a plain or prairie); ?laguna (lagoon [2]); ?levee (S. & W. in cultural sense); ?lime sink; mixed land; ?mulatto land; oak swamp; orange orchard (?S. & W.); oyster bar; oyster-shell bank; pine barren (chiefly S.–DAE); pine flat?; ?pine ridge; prong; reed brake; ?rice swamp; ?river swamp; salt-water marsh; savanna (savanna covered with scattered trees); ?savanna land; sea island; sugar land; ?swamp (boggy or marshland stream); ?tidewater (water affected by the tide, or a region where such is the case); wet glade (according to the OED citation of Bartlett [1859] under glade, glades are "so called in Maryland, where they are divided into wet and dry glades").

(c) LOCALISMS

Although *everglade* (sf.)[14] may now be part of the common stock of American English, there is hardly any doubt that the term originated in Florida. (For a discussion of the origin and formation of this word, see the glossary.) As a place name in the plural form with a singular sense, the term is not known to exist outside of the state. Since the only quotations given for a few terms listed in the DAE as Southernisms are taken from Florida literature, it is possible that the words are state localisms: *e.g., bitter land, cabbage hammock, cabbage land, Cedar Key* (sf.) (under *cedar*), *shell hammock, swammock* (sf.), and *tupelo swamp*.

The DAE comments that *kay(o)* and *key* (sf.) are used "chiefly off the Florida coast," but does not list the form *cay(o)*, which the OED says was originally applied to the islets around the coast and islands of Spanish America. Another term which seems to be used locally is *cut* in the sense of *inlet. Mountain* is used once to designate a clump of cypress trees. Both *fountain* and *spring* are used with reference to an oceanic spring. *Gall* (cold, acid swamp on which gall bushes grow —strictly speaking, a watercourse thinly covered with soil) is probably

---

[14]An effort has been made to recognize those terms which have survived to the present; and those words which have been observed in modern usage are indicated by "(sf.)," signifying "survived form."

not used outside Florida. A place where a stream has forced a passage through the coast is called a *gap*.

Although it is impossible to say conclusively, the following expressions may be localisms whose usage is confined to Florida: *outwatering* (mouth or place of exit of a stream into the sea), *marsh* (low ground sometimes inundated so that the waters collect and drain off in a stream; a kind of drain), *head* (submerged rock or reef), *?rush land* (the one quot. in the OED under *rush* yields no information on area of usage), and the short forms *bridge* (natural bridge—*q.v.*), *cypress* (cypress swamp), *field* (floating field), *hammock* (hammock land), *island* (floating island), and *plain* (floating plain). *Boil* (of a spring), *canal* (connecting channel), and *dam* (sf.) (a natural barrier temporarily closing an inlet) may be used in areas other than Florida, but there is no evidence at hand to support this assumption.

The majority of the Florida localisms are new compounds and an attempt has been made to make their selection on a scientific basis. Therefore the compounds in this group have been rated in the following order: (1) those terms in which the stress seems to fall on the first syllable, or at least the second syllable of the first component; (2) those terms consisting of a noun followed by a noun, some of which have an even stress on both elements; and (3) those terms which may not be stressed as in (1) or (2) above, but whose inclusion seems justified on the basis of semantic considerations and the nature of the available evidence.

If there is no way of knowing exactly how the inhabitants of Florida pronounced words three-quarters of a century or more ago, at least modern pronunciation can be used as a guide to the speech habits of the past. Accordingly, the problem of stress has been studied in the light of contemporary usage. Those compounds which fall into the first group (*i.e.*, with stress on the first syllable, or the second syllable of the first component) are as follows:

bay head (sf.), bay land, bay pond, boat channel, ?branch land, cabbage-bluff, cabbage grove, cabbage knoll, ?cabbage land, cabbage pond, cabbage swamp, Cattle-ford, clayhole, cockle bank, cockle bluff, coquina land, coral bank, Cowford, creek branch, cypress bog, cypress-branch, cypress grove, cypress hammock, cypress island, cypress savanna, cypress sink, eddy cove, eddy current, eddy water, hammock island, hammock savanna, island swamp, land carriage, lily swamp, lime grove, lime pit, line branch, magnolia swamp, mangrove forest, mangrove island, mangrove islet, mangrove key, mangrove land, mangrove swamp (sf.), maple grove, marl-bed, marl hammock, marl land, marsh island, mulberry hammock, myrtle swamp, myrtle thicket (sf.), oakfield, orange land, oyster clift, oyster hill, oyster shoal, palmetto flat, palmetto land, palmetto scrub, pine glade, pine grove, pine hammock, pine hummock, pine island, pine knoll, pine level, pine opening, pine range, pine tract, rice tract, ?salt flat, salt lagoon, sand bank (sand hill), sand hillock, sand kay, sand key, sand point, scrub hammock, sedge-marsh, sedge swamp, spruce hill, spruce ridge, thicket-wood(s), turpentine tract, turtle hole, water run.

One subclassification of the same group (1) consists of expressions formed by a noun preceded by a compound, *e.g.:*

backbone ridge, back-water swamp, bay-bush flat, cabbage-tree hummock, cabbage-tree Island, cabbage-tree land, clear-water lake, clear-water pond, fan-palmetto barren, flag-grass pond, freestone spring, fresh-water key, fresh-water marshland, fresh-water rivulet, fresh-water spring, fresh-water swamp, fresh-water tide-swamp, high-hammock land, live-oak grove (sf.), live-oak hammock, live-oak hummock, live-oak land, live-oak swamp, live-oak thicket, loblolly-bay swamp, mangrove-swamp land, red-bay hammock, red-clay land, river-swamp land, saw-grass marsh, saw-grass meadow, saw-grass pond (sf.), saw-grass savanna, saw-palmetto flat, saw-palmetto land, sea-sand hill, spruce-pine ridge, sweet-water country, sword-grass pond, tide-river swamp, tidewater channel, water-oak swamp, wild-orange grove.

Those terms falling into the second category (noun followed by noun, some of which have an even stress on both elements) are as follows:

beech hammock, cane hammock, cane pasture, grass knoll, grass lake, grass marsh, grass meadow, grass point, grass pond, grass savanna, gulf shore, oak grove, ?oak hammock, oak hill, oak scrub, oak thicket, oak upland, oak wilderness, Oat Point, palmetto hammock, palmetto jungle, palm hammock (sf.), pine pond.

Terms classified under (3) above, which lack the conditions of stress of (1) and (2), have been accepted on the basis of evidence and semantic considerations. The one factor considered of greatest importance here is what might be called the principle of logical independence and cohesion; that is to say, for example, the expressions *blowing spring* and *low hammock* refer to permanent, visible or audible objects. Before terms were added to this group certain corroborative details were considered, such as the quality of the source of information, the tone or plausibility of the quotation, and other confirming facts (*e.g.,* place-name evidence or analogical formations—*cf. fast land* in the DAE with *fast ground* below). The compounds in this category consist of nouns preceded either by an adjective or a participle, *e.g.:*

blowing spring, farming country, fast ground, firm ground, flat pineland, floating field, floating plain, fresh lake, fresh marshland, high hammock (sf.), high swamp, low hammock (sf.), open grove, open wood(s), out shore, sobbed land, sour ground, sour grove, swimming creek, wet savanna, wrecking ground.

There is no way of telling what percentage of the neologisms are peculiar to Florida. Nevertheless, those terms which this writer considers as probably true Florida localisms are as follows: *Everglades* (pl. with a sing. meaning), *Cedar Key, swammock, key* and the variants *cay(o), kay(o), cut* (inlet), *mountain* (clump of trees), *fountain* and *spring* (with ref. to the oceanic spring near St. Augustine), *gall* (watercourse thinly covered with soil), *hammock bridge* (natural bridge), *bay head, bay land, cockle bank, cockle bluff, coquina land, cypress hammock, hammock savanna, lime grove,* the seven *mangrove* compounds, *sand kay* and *sand key, bay-bush flat, fresh-water key, live-oak hammock, cane hammock, cedar hammock, oak hammock, blowing spring, flat pineland, high hammock, low hammock, open grove, open wood(s),* and *wrecking ground.*

(6) Quotations Which Antedate the DAE and the OED

(a) THOSE TERMS WHOSE QUOTATIONS ANTEDATE THE DA, THE DAE, AND THE OED

The earliest quotation in the glossary for *savanna* (*i.e.,* a savanna covered with scattered trees) precedes that in the DAE by 99 years, and that in the OED by 61. Both *laguna* and *open* (natural clearing) occur in the Floridian records 75 years before the DAE examples. The following terms are arranged in the order of diminishing number of years with which their illustrative quotations antedate those given in the DAE:[15]

[15]Some of the terms do not appear in the OED; however, some of the quotations for other terms are repeated in the DAE.

shell bank (73 yrs.); fresh river (*c.* 72 yrs. and precedes OED by *c.* 105 yrs.); sand bluff (68 yrs.); open country (66 yrs.); cabbage hammock (64 yrs.); cabbage land (64 yrs.); haulover (64 yrs.); sea island (55 yrs. and OED by 99-100 yrs.); shell hammock (49 yrs.); cut-off (41 yrs.); pasture range (37 yrs.); rolling land (35 yrs.); Gulf Stream (26 yrs. and OED by 32 yrs.); cypress pond (27 yrs.); fresh-water lake (27 yrs. and OED by 12 yrs.—under fresh); inland swamp (27 yrs.); salt lake (24 yrs. and OED by 61 yrs.); oak ridge (23 yrs.); pine ridge (22 yrs.); sand flat (21 yrs.); rolling country (19 yrs.); sand-bar (15 yrs. and OED by 41 yrs.); tideland (15 yrs.); swammock (12 yrs.); bitter land (10 yrs.); pine forest (8 yrs. and OED by 31 yrs.); backbone (plateau) (7 yrs.); mud shoal (7 yrs.); alligator hole (6 yrs.); anchorage ground (2 yrs.).

(b)   THOSE TERMS WHOSE QUOTATIONS ANTEDATE THE DA AND THE DAE BUT NOT THE OED

There is a span of 202 years between the first quotation on *promontory* in the glossary and that given in the DAE. The next longest interval of years occurring between these records and those of the same dictionary is 99 years for the term *lake*. The following words are also given in the order of diminishing number of years with which their examples antedate those of the DAE:

vale (79 yrs.); hill (73 yrs.); landing-place (73 yrs.); meadow (73 yrs.); tank (natural pond) (73 yrs.); marsh ground (*c.* 69 yrs.); port (69 yrs.); pasture (grassland) (61 yrs.); wet land (61 yrs.); channel (deep part of a stream) (? 59 yrs.); point (tapering land running into the sea) (59 yrs.); opening (in forest) (55 yrs.); creek (inlet of sea or river) (*c.* 54 yrs.); table-land (51 yrs.); marsh (marshland) (49 yrs.); flat (shoal; low-lying land) (47 yrs.); shoal (*c.* 47 yrs.); wood (45 yrs.); river (44 yrs.); cape (39 yrs.); road (35 yrs.); sand hill (33 yrs.); low country (31 yrs.); key (30 yrs.); plateau (30 yrs.); wilderness (29 yrs.); dead water (26 yrs.); plain (small tract of level land free of trees) (21 yrs.); grazing-ground(s) (13 yrs.); harbor (13 yrs.).

(B)   ANALYSIS ON THE BASIS OF RELATED FEATURES

When on the basis of related features one surveys the entire field of topographic terms, one is impressed anew with their apparently interminable variety and specificity of meaning. For example, merely the consideration of those features in Florida which are characterized by being composed of sand will illustrate their diversity: *e.g., sand* (shore), *sand-bar, sand bank, sand barren, sand beach, sand bluff, sand flat, sand hill, sand hillock, sand kay, sand key, sand point, sand ridge,* and *sea-sand hill.*

All topographical expressions are primarily divided into two groups, namely: (1) those descriptive of land features, and (2) those referring to water features. Because of the fact that what we speak of as *water* is actually land covered with water, all topographic forms occurring on the bottom of water features (such as *sand-bar*) are discussed under the *land* classification.

(1) Land Forms

(a) LAND FEATURES INVOLVING WATER

1. *Those wholly or partially surrounded by water.*—In Florida, land which is completely surrounded by water is denoted by two general terms, *island* and *key*. The latter, with its Spanish forms *cay(o)* and *kay(o)*, is used to describe a small island or partly uncovered reef, and also a bank, bar, or group of rocks—one cluster is called the "Rocky Keys," a peninsula (Key Largo—which today is classified as an island),[16] and collectively, the archipelago known as the Florida Keys. *Key* is applied once to a marsh island, and also to an islet in the Everglades. In one reference to West Florida, keys are differentiated from the shell banks only in being detached from the coast. Both *key* and *island* are combined with other words to form the more specific *cabbage-tree island, cedar island, Cedar Key, cotton island, cypress island, desert island, fresh-water key* (a key located off the estuary of a river and thus at least partially surrounded by fresh water), *hammock island, island swamp, marsh island, pine island, sand kay, sand key, sea island, sedge island,* and the forms listed as attributive constructions—*bluff island, creek island,* and *swamp island*. What is called a *mangrove island* or *mangrove key* may or may not be completely inundated: the Martyrs are referred to as "broken (*i.e.,* disconnected) islands," and are further classified into "the high, and the low or drowned islands." The "drowned" type of mangrove island either has no firm ground or

---

[16]*Webster's Geographical Dictionary* (Springfield, Mass.: G. & C. Merriam Co., 1949), under "Florida Keys."

is covered with water at high tide; however, some mangrove islands are high enough to support other vegetation. *Isle, islet* and *mangrove islet* belong with this group. A group of islands is called an *archipelago*. *Field, island, floating field, floating island, floating plain,* and *plain* are used in reference to drifts of vegetation of sufficient size to resemble small islands afloat. One writer describes a *floating island* which has sunk. The designation of a narrow strip of coastland (actually an island) which parallels the mainland as *double land* does not coincide with the nautical definition quoted by the OED—"that appearance of a coast when the sea-line is bounded by parallel ranges of hills, rising inland one above the other." *Neck* is used synonymously with the last-mentioned term once.

Land bordered by water on three sides, both when it projects into the sea and when it lies in the bend of a stream, is usually designated as a *peninsula*. However, *cape, elbow, head, headland, promontory, spit,* and *tongue* are applied to similar extensions of land. *Pitch* is used to denote that portion of a cape, reef, or shoal which extends farthest into the sea. *Point* is used with reference to a projecting piece of marsh or end of a reef, sand-bar, or sand bank; a cape; a tongue of land; and the East Florida peninsula, especially the lower part thereof; and combines to form *grass point, Oat Point,* and *sand point,* and the attributive *bluff point* and *marsh point.*

Land touching water on two sides is called a *carrying place, causeway, haulover* (spec., a narrow isthmus), *isthmus, natural bridge*[17] (*q.v.*) or *bridge,* or *neck* (the land in the bend of a river; also, the East Florida peninsula; the term is used once with reference to a *point*).

2. *Land forms bordering water.*—Land forms bordering water are designated as *beach, bluff* (spec., elevation on river-bank partially inundated at high tide), *brink, coast, coast country, coastland, coastline, gulf coast, gulf shore, landing, landing-place, levee, nook* (spec., a beach), *out shore, river-bank, sand beach, sea-bank, sea-beach, seaboard, seacoast, sea-shore, shell beach, shore, shore line, slide* (river-bank down which alligators slide), *strand,* and *?watering-place.* In one reference to a beach which has been formed by the action of the sea

[17]One of these natural bridges is indicated on the Florida State Road Department *Map of Alachua County* (prepared in cooperation with the Federal Works Agency Public Roads Administration, 1936; revised January, 1948), where the Santa Fe River is shown to sink below ground for approximately one mile, just northeast of High Springs.

but which separates an inlet from the sea there may be an overlapping of two meanings of bank—(1) sloping margin of a watercourse, and (2) shelving elevation in the sea near the surface. *Sand* is used once to denote a shore, and also a tract of sand along a shore. *Sand bank* is used collectively once to designate the Florida Keys, the Florida Reef, and adjacent sand-bars.

3. *Submerged areas.*—The following terms are used to denote areas below the surface of water: *anchorage, anchorage ground, anchoring-ground, bottom, bed, channel* (bed of watercourse), *ground, hold* (holding ground—*q.v.*), *holding ground* (anchoring ground), and *sounding*. *Cavern, cliff,* and *precipice* are used with reference to features at the bottom of a spring. An area which is shallow, or an elevation in the sea or course of a stream which constitutes an obstruction to navigation, is designated as a *bank, bar* (ridge of sand thrown up from the bottom by either the pressure of a current coming into contact with a body of water, or the force of the sea opposing a bay; also, those bars commonly found on the Atlantic with varying depth, called "shifting"), *breaker, coral bank, coral reef, flat* (a shallow or shoal), *head* (submerged rock or reef), *middle ground, mud bank, mud shoal, oyster bank, oyster bar, oyster bed, ?oyster clift, ?oyster hill, oyster reef, oyster rock, oyster shoal, pitch* (of reef or shoal), *rapid* (also said to exist in a bay, or inlet), *reef* (with ref. to an extensive formation—including the keys, banks, shoals, and sunken rocks—which is composed principally of coral banks on a stratum of stone; namely, the Florida Reef, sometimes called the "General Florida Reef"; also, the Carysford Reef), *ripple, rippling, rock* (reef, oyster reef), *sand bank* (sand-bar), *sand-bar* (shifting sand-bar, a phenomenon very common along the Florida coast; an island), *sand ridge, shallow, shelf* (poss. the shelves in Florida waters are oyster beds), *shoal bank* (attrib.), *spit* (a reef), *wharf* (rocky reef), and *wrecking ground* (the Florida Reef region, where countless ships were wrecked). De Brahm (1773) appears to use *shoal* to denote an island or key consisting of rocks and their sand covering; however, if he is referring to sand-bars, those he mentions are high enough to have sand hills. One author mentions dry *shoals.* (For the distinction between *bank, bar, reef,* and *shoal,* see the discussion under *shoal* in *Webster's Dictionary of Synonyms.*) Finally, a *mangrove island* may be an area several acres in extent which supports mangrove vegetation but does not contain a single foot of dry land.

4. *Saturated land.*—Saturated land falls into three general groups; namely, *bogs, marshes,* and *swamps.* Although the three terms are often used indiscriminately, a *swamp* differs from a *marsh* in being timbered and not usually covered with water, and from a *bog* in not consisting primarily of decaying vegetation.

In detail, land which is wet and spongy is called *bog, cypress bog, morass* (spec., a boggy pond), *Ever-Glade morass* (attrib.), and *river morass* (attrib.). One author classifies *galls* as a kind of swamp, but they also are spongy tracts, being more specifically designated as *bay-gall, cypress gall, bitter land, reed-brake, sour ground,* and *sour land.* Another type of wet land which quivers or yields under foot is termed *quagmire* or *quicksand.*

Despite the fact that one writer considers *savannas* as a type of swamp, their nature—being very spongy even when dry—resembles that of bogs and galls. In Florida, a *savanna* is basically understood to be any grassland possessing some degree of saturation. The earliest writer to go into detail, De Brahm (1773), gives the fact that the soil is not sandy enough to allow the water to penetrate as the reason that savannas are (1) under water most of the time, and (2) very spongy even when dry. Romans (1775) explains savannas as a kind of drain for the higher adjacent lands; and Williams (1827) accounts for them as being reservoirs of water, like swamps, but distinguished from the latter by being covered with grass and herbs instead of trees and vines. On the other hand, though savannas are as a rule flooded, or "drowned," sometimes they are so dry that fires sweep over them and destroy the grass upon them. Because a savanna is characteristically low, wet, and grassy, it bears a close resemblance to an *everglade*—the former term being used synonymously with *glade* and *wet glade*; moreover, a particular savanna is referred to once as a "sea of grass." Savannas are said to correspond to what is called *intervale land* in New England. This type of land is referred to specifically as a *basin, flat, marsh, plain, moist prairie,* and a *waste.* Since no mention at all is made of the saturation element, it is to be doubted that the second DAE definition of *savanna* as "flat grassland covered with scattered trees" is accurate. At any rate, the three authors who refer to hardwood vegetation on Florida savannas make it clear that moisture is characteristic of this type of land. The corrected second definition of *savanna,* then, would read, "a savanna covered with scattered trees." There is another type of savanna characterized by high ground and hillocks, which occurs chiefly in West Florida, especially in the immediate vicinity of rivers. It is possible that such savannas are identical with *second bottom* (*q.v.*). The term combines to form *grass savanna, savanna land, saw-grass savanna,* and *wet savanna;* with reference to hardwood vegetation: *cypress savanna, hammock savanna, pineland savanna* (attrib.), *pine savanna;* and *savanna country, savanna ground, savanna plain,* and *savanna swamp* (all attrib.).

Marshes and swamps differ from bogs, galls, and morasses in having a lesser degree of soil acidity and therefore more vegetation than the latter group. Furthermore, *marshes* (low-lying land partly or completely inundated) are distinguished from swamps in having no trees. There are four principal types of marshes in Florida: *fresh marsh* or *fresh-water marsh, salt marsh* or *salt-water marsh* (also, *salt flat; marsh flat* [attrib.]; *mud flat*), *hard marsh,* and *soft marsh. Marsh ground* and *marsh island* also occur. Marshes differentiated according to the prevailing vegetation are *grass marsh, reed-marsh, saw-grass marsh,* and *sedge marsh.* The form *marshland* also occurs in the collocations, *fresh marshland* and *fresh-water marshland.* Low ground which is sometimes inundated so that the waters collect and drain off in a stream is called a *marsh* or *drain.* A marshy depression is designated as a *swale.*

However, the term most widely used for saturated lowland usually overgrown with vegetation is *swamp.* Regarding the distinction between swamps, marshes, and meadows, Martha Jane Gibson says in " 'Swamp' in Early American Usage" (*American Speech,* X [Feb., 1935], p. 35) that the sword *swamp* denoted "a certain condition of soil—not inundated, as were meadows; not extremely boggy, as were marshes; and yet a soil too wet for easy going on foot, or for actual cultivation with the plow, but one at the same time rich and productive of either trees, underwood, or grass for pasturage." According to Moore's *Dictionary of Geography,* the dampness in a swamp is the result of either the flatness of the land, the presence of rocks impervious to moisture, or the growth of vegetation. "A swamp is often formed when a lake basin fills up, for the surface is so flat that the *Run-off* of rain water is very slow, and in the damp soil vegetation grows and helps to maintain the swampy conditions."[18]

The fact that there are so many varieties of swamps renders precise

[18]W. G. Moore, *A Dictionary of Geography* (Harmondsworth, Middlesex: Penguin Books, 1949), p. 159.

definition very difficult. On the basis of the Florida records swamps may be classified according to (1) location: *back swamp, cove swamp* (attrib.), *high swamp, inland swamp* (as opposed to the coastal types), *island swamp, savanna swamp* (attrib.); (2) nature: *dismal swamp;* (3) characteristic vegetation: (a) hardwood—*ash swamp, bay-gall swamp* (attrib.), *bay swamp, cedar swamp, cypress* (cypress swamp), *cypress swamp, gum swamp, live-oak swamp, loblolly-bay swamp, magnolia swamp, mangrove swamp* (a salt-water swamp in which mangrove trees grow; found only near the seacoast or on an island), *maple swamp, myrtle swamp, oak swamp, pine-barren swamp* (attrib.), *tupelo swamp, water-oak swamp,* and (b) other—*cabbage swamp, cane swamp, lily swamp, palmetto swamp, rice swamp* (also, *rice land, rice tract*), and *sedge swamp;* and (4) special association with water: *back-water swamp, creek swamp, fresh-water swamp, fresh-water tide-swamp, mangrove swamp* (being a salt-water swamp), *river swamp, tide-river swamp,* and *wet swamp.*

Swamp land (said originally to be a basin filled by deposits washed in from the adjacent higher land) occurs both separately and in two combinations, *mangrove-swamp land,* and *river-swamp land.* Hammock land which is sufficiently low to resemble swamp land is given the telescopic form, *swammock. Sugar land* (which some writers classify as hammock land), *sobbed land* (having an almost impenetrable subsoil), and *wet land* are probably identical with *swamp land.*

Since the tupelo tree belongs to the same genus (*Nyssa*) as the gum, it is probable that *tupelo swamp, gum swamp,* and what are called the "true back swamps" (which bear scarcely any other tree than the tupelo) all refer to the same type of swamp.

The most extensive undrained area in the state is the *Everglades* (for details, see the glossary), a region which includes savannas, hammocks, lagoons, and grass ponds. This area is also referred to as a *basin,* or the *Glade* (nowadays it is frequently called "the 'Glades"). The form *Ever Glade Morass* (attrib.) occurs once. Also, *down, glade, pine glade,* and *wet glade* are used in the more limited sense of *everglade.*

5. *Land which is periodically or sometimes inundated; alluvial land.*—The low-lying land adjoining a river is commonly designated *bottom, bottom land, low ground, river bottom,* or *river-bottom land;* these terms correspond to the New England *interval* or *intervale land,* both of which occur in Florida records (the latter only once). The

second level of bottom land, rising between the interval and the pine barren, is known as *second bottom*. When the same type of land is overgrown with canes, it is called *cane bottom, canebrake, cane hammock, cane land,* or *cane pasture*. Sometimes poorly drained land is denoted by the more general *drowned land, flatwoods, low country, low hammock,* and *lowland*. Alluvial land forming in a more or less triangular shape at the mouth of a river is known as a *delta. Meadows* are usually subject to inundation; various kinds of meadows are termed *grass meadow, meadow ground, meadowland,* and *saw-grass meadow. Wet prairie* is used once to denote a similar terrain which is periodically overflowed.[19]

(b) LAND FEATURES INVOLVING A CONSIDERATION OF HEIGHT

1. *Low, level areas.*—The general term for a wooded, level area which is higher than swamp land yet lower than most pineland is *hammock*. Actually, though *hammock* is sometimes used synonymously with *swamp*, the former is distinguished from the latter by being more elevated and drier, having a shrubby undergrowth, and also in having a stiffer soil of loam and red clay, sand, and lime; but a hammock, like a swamp, is timbered with oak, magnolia, or beech. However, a hammock differs from (1) a savanna in being wooded, and (2) from pineland in having underbrush. *Hummock* (which is less common in Florida) appears to apply to an area somewhat elevated above its surroundings; but the variant form *hammock* (which sometimes does mean *upland*) seems to be used in Florida mostly to denote any wooded, level area. The soil of this type of land is said to be composed of a white sand on which streams have cast vegetation which in turn has become humus; and therefore hammock soil is said to have greater depth than that of the flatwoods or pinelands. *Hammocks* are low, wet lands that never require draining, and are sometimes identified with *river bottom*. At any rate, hammocks usually have both a watery nucleus and a forested exterior (generally oak and hickory land), and

[19]According to Kurath (Kurath, Hans, *A Word Geography of the Eastern United States* [Ann Arbor: University of Michigan Press, 1949]), the most common expressions in the Midland and South for low-lying flat meadow lands and fields adjacent to watercourses are *bottoms* and *bottom lands,* the former occurring more frequently in North Midland, and the latter being the usual term in South Midland and the South. By the same authority *flats, low-lands,* and *interval(e)* are used more often in the North, *low-grounds* and *savannah* (*sic*) being the common designation in the South.

are always thickly timbered and densely overgrown with shrubbery. There are various types of hammock lands, such as *high hammock*, the "light" (*i.e.*, high, sandy and light in color), as opposed to the "heavy," or low and dark gray, and *shell hammock*. Another variety is the *low hammock*—a type of "heavy" hammock said to have a more tenacious soil than the high and "light" hammock. Many hammocks such as the following have a characteristic growth: *beech hammock, cabbage hammock, cane hammock, cedar hammock, Coconut Hammock, oak hammock, palmetto hammock, palm hammock, pine hammock, red-bay hammock*, and *scrub hammock*. *Hammock land* and *hummock* combine with other words to form *high-hammock land, cabbage-tree hummock, live-oak hummock, pine hummock*, and *hummock land*.

Lowland which is sufficiently free from overflowing to be usable for pasture or farming is called a *flat*. Other types of level areas are denoted by *bay-bush flat, marsh flat* (attrib.), *mud flat, palmetto flat* (which is dry), *pine flat* (which is high), *salt flat* (a kind of marsh), *sand flat, saw-palmetto flat, flat-land, flat pineland*, and *flatwoods*. An area having a level surface is called a *level*, or more specifically, *pine level*. A small tract of level land which is treeless or nearly so is said to be a *plain, desert plain* (attrib.), *grass plain, pine plane, pine-wood plain* (attrib.), *savanna plain* (attrib.), or *waste plain* (attrib.). *Meadows, savannas*, and the *Everglades*, have already been mentioned in the discussion on saturated or frequently inundated areas. Although *prairie* can be used to refer to rolling land, it is assumed that since so much of Florida is flatland most of the prairies there are level. The last mentioned term combines to form *grass prairie, morning-glory prairie, open prairie, wet prairie, prairie country, prairie ground* (attrib.), and *prairie land*.

2. *Elevations.*—Since most of Florida is low and flat, there are few significant elevations, and no mountains in the usual sense, within the state. However, two eighteenth-century writers (both of whom probably took their information secondhand) speak of *mountains* in Florida; while two more recent authors refer to *mountains* in connection with place names, the one explaining the "White mountains" as a range of hills, and the other specifying the "Blue Mountains" as clumps of cypress trees. With regard to the interchange of usage between *mountain* and *hill* (the latter being the common term for the more conspicuous eminences in Florida), it should be pointed out that what

is called a *hill* in one area would be designated a *mountain* in another, and vice versa, depending on the more or less mountainous character of the particular district. According to the NID, "In generally flat countries, any small hill, a few hundred feet in height, may be locally termed a mountain." The collocations formed with the latter term are *hickory hill, oak hill, pine hill, sand hill* (In contrast to the sand hills to the north, those characteristic of Florida are regular in form and generally covered with grass and other vegetation; in fact, some of these hills are forested. One writer explains these formations as originally sand islands surrounded by marshes and lagoons.), *sea-sand hill, spruce hill,* and *upland hill* (attrib.). A small hill is said to be a *hillock* (also, *sand hillock*), *knap, knob, knoll* (also, *cabbage knoll, grass knoll, pine knoll*), *mound, rise, rising,* or *rising ground.* Both *swell* (also *pineland swell* [attrib.]) and *slope* are used to denote a stretch of rising ground. A piece of ground rising from a level tract is sometimes designated an *island. Mount* is applied to a hill which is conical, and perhaps more prominent than a *mound.* A hill with a pointed summit is called a *peak;* the expression *sand-hill peak* (attrib.) occurs once on a map. The topmost point or ridge of a hill is called the *summit.*

The following terms are often or characteristically used in reference to elevations above, bordering, or near water: *bank* (sloping margin), *bluff* (elevation on river-bank partially inundated at high tide; in Florida, bluffs apparently never exceed 100 feet in height), *brink* (esp. when rising abruptly), *Cabbage-bluff, bluff point* (attrib.), *claybank, clay bluff, cliff, coast-ridge, cockle bank, cockle bluff, mound* (spec., a bluff), *mount* (spec., a bluff), *levee, oyster clift* (cliff on which oysters grow, and therefore sometimes under water), *oyster hill* (prob. a rock sometimes inundated so that oysters may grow on it), *oyster-shell bank, pine bluff, promontory* (spec., a mount), *river-bank, rock(s)* (with ref. to the Keys), *sand bank, sand bluff, sea-bank* (sand hill), *shell bank, shell hammock,* and *slide* (for alligators). Sometimes *hammocks,* and especially *hummocks,* are slight elevations above an adjacent marsh, swamp, or creek.

The higher land of a region, as opposed to the valleys and plains, is called *upland, upland hill* (attrib.), or—when overgrown with oaks— *oak upland.* (According to Williams, the uplands in West Florida are clay formations.) Other terms denoting land of some elevation are *fast ground, fast land, firm ground, firm land, high hammock, high-hammock land, highland* (plain or pine barren as opposed to a swamp or lowland), and *high swamp*. Elevations which have a level surface are designated as *flat, pine flat, plain* (vast flat ridge or plateau), *plateau* (dividing ridge of the central Floridian peninsula), *platform, table-land*, and *terrace*.

An elevated ridge of earth which is sometimes as high as a hill, but usually not associated with water, is denoted by *bank*. High land forming a watershed between two streams is termed a *divide*. Moreover, the East Florida dividing ridge located in the central part of the peninsula is denoted by *backbone, backbone ridge, dividing ridge* (not necessarily the highest land in a region), and *ridge*. The last-mentioned term is also applied to a range of hills (usually, sand hills), and occurs in the following combinations (sometimes with reference to the predominating tree growth): *blackjack ridge, coast-ridge, hammock ridge* (attrib.), *oak ridge, pine ridge, sand ridge, shore ridge* (attrib.), *spruce-pine ridge*, and *spruce ridge*. A ridge, or especially a projecting part or offshoot of a ridge, is called a *spur*.

3. *Concavities or areas partially or totally surrounded by elevations.* Subterranean concavities are denoted by *cave, cavern, cavity* (a subterranean void often connected with a watercourse; also, a hollow or conical depression in the surface of the earth), *chasm* (cleft in bottom of spring, or fissure in cave [apparently caused by a watercourse]) and *hole* (cavity in the earth or rock; cave). The following terms are used in reference to breaks or depressions in the surface of the earth: *abyss, bottom* (valley, hollow), *break* (a gap in the shore line produced by the flooding of an inlet; a round and sloping depression in the earth's surface—a small basin or hollow), *burrow* (of gopher), *dale, dell, gap* (notch in range of hills; notch in forest line), *glen* (secluded, narrow valley—in Florida—between hills), *gulf* (gully), *gully, hollow* (ravine; valley; depression, sink), *lime pit, lime sink, limestone sink, pit* (gopher hole), *ravine, sink* (basin, depression; also, sink hole), *sink hole, swale* (moist depression), *vale*, and *valley*.

(c) FORMS ASSOCIATED WITH OR CHARACTERIZED BY FLORA AND FAUNA

The terms *alligator hole* (nest, or sink), *Cattle-ford, cattle range, Cowford, hillock* (thrown up by a salamander), *pasture-ground* (for birds), *range* (for cattle), and *turtle hole* are used to designate areas in Florida which are associated with or produced by animals other than corals and shellfish. *Coral bank* and *coral reef* refer to submerged formations consisting of the skeletons of this minute type of animal. Marine shells are the prevailing element in (the first component of) *coquina land, shell bank, shell beach, and shell hammock.* Areas dominated by bivalve molluscs (which are abundant) are designated as *cockle bank, cockle bluff, oyster bank, oyster bar, oyster bed, oyster clift, oyster hill, oyster reef, oyster rock, oyster-shell bank,* and *oyster shoal.*

A great proportion of the terms in the glossary relate to the *flora* of the state. Those expressions which designate areas supporting some type of growth but none in particular are as follows:

brake, brushwood, coppice, copse, cove (meadowland adjoining a small inlet), desert (wild, uninhabited region, including forest land; a swamp), dismal swamp, field (floating field), floating field, floating island, floating plain, forest (esp. with ref. to the open groves of Florida), forest land, ?fresh-water swamp, fresh-water tide-swamp, gall, garden (natural grove), grazing country, grazing-ground(s), grazing land, grazing tract, grove, hammock, hammock island, hammock land, hammock savanna, hardwood land, high hammock, high-hammock land, high swamp, hummock, hummock land, island (grove or clump of trees in a prairie), island swamp, islet (grove or clump of trees in a plain or prairie), jungle, lawn, low hammock, marl hammock, marsh (meadow), meadow, meadow ground, meadowland, mixed land, open grove, open prairie, open wood(s), orchard, pasture, pasture-ground (for birds), pasture land, pasture range, plain (floating island), point (tapering woodland extending into prairie), prairie (meadow; also, savanna or grass opening in a forest), prairie country, prairie land, savanna, savanna land, scrub, scrub hammock, scrubland, swammock, swamp, swamp land, tide-river swamp, timbered country, timbered land, timberland, undergrowth, wet prairie, wet savanna, wet swamp, wild, wild country, wilderness, wild land (forest), wood, woodland.

The fact that probably the most common type of vegetation in the entire territory is pine accounts for the great number of *pine* collocations (twenty-three in all). The Florida *pine barrens* differ from those farther north in that the trees in the former stand at some distance from each other, so that it is possible for the grass to grow underneath; thus, this type of land is sometimes referred to as "open." There are two types of pine barrens: the one more elevated and dry, and the other—being interspersed with ponds and lakes—low and sobby or wet. The more general *pineland* is classified by De Brahm (1773) according to elevation, soil, and product; namely, the low and black, the "middling" high and white, and the very high and yellow, which produce the shrubby pine, white spruce pine, and yellow pine, respectively. Sometimes this type of land is elevated and dry, rolling, and even rocky. The two distinguishing features of Florida pinelands are that (1) they resemble open groves, and (2) they are studded with rich hammock and swamp lands. Other areas on which the predominating growth is pine are *pine-barren land, pine bluff, pine country, pine flat, pine forest, pine glade, pine grove, pine hammock, pine hill, pine hummock, pine island, pine knoll, pine level, pine opening, pine plain* (pine plane), *pine range, pine ridge, pine savanna, pine tract,* and *pine wood.*

The characteristic growth is also indicated by the first element of the following terms:

ash swamp, bay-bush flat, bay-gall, bay head, bay land, bay swamp, beech hammock, blackjack ridge, cabbage-bluff, cabbage grove, cabbage hammock, cabbage land, cabbage swamp, cabbage-tree hummock, cabbage-tree island, cabbage-tree land, cane bottom, canebrake, cane hammock, cane land, cane pasture, cane swamp, cedar hammock, cedar island, Cedar Key, cedar swamp, Coconut Hammock, cornland, cotton island, cotton land, cypress (cypress swamp), cypress bog, cypress gall, cypress grove, cypress hammock, cypress island, cypress savanna, cypress swamp, fan-palmetto barren, flat pineland, flatwoods, grass knoll, grassland, grass marsh, grass meadow, grass plain, grass point, grass prairie, grass savanna, gum swamp, hickory hill, hickory land, indigo land, lily swamp, lime grove, live-oak grove, live-oak hammock, live-oak land, live-oak swamp, live-oak thicket, loblolly-bay swamp, magnolia swamp, mangrove forest, mangrove island, mangrove islet, mangrove key, mangrove land, mangrove swamp, mangrove-swamp land, maple grove, maple swamp, morning-glory prairie, mulberry hammock, myrtle swamp, myrtle thicket, oakfield, oak grove, oak hammock, oak hill, oak-land, oak ridge, oak scrub, oak swamp, oak thicket, oak upland, oak wilderness, Oat Point, orange grove, orange land, palmetto flat, palmetto ground, palmetto hammock, palmetto jungle, palmetto land, palmetto scrub, palmetto swamp, palm hammock, peach land, red-bay hammock, reed-brake, reed-marsh, rice land, rice swamp, rice tract, rush land, saw-grass marsh, saw-grass meadow, saw-grass savanna, saw-palmetto flat, saw-palmetto land, sedge island, sedge-marsh, sedge swamp, ?sour grove (prob. wild-orange grove), spruce hill, spruce-pine ridge, spruce ridge, sugar-cane land, sugar land, tupelow swamp, turpentine (*i.e.,* pine) land, turpentine tract, water-oak swamp, wild-orange grove.

(d) OPEN AREAS

Treeless areas, or those tracts on which there is a scattered growth of trees, are denoted by *barren(s), plain, prairie,* and *savanna* (already discussed under the heading of "Saturated Areas"), and the collocations into which they enter: namely, *fan-palmetto barren, desert plain* (attrib.), *grass plain, grass prairie, morning-glory prairie, open prairie, pine barren, pine-barren land, pine plain, pine-wood plain* (attrib.), *prairie country, prairie ground* (attrib.), *prairie land, sand barren, savanna plain* (attrib.), *waste plain* (attrib.), and *wet prairie.* An opening in a forest is designated a *glade, lawn, open, opening,* or *pine opening.* Open land in general as opposed to woodland is denoted by *field.* A forested area which is clear of underwood, and in which the trees stand at some distance from each other, is known as an *open grove* or *open wood(s).*

(e) BARREN AREAS

The terms *barren(s)* (and its collocations, all of which were mentioned under "Open Areas"), *desert* (barren region)—and the forms listed as attributives under *desert* (*desert beach, desert coast, desert country, desert plain,* and *desert waste*), *desert island, waste* (spec., a *savanna*), and *waste land* are used to describe arid regions. *Scrub, scrub ground* (attrib.), *scrub hammock, scrubland,* and *oak land* (where one writer—1743—refers to *scrubby oak-land*) denote sterile areas overgrown with brushwood and stunted trees.

(f) LAND FORMS CLASSIFIED ACCORDING TO SOIL

Those land features which are composed of characteristic types of soil are as follows:

claybank, clay bluff, coquina land, lime pit, lime sink, limestone country, limestone land, limestone sink, marl-bed, marl hammock, marl land, mud bank (in river or harbor), mud flat, mud shoal, mulatto land, peat bed, red-clay land, red land, sand (tract of sand along shore), sand bank, sand-bar, sand barren, sand beach, sand bluff, sand flat, sand hill, sand hillock, sand kay, sand key, sand point, sand ridge, sea-sand hill.

(g) INDEFINITE AREAS

Those areas which have a less well-defined appearance or extent than the other terms in the glossary—but which are included because of their specific association with the territory of Florida—are as follows:

coast (tract or region), coast country, continent, country, farming country, farming land, firm land (mainland, continent), forest (wilderness), grazing country, grazing-ground, grazing land, grazing tract, ground (sea bottom; portion of the earth), gulf coast, high land, lake country, land, limestone country, low country, open country, pasture range, prairie country, prairie land, range, sweet-water country, waste (wild region), waste land, wild, wild country, wilderness, wild land, woodland (wooded region), wrecking ground.

(2) *Water Forms*

(a) COASTAL

The extensive bodies of water adjoining the Florida coastline are generally referred to as the (Atlantic) *Ocean,* on the east, and the *Gulf* (of Mexico), on the west and sometimes as the *sea(s)* on both sides of the state. Actually, *ocean* and *gulf* are sometimes used interchangeably with reference to the seas on both sides of the East Florida peninsula. Another term frequently used synonymously with *gulf* is *bay* (esp., "Bay of Mexico"). Although the distinction between these two terms is not always clear, the OED states that a *bay* is wider in proportion to its amount of recession (into the land), while a *gulf* is rather a landlocked portion of the sea opening through a strait (see *bay* in the glossary). The word *bay* is also used specifically to denote a harbor, nook, bay within a bay, or an arm or prong.

Other terms besides *bay* and *gulf* which are applied to the indentations in the shore line are *bayou* (bay, harbor), *bight* (which has more curvature than a bay; spec., a recess in an inlet), *cove* (small bay, recess in shore), *lagoon* (bay), and *opening* (bay, gulf). A small opening into the coastline is also called an *arm* of the sea (spec., lagoon, branch of a bay), *cod* (of bay), *hole* (bay; inlet, cove), *inlet* (bay, nook), and *nook* (sheltered inlet). *Prong* is applied once to the branch of a bay. *Lake* is used once in reference to a bay (now called Florida Bay). *Sound* is also used to designate a bay, or arm of a bay. A narrow coastal inlet is called a *creek, cut, estuary,* or *salt creek.*

Aquatic areas whose surroundings afford natural shelter for ships are denoted by *basin* (harbor, main body of bay), *cove* (road, roadstead), *dock* (cove, harbor), *harbor* (spec., inner and outer harbor of the Tortugas—see *harbor* in the glossary), *haven, port, road* (spec., a cove), *roadstead* (bay, harbor), and *seaport.*

Those coastal waters which serve as a connecting link between larger bodies of water are designated as *boat channel, channel* (considered wider than a strait; spec., a sound), *cut* (inland passage), *gut* (channel), *inland passage* (spec., a sound), *pass* (spec., the communication between the St. Johns and St. Marys Rivers; also, a passage smaller than a channel), *?ship channel, sound,* and *strait* (what is now called the Straits of Florida was formerly called the Gulf of Florida or Straits [or "Channel"] of Bahama), and *tidewater channel.* The entrance to a *channel* (strait) is referred to as the *chop(s).* A narrow part of a sound or strait, as well as a labyrinth of narrow channels (occurring once), is called the *narrow(s).*

The oceanic spring located below St. Augustine, and recorded here as a *fountain* or *spring,* is one of the natural phenomena of the state. Another oddity is what the sailors call *rip-rap(s)*—a rippling caused by the coming of the Gulf Stream into contact with a strong eddy. A strong swift current running along the coast (here, the Florida Keys) between a reef or bar and the shore is said to be a *set.* The waters of the sea which form *counter-currents* or whirlpools are designated as *eddy, eddy current,* or *eddy water* (eddying water occurring close to shore). Both *coast* and *shore* are used to denote the waters along the shore.

Perhaps the best-known example in Florida of an extended water area connected with the sea by means of inlets (a feature which is also called a *salt lagoon, ?salt lake,* or *salt-water river*) is Indian River—specifically referred to here as a *bay, inland sea,* or *lagoon.* What is now called Lake Worth is a similar body of water.

(b) INLAND

1. *Bodies of water.*—The following terms are applied to bodies of water unconnected with the sea: *alligator hole* (sink), *basin* (sink;

pool of a spring; lake forming the catchment area of a stream), *clay-hole* (a pond), *clear-water lake, clear-water pond, cove* (a well-known low area on the Withlacoochee River near Ocala: in the singular the term signifies a shallow lake containing hammock islands [*q.v.*], or a swamp; in the plural the reference is to the small bays or inlets of this region), *dead lake* (listed in the glossary under *lake*) or *dead water* (here, a lake having no regular outlet), *fresh lake, fresh-water lake, fresh-water pond, hole* (small pond), *lagoon* (shallow, fresh-water pond or lake connecting with or near a river or lake), *laguna* (lake), *pool* (small body of standing water; also, a puddle), *salt pond* (here, a pond located on an island), *slough* (pond), and *tank* (natural pond). There is also one type of *lake* whose waters sink or disappear altogether. With regard to the distinction between a pond and a lake, the NID states in its commentary on *lake*, "When a body of standing water is so shallow that aquatic plants grow in most of it, it is usually called a pond." *Pond* also occurs in the senses of *basin*, and *salt-water pond*. Some ponds are explained as being expansions of subterranean waters; and one type of pond shrinks within its bounds or dries up altogether. *Sinks* and *sink holes* are very common in Florida. Sometimes the sinks act as subterranean outlets or drains of other waters, such as a lake or pond. According to Williams (1837), a sink hole is caused by a caving-in above a subterranean reservoir. A similar, if not identical, formation is called a *pothole* (*q.v.* in the glossary).

Inland bodies of water in which characteristic vegetation is found are denoted by *bay pond* (pond in which bay trees grow), *cabbage pond* (pond supporting a growth of cabbage palmettos), *cypress pond, cypress sink, flag-grass pond, grass lake* (here, the Everglades), *grass pond, island* (cypress pond), *pine pond, saw-grass pond,* and *sword-grass pond.* On the other hand, an *open pond* is a pond whose surface is unobstructed by trees or other vegetation—possibly in contradistinction to the cypress ponds.

2. *Watercourses.*—According to the highly individualistic De Brahm (1773), running waters should be classified as "Streams, Rivers & Rivulets; the last as not navigable Branches of Rivers or Streams. The Rivers as Navigable Waters emptying into Streams, & the Streams as navigable Waters disemboguing into the Ocean." However, the common generalized term for watercourses is *stream*, which occurs in two senses, namely: (1) a course of flowing water forming a river, rivulet,

or brook; and (2) the current of a river. Both *watercourse* and *water* (in the sense of flowing water) occur, but not so frequently as *stream*. The larger and more important streams are usually called *rivers;* but in the Florida records the same term is sometimes used interchangeably with *branch, brook, creek* (tributary brook), *drain,* and *rivulet* (once). With regard to this problem, the NID states, "In parts of the United States and Canada, esp. in New England, *river* is applied to streams the size of brooks, while streams of river size are sometimes called *creeks.*"

Fresh river, fresh-water brook, fresh-water creek, fresh-water river, and *fresh-water rivulet* (*run*) designate streams whose waters are specified as fresh. The sources (or waters connected with the source) of a stream are denoted by *fountain, head, head branch, head spring, headstream, headwater(s), run* (spring), *source, spring, spring branch, spring creek, springhead,* and *well* (spring forming pool or stream). Springs are further classified under *basin spring* (attrib.), *blowing spring* (spring which makes a flapping sound as it boils up), *freestone spring* (spring lacking most minerals), *fresh spring, fresh-water spring, mineral spring, Pine-Barren spring* (attrib.), *salt spring, sulphur spring,* and *warm spring.* The bubbling upheaval of water above the surface and in the center of a spring is called a *boil.*

Subterranean streams, which are very common in certain parts of Florida, are denoted by *channel, fountain, passage, river* (esp. one that sinks, runs underground for a part of its course, and reappears), and *watercourse.*

Mention has already been made (under "Saturated Areas" of land) of the *bay-galls, cypress galls* and *galls* which are said to be actual watercourses covered with a thin layer of the coldest type of soil. Retrogressing streams are denoted by *slew, slough* (narrow stretch of backwater), *slue,* and *swamp* (a slough)—the excess water forced back in a stream being called *backwater.*

The path or direction taken by a stream is termed its *course.* A long straight stretch in the course of a stream is known as a *reach,* while the convolutions or curves of a stream are referred to as *bend, elbow, meander(s), turn, turning,* and *winding(s).* The embranchments from a course are denoted by *arm* (branch of river), *branch, fork* (point of juncture of two or more streams; also, a tributary stream forming one part of a fork), *junction, line branch* (tributary), and *prong.* A sudden descent, or series of such descents, in the course of a stream is designated a *cascade* (small waterfall), *fall(s)*, or *rapid(s)*. A dilation in a river (esp. the St. Johns) is called a *bay, inland sea*, or *lake*. Shallow places in a stream suitable for the crossing of animals are denoted by *Cattle-ford, Cowford, crossing, crossing place, ford,* and *pass* (ford). A narrow part of a river is called a *narrows* or *gateway*. The place of entry of a river into a lake is also spoken of as a *gateway*, or *mouth* (which also signifies the outfall of a river; however, the sense of *outlet* rather than *entrance* occurs three times). The point at which a body of water discharges into the stream which drains it is termed an *outlet*. The tidal mouth of a river—where the tide meets the current of fresh waters—is designated as an *estuary*. Moreover, the place of exit of a stream into the sea is called an *outwatering*.

Other terms denoting watercourses are *bayou* (sluggish branch or creek), *canal* (natural watercourse connecting other streams or bodies of water), *channel* (watercourse), *creek branch, current* (stream), *cut-off* (sluggish stream connecting two rivers), *cypress-branch, ditch* (channel), *feeder* (stream flowing into a body of water), *gutter* (creek), *lane* (channel), *outlet* (stream), *rill, sluice* (small stream carrying off overflow water; spec., a river), *streamlet, swamp* (boggy stream), *swimming creek* (stream too deep to be crossed by wading), *torrent, water run, watershed* (drain; also, gathering ground of a river system), and *water-stream*.

(C)　Difficult Terms

On the basis of the one quotation in the glossary it is impossible to tell whether or not *lane* is used merely in the sense of a narrow passage (here, a channel), or given the Scottish meaning of a sluggish stream of water. Another puzzling term is *race*, which usually means a strong current in the sea, but which here denotes an island; perhaps the reference is to the current on one side of the island. It is not clear what is meant by "shelves with mouthes," unless possibly *mouth* refers to a channel providing a passageway for boats through a shoal which forms a kind of shelf.

One supposition given by the DAE is that *old river* (sf.) signifies "?The former bed of a river which has cut itself a new channel." On the other hand, it is possible that the term denotes a river which has remained within its customary bounds as contrasted with a stream which has recently been formed by the bursting of old confines.[20] The 1634 DAE quotation ("The Land . . . is bounded . . . west with the old River & East with the new River.") might thus be interpreted. Perhaps the answer is contained in what the NID says regarding the age of rivers: "A river has its stages of development, youth, maturity, and old age. In its earliest stages a river system drains its basin imperfectly; as valleys are deepened, the drainage becomes more perfect, so that in maturity the total drainage area is large and the rate of erosion high. The final stage is reached when wide flats have developed and the bordering lands have been brought low." At any rate, the DAE editors are probably correct in questioning the definition which they give. For one thing, the quotation given in the glossary refers to a "run or branch of an old river"; and it is highly questionable that the writer had the bed of a desiccated stream in mind for the first two terms. There must have been water in the "run or branch," else the author probably would have said there was not; and how can an "old" (*i.e.*, dry) river have a wet tributary?

VIII. *Form of the Glossary*

Each entry in the glossary is arranged according to the following sequence of elements: first, the topographic term, which is listed in its proper alphabetical order (compounds being considered for this purpose as if spelled as one word); second, the definition; and third, the illustrative quotation. Wherever possible, full definitions have been cited from the standard dictionaries. In general, the authorities have been used in the following order of preference: (1) *Dictionary of American English;* (2) *Oxford English Dictionary;* (3) *Webster's New International Dictionary;* (4) *Century Dictionary;* and (5) *English Dialect Dictionary.* The absence of a dictionary reference signifies that the term in question is not defined by any of the standard dictionaries, and that the definition given is new.

Where usage following the year 1874 has been recorded by either the DAE (*e.g., prong,* which is brought up to 1913) or the OED, it has

---

[20]The DAE, OED, and NID do not recognize such a thing as a "new river"; but judging by the number of streams in Florida alone which are called by this term as a place name, there can be no doubt that such a phenomenon actually exists.

not been considered necessary to supply the latest possible illustration within the bounds of this inquiry. Rather the emphasis has been placed on the earlier material. Nor have matters of pronunciation (other than the relation of stress to the formation of compounds—discussed *supra* pages 35-37) been included since that type of information is available in the dictionaries.

Whenever special meanings or new meanings have occurred they have been noted in the introductory remarks comprising the definition section preceding the illustrative quotations. Those quotations which have a particular significance are indicated in the definition section by date: thus, the definition-discussion of *bluff* mentions "rising ground (1784)," which is a reference to a specific meaning illustrated by the 1784 quotation under that term.

The quotations themselves have been arranged in the following order: (1) illustrations of the entry; (2) illustrations of the entry when preceded by a qualifying term; and (3) illustrations of attributive formations with the entry which are not yet accepted as compounds in their own right (see the discussion of the formation of compounds on pages 25-27). In the instance of (2) and (3) just mentioned the arrangement is alphabetical according to the qualifying term, or the attributive, respectively. Cross-references are listed below the quotations of the more important terms.

In the source references upper-case Roman numerals indicate volumes, with the exception of the complex Congressional references where "vol." is used for that purpose; also, page references are always separated from volumes and documents by a period: *e.g.*, "1731 C I. 70," "1855 USCSED vol. 756 [Document] #76.5." Excepting those cases in which a source has been quoted only a few times, all the dictionaries and sources utilized in the glossary have been cited by letter abbreviation. A key to the abbreviations is given below.

IX. *Key to Abbreviations*

A	Adair, James, *The History of the American Indians.*
(A.)	In introductory comments only: signifies that the DAE considers this term an Americanism.
AG	*The American Gazetteer.*
ALLEN	Allen, Sarah, *A Narrative of the Shipwreck . . . of Mrs. Sarah Allen. . . .*
ASPIA	*American State Papers, Indian Affairs* (U.S. Congress).

ASPM	*American State Papers, Miscellaneous* (U.S. Congress).
ASPMA	*American State Papers, Military Affairs* (U.S. Congress).
ASPNA	*American State Papers, Naval Affairs* (U.S. Congress).
ASPPL	*American State Papers, Public Lands* (U.S. Congress).
AUDUBON	Audubon, John James, "Three Floridian Episodes," in *Tequesta.*
AUG	Morse, Jedidiah, *The American Universal Geography.*
B	Bartram, John and William: 1765-1766 B refers to the *Journal* of John Bartram in STORK; 1791 B refers to William Bartram's *Travels through North and South Carolina, Georgia, East and West Florida.*
BARR	Barr, Capt. James, *A Correct and Authentic Narrative of the Indian War in Florida.*
BILL	Bill, Ledyard, *A Winter in Florida.*
BRINTON	Brinton, Daniel Garrison, *Notes on the Floridian Peninsula* (1859), and *A Guide-Book of Florida* . . . (1869).
BRYANT	Bryant, William Cullen, *Letters of a Traveller.*
BYRNE	Byrne, Bernard M., *Letters on the Climate, Soils, and Productions of Florida.*
C	Catesby, Mark, *The Natural History of Carolina, Florida, and the Bahama Islands.*
CADOGAN	Cadogan, George, *The Spanish Hireling Detected.*
CARROLL	Carroll, B. R., *Historical Collections of South Carolina.*
CD	*The Century Dictionary.*
DA	Mathews, M. M., *A Dictionary of Americanisms on Historical Principles.*
DAE	Craigie, *et al.*, *A Dictionary of American English on Historical Principles.*
DARBY	Darby, William, *Memoir on the geography,* . . . *of Florida.*
DRAKE	(Bigges, Walter), *A Summarie and True Discorse of Sir Frances Drakes West Indian Voage.*
E	Ellicott, Andrew, *Journal.*
EDD	Wright, Joseph, *The English Dialect Dictionary.*
ESB	Smith, Buckingham, *Espiritu Santo Bay.* . . .
F	Forbes, James Grant, *Sketches, Historical and Topographical, of the Floridas.* . . .
FAIRBANKS	Fairbanks, George R., *The History and Antiquities of the City of St. Augustine, Florida.*
FHQ	*The Florida Historical Quarterly.*
FICSP	Adams, J. S., *Florida: Its Climate, Soil, and Productions.*
FLORIDA PIRATE	*The Florida Pirate, or An Account of a Cruise in the Schooner Esperanza.*
FRLCSH	*A Full Reply to Lt. Cadogan's Spanish Hireling.*
G	Gauld, George, *Observations on the Florida Kays, Reef and Gulf.*
GADSDEN	A report by Col. James Gadsden on the possibilities of road construction from St. Augustine to Cape Florida, in ASPMA III. 118-120.
GHDPOPW	*A Geographical and Historical Description of the Principal Objects of the Present War in the West-Indies.* . . .
GME	Morse, Jedidiah, *Geography Made Easy.*

H	Hawks, J. M., ed., *The Florida Gazetteer.*
HAKLUYT	Hakluyt, Richard, *The Principall Navigations,* . . . 1589 and 1600 eds.
HAWKINS	Hawkins, Sir John, *A true declaration of the troublesome voyadge of M. John Haukins to the* . . . *west Indies.* . . .
HEWATT	Hewatt, Alexander, *An Historical Account* . . . *of South Carolina and Georgia.*
HEYLIN	Heylin, Peter, *Microcosmos* . . . (1621), and *Cosmographie* . . . (1652).
HUTCHINS	Hutchins, Thomas, *An Historical Narrative and Topographical Description of Louisiana, and West-Florida.*
IJ	*Incidents of a Journey from Abbeville, S.C., to Ocala, Fla.*
J	Jefferys, Thomas, *A Description of the Spanish Islands.* . . .
KEASBEY	Keasbey, Anthony Quinton, *From the Hudson to the St. Johns.*
KIMBER	Kimber, Edward, *A Relation,* . . . *of a Late Expedition to the Gates of St. Augustine.* . . .
L	Laudonnière, René, *A Notable Historie containing foure voyages made by certayne French Captaynes Vnto Florida.* . . . (*Note:* The pagination of this work is consecutive on every other page: the left page bears no number and is labelled here with the letter *L; e.g.,* "6L" signifies the left side of the sixth leaf.)
LANMAN	Lanman, Charles, *Adventures in the Wilds of the United States.*
LE BLANC	Le Blanc, Vincent, *The World Surveyed.* . . .
MAG	Morse, Jedidiah, *The American Gazetteer.*
MELISH	Melish, John, *A Military and Topographical Atlas of the United States; Including the British Possessions & Florida.*
MS.	De Brahm, John Gerard William, ". . . East Florida" (manuscript). (*Note:* Some pages of this work are not numbered: a page reference enclosed in parentheses indicates that the quotation occurs on one of the unnumbered pages following the last preceding numbered page—which is the page reference given.)
NAWIG	*The North-American and the West-Indian Gazetteer.*
NID	*Webster's New International Dictionary.*
NVSM	*The Narrative of a Voyage to the Spanish Main.*
NWR	*Niles Weekly Register.*
OLDMIXON	Oldmixon, John, *The British Empire in America.*
OSBORNE	Osborne, Thomas, *A Collection of Voyages and Travels.* . . .
OED	*Oxford English Dictionary.*
POPE	Pope, John, *A Tour through the* . . . *United States* . . . *and the Floridas.*
PREBLE	"A Canoe Expedition into the Everglades in 1842," in *Tequesta.*
PURCHAS	Purchas, Samuel, *Purchas his Pilgrimes.*
R	Romans, Capt. Bernard, *A Concise Natural History of East and West Florida.*
RCBH	*The Report of the Committee of both Houses.* . . .

RIBAULD — Ribaut, Jean, *The VVhole and true discouerye of Terra Florida*. . . .

ROBERTS — Roberts, William, *An Account of the First Discovery and Natural History of Florida.*

S — *A Scrapbook of Newspaper Clippings Relating to Florida, 1851-1894.*

SAR — Eagan, Dennis, *Sixth Annual Report of the Commissioner of Lands . . . of the State of Florida.* . . .

SIEBERT — Siebert, Wilbur Henry, *Loyalists in East Florida, 1774 to 1785.*

SIMMONS — Simmons, William Hayne, *Notices of East Florida.*

SMITH-F — Smith, Buckingham, *Memoir of Hernando . . . Fontaneda.* . . .

SMITH-N — Smith, Buckingham, *Notes by the translator,* in *Memoir of . . . Fontaneda.*

SPRAGUE — Sprague, John T., *The Origin, Progress, and Conclusion of the Florida War.*

SSW — *A Sketch of the Seminole War.* . . .

STCS — "The Selection of Tallahassee as the Capital"—the W. H. Simmons *Journal* quoted in *FHQ;* see Williams J. L.

STCW — "The Selection of Tallahassee as Capital"—the J. L. Williams *Journal* quoted in *FHQ;* see Williams, J. L.

STORK — Stork, William, *A Description of East Florida.*

USCHD — *United States Congress, House Documents.*

USCHED — *United States Congress, House Executive Documents.*

USCHMD — *United States Congress, House Miscellaneous Documents.*

USCSD — *United States Congress, Senate Documents.*

USCSED — *United States Congress, Senate Executive Documents.*

V — Vignoles, Charles Blacker, *Observations Upon the Floridas.*

VIAUD — Viaud, Pierre, *The Shipwreck . . . of Monsieur Pierre Viaud.*

VRV — Hakluyt, Richard, *Virginia Richly Valued.* . . .

W — Williams, John Lee, *A View of West Florida* (1827), and *The Territory of Florida* (1837).

WALKER — Walker, Fowler, *The Case of Mr. John Gordon.*

WFH — *A Winter from Home.*

WYNNE — Wynne, John Huddlestone, *A General History of the British Empire in America.*

Y — Young, Capt. Hugh, "A Topographical Memoir on East and West Florida with Itineraries," *FHQ.*

GLOSSARY

A

ABYSS. An unfathomable cavity; a profound chasm. OED.

1837 W 148 [The orifice of the sink] is a vast abyss, situate on the north side of the savanna.

ADIA. Poss. a place name consisting of the short form of the Greek *adiabatos,* "not fordable." Another possibility is that *Adia* has some connection with the dialectal *Ade* applied by navigators of the Severn to reaches where there are eddies in a river, as Swinny Ade, near Coalport (EDD). Also, the term may be a misspelling of Aisa Hatcha near the St. Johns.

1786 in SIEBERT II. 57 There were Several Settlements ... made upon ... 1st. Mount Oswald ... 4th. The Adia upon the Halifax River & 5th. The Swamp inland between the two Rivers.

ALLEY. A walk in a wood bordered with trees. OED.

1587 L 40 At the comming out of the village of Edelano to go vnto the riuers side a man must passe through an allie aboute three hundred paces long and fifti paces broade: on both sides whereof greate trees are planted, the boughes whereof are tied together like an arche, and meet together so artificiallye that a man woulde thinke it were an arboure made of purpose, as faire I saye, as any in all christendome, although it be altogether naturall.

ALLIGATOR HOLE. The DAE general definition of the term as a nest or hibernating place is illustrated here in detail. The 1873 writer gives a minute description of an alligator nest in mud covered with cane or grass; on the other hand W. Bartram (1791) specifies the hole as a sink

frequented by alligators. DAE 1797. Prob. Southern. DA 1791 (1793).

1791 B 238 Our chief conducted me another way to show me a very curious place, called the Alligator-Hole, which was lately formed by an extraordinary eruption or jet of water; it is one of those vast circular sinks ... This remarkable one ... is about sixty yards over, and the surface of the water six or seven feet below the rim of the funnel or bason: the water is transparent, cool, and pleasant to drink, and well stored with fish; a very large alligator at present is lord or chief.

1837 W 147 Tallahasse [is] ... one hundred miles south west from the Alligator Hole.

1873 S 5, 6 The alligator makes large holes in these swamps and savannas. He covers the holes with dried cane, grass and whatever he can find of a similar nature. This covering is raised like a cone, and is two or three feet in height. There is a hole in one side of the covering, through which the 'gator crawls out and in. In these holes the female alligator raises her family ... The greatest alligator hole in Florida is on the ocean side of the Indian River.

ANCHORAGE. Anchorage ground (*q.v.*). OED.

1563 RIBAULD 12-13 Yet the holde & ankerage was so good, that one cable & one anker held vs fast.

1797 MAG under *Espiritu Sancto* Espiritu Sancto, a bay on the W. coast of East Florida ... has a good harbor, 4 fathom water, and safe anchorage.

1830 ASPNA IV. 966 The anchorage is clear of rock.

1855 USCSED vol. 756 #76.4 Cedar Keys ... has an anchorage of about a mile in extent.

ANCHORAGE GROUND. An anchoring-ground. DAE 1824 (fig.). (A.)

1822 ASPNA IV 963 The watering place is two miles from the anchorage ground.

1836 ASPMA VII 276 The commanding general therefore directs you . . . to anchor in the nearest . . . anchorage-ground to the mouth of that stream.

ANCHORING-GROUND. Ground suitable for anchoring. OED 1740 under *anchoring.*

1796 G 11 The best anchoring ground is nearest the east bank.

ARCHIPELAGO. A group of islands. OED.

1821 F 105 From the peculiar situation of these keys . . . little doubt can be entertained that instead of being haunts for Picaroons of all countries, they will be changed into the residence of some industrious people, and become, at no distant period, the Archipelago of the Western World.

1823 V 43 The westward [prong] continues on till the channel is lost in the archipelago of mangrove keys at the north end of Meritt's island.

1837 W 131 Four miles east of the Oclockony Bay, there is a little archipelago of islands.

ARM (OF LAND). A portion of land—the Everglades, or a hammock—projecting from the main body. "Now local." DAE 1654. The sense is extended to mean the spur of a ridge (1823).

1823 V 73 One spur . . . runs parallel to the coast on the west of the great Alachua savanna, where it meets another arm coming from the north-east.

1871 H 43 In some instances, arms of the hammock project out between these high hills.

1874 S 27, 28 [The traveller] must draw his boat over an arm of land completely encircling the lake and cutting it off from the glades . . . All day long were we in this arm of the Everglades.

ARM (OF WATER). One meaning quoted by the DAE (1635) is that of an inlet of the sea, in which sense the word is referred to variously as a lagoon, channel, or branch of a bay. The other DAE (1622) interpretation as a branch of a river is found twice (1587; 1827), and is also applied to an inlet from a pool (1870).

1563 RIBAULD 32 This arme doth deuide, & maketh many other Iles of May, as also many other great Ilandes . . . This riuer . . . we haue called Sene.

1587 L 33 The village of Sarauahi [was] . . . scituated vppon an arme of the riuer.

1770 WYNNE 329 [Anastatia island is] divided from the main land by a narrow channel, called Matanza river, though in reality an arm of the sea.

1775 R 267 This pretended river is one of those arms of the sea commonly called a *Lagoon.*

1784 HUTCHINS 75 About eight miles from Rose island . . . the bay turns more to the eastward, and is divided into two large branches or arms.

1823 STCW 39 Between this peninsula and the spot where we lay there runs an arm of water.

1827 W 22 An arm of the Appalachicola has lately burst into the Chapola.

1831 USCSD 17 The eastern arm of St. Andrews bay is a beautiful channel of water.

1870 BILL 102 Keeping the edge of the river, we came where several old slabs . . . lay across the arm of a projecting pool.

ASH SWAMP. A swamp in which ash is the predominant tree. DAE 1668. (A.)

1765 B 7 The banks of this fine river are a continual alternate change of pine-land, bluffs, cypress, swamps, marshes, and rich ash, and maple-swamps.

1766 B 10 Generally a cypress-swamp interposed between the pine-lands and swamps of ash.

B

BACKBONE. The general concept given in the DAE (1876–not referring to a mountain) is "the ridge of highest elevation in a locality"; the first quotation below refers particularly to the dividing ridge of the Florida peninsula.

1869 FICSP 116 Lake Harris is situated upon the dividing ridge or "backbone" between the Gulf and the Atlantic.

1873 S 8 The [Indian] mound was on a little ridge that forms the backbone of the island.

BACKBONE RIDGE. A dividing ridge; here, with reference to the divide located in the upper part of the East Florida peninsula.

1869 BRINTON 38 ftn. This "Back-Bone Ridge," as it has been called, has a rounded and singularly symmetrical form when viewed in cross section.

BACK COUNTRY. The undeveloped district lying to the rear of a peopled area. DAE 1755. (A.) DA.

1821 F vii The Apalachicola river [will supply] . . . any settlements which may be made upon it, with a rich and valuable back country.

1823 STCW 39 The back country for some miles is intersected with swamps.

1837 W 13 The back country presents a singular alternation of savannas, hammocks, lagoons and grass ponds, called altogether the Everglades.

BACK LAND. Land lying behind the more settled areas. DAE 1681. (A.)

1787 in SIEBERT II. 246 Amongst the back land upon the tract there was some Swamp very good.

BACK SWAMP. In general, a swamp remote from civilization; spec., (1) an inland swamp too saturated to produce undergrowth; a tupelo

swamp (1775); (2) a river swamp, or the land adjacent to and lower than the banks of a river (1823). DAE 1772 (no def.). (A.)

(1) 1775 R. 29 The back or inland swamps answer in situation to what are called the meadows or savannahs (among the pine lands) their soil being rich, occasions them to bear trees. The true back swamps, that are in wet seasons full of standing water, bear scarcely any other tree, than . . . tupelo; the continuance of water on this kind of ground, is the reason why scarce [sic] any undergrowth is found here. There are swamps also called back swamps, but they are either at the head of some stream, or have more or less water running through them.

1784 in SIEBERT II. 301 5840 Acres back swamp uncleared.

(2) 1823 V 90 Sometimes the land immediately on the river banks is rather higher than the grounds a little behind, which are then called back swamps; these are nearly constantly full of water, and have chiefly tupelo growth, and no underwood.

BACK WATER. The excess water of a stream held or forced back by flooding or–here–the tide. DAE 1654.

1787 in SIEBERT II. 204 [The said tract has] a command of back water . . . from the Six Mile Creek By the Tide.

BACK-WATER SWAMP. A swamp adjoining back water.

1787 in SIEBERT II. 209 The swamp upon the land was a back water swamp.

BANK. The underlying meaning of bank is a small raised area, but in the main the term is used to designate the following: (1) the sloping margin of a watercourse; (2) a shelving elevation in the sea near the surface (OED 1605); and (3) a raised shelf or ridge of ground. OED. The first sense is extended to apply to the slanting ground surrounding a lake or pond, or that adjacent to a swamp. However, the height of the slope is inconsequential, and may vary from a few feet to several hundred (1827; 1874). In legal phraseology, the term includes both the alluvion and land between high and low water mark, and the shoals and sand-bars sometimes covered by water (1825). The second quotation dated 1825 illustrates the obsolete meaning of *sea-coast* or *shore*. In the reference to a beach formed by the action of the sea but which separates an inlet from the sea (1769), there may be an overlapping of meaning between (1) and (2). At any rate, under (2) the word is commonly employed here to denote a submerged sand-bar, ridge of soundings, or coral reef. In the reference to a high bank over which a stream flows (1823) the shade of meaning is not too far removed from (3). Nevertheless the important distinction implied in (3) is the fact that the form has no essential connection with water. The actual meaning shown in these examples is rather a heap of earth, or a hill.

(1)   1589 DRAKE map of St. Augustine   A vvood grovving hard by the riuer side, hauing betvveene it & the riuer side a high banke of sand.

1609 VRV 34   The calieuermen and crossebowmen shot at them from the banke [of a great lake].

1652 HEYLIN 116   *Fort de Charles* ... [was] built by the *French* upon the Banks of the River Maio.

1731 C I. 50   [The yellow breasted Chat] frequent the Banks of great Rivers.

1766 B 22-23   Coasted the west side of the lake, which was part sandy-beech, part marsh, some cypress-swamp, and much oak banks.

1787 in SIEBERT II. 208   [There were] twenty [acres] on the bank of the Swamp of Six Mile Creek.

1791 B 81   I made a convenient and safe harbour ... under an elevated bank, on the West shore of the river.

1818 Y 142   Passed an open pond ... with high banks.

1821 F 79   The *Cattle Ford* ... has below it a marsh on both sides, with high oak banks.

1822 SIMMONS 37   The banks of the lake are, in some places, elevated.

1825 ASPPL IV. 201   The *bank* ... includes shoals and sand bars, covered with water at ordinary stages of the sea or river, as well as the band of land lying between high and low water mark ... As soon as ... alluvions are formed free from inundation ... they become *private* property. The property of the *banks* belongs to those whose fields or lots are contiguous to the sea, bay, or river.

1825 ASPPL IV. 632   Your memorialist claims title to a tract of land ... situated on ... *the banks of the sea.*

1827 W 34   The bank is two or three hundred feet high; it commands a beautiful and extensive wild prospect of the Appalachicola.

1852 WFH 35   The river Suwannee ... is a clear, rapid stream, with bold rocky banks.

1874 SAR 58-59   The banks ... are precipitous and high, at some points rising from the water's edge as boldly and precipitously as a rock to the height of from ten to forty feet, at others looking as if they had been graded, one grade rising above another to the height of 100 feet.

(2)   1563 RIBAULD 12-13   Our ... men ... retournying ... declared that they had founde ... viij fadom of water at the hard bancke of the sea.

c. 1565 Hawkins voyage, in HAKLUYT (1589) 541   The French men ... trauelled to the Southwest of the cape, hauing found the same dangerous, by meanes of sundry banks.

1769 STORK 10 Hallifax river . . . is separated from . . . [the sea] only by a sandy beach, in some parts a mile, in others two miles broad. This beach or bank seems to be formed by the sands; which, either by hurricanes, or in a course of ages, have been washed up by the sea.

1773 MS. Map 303 Bank of Rocks under Water called the Grupper Bank.

1776 NAWIG under *Florida, East* [The incessant wearing away, has divided . . . [its southern extremity] into a great number of islands, keys, banks, and rocks.

1778 *The Present State of the West-Indies, etc.* 45　　Its sea-shores have a prodigious quantity of banks of pearl oysters.

1784 HUTCHINS 74　It is necessary to incline a little towards the western reef, which has deep water close to it, in order to avoid the 10 feet [*sic*] bank that there extends about half a mile SW from the point of Rose island.

1796 G 6, 20　The currents on the *Tortugas Bank* sometimes set to the westward, sometimes to the eastward . . . At New Inlet . . . a bank of soundings about 5 leagues broad begins to cover the beach.

1803 E 264-5　On our coast the Stream passes nearly along the great bank of soundings.

1823 STCW 23　The stream [entering the earth] . . . falls into this gulf over a bank twenty or thirty feet in height.

1837 W 40　Five or six miles west of the Tortugas, there is a large bank of coral rock.

(3)　1823 STCW 21　The old Tallahassee village . . . extends over a high and uneven bank . . . descending westwardly to a very large marsh.

1827 W 69　Extensive banks of shells are also found every where near the coast.

1839 *Winter in West Indies* 142 St. Augustine . . . is situate . . . upon the highest land in the vicinity, being a kind of high bank formed of sand and shells.

See also (1)　LAGOON BANK (attrib.); RIVER-BANK; SEA-BANK;　(2)　CORAL BANK; MUD BANK; OYSTER BANK; SAND BANK; SHOAL BANK (attrib.);　(3) CLAYBANK; COCKLE BANK; OYSTER-SHELL BANK; SAND BANK; SEA-BANK; SHELL BANK.

BAR. Also, BARRE. Basically a bar is any subaqueous bank of sand which obstructs navigation, occurring in a river or harbor or at the mouth of an inlet or lake. DAE *c.* 1656. More accurately, these hindrances appear to be ridges of sand thrown up from the bed or bottom by either the pressure of a current coming into contact with a body of water—*e.g.*, where a river joins a lake (1874) or meets the sea (1871)—or the force of the sea opposing a bay (1784). Particularly on the Atlantic coast the bars are constantly "shifting," *i.e.*, varying in depth (1769; 1796; 1829). The word is extended to describe both a dry sand-bar (1775), and a key or island (1823).

1563 RIBAULD 28　We durste not hazarde to enter wyth our shyppe, by reason of a Barre of Sande, that was at the enterye of the Porte.

1587 L 52　My boat . . . by this tyme was passed the barre of the Ryuer.

1741 *Introd. to Report on Gen. Oglethorpes Exped. to St. Aug.*, in CARROLL II. 351-2 Col. *Moore* . . . proceeded in the Vessels directly to the Bar of *St. Augustine* Harbour.

1765 B 4　There is a great barr opposite to the town.

1769 STORK 7 ftn.　The depth of the bars of the harbours on the eastern shore of East-Florida, cannot be exactly ascertained, as the tides there are chiefly regulated by the winds; a strong westerly wind will make but six feet, and an easterly wind 12 feet water upon the bar of St. Augustine, at low water.

1775 R xx The mouth of *Rio Seco* . . . is very seldom open, having a narrow bar of dry sand before it.

1784 HUTCHINS 73-74 The bar of Pensacola is of a semicircular form, with the convex side to the sea, and lies at a considerable distance from the land, occasioned, no doubt, by the conflict between the sea and the bay.

1796 G 20 Hillsborough Inlet has a very shifting bar, sometimes not admitting a boat; and at other times 6, 8, or even 10 feet water have been found upon it.

1822 SIMMONS 27 Were it not for the bar of Lake George, a ship of the line might ride here.

1823 V 84, 121 The rapid current of the gulf stream along this part of the Florida coast has the effect of closing the bars of the inlets . . . Due south from [Newfound Harbor] . . . and four miles off is *key Looe,* a little sandy bar or island.

1829 USCHED vol. 187 #147.13 *St. John River* . . . has a shifting bar, which obstructs its entrance into the sea; the least depth on the bar is 6 feet at low tide, and 12 feet at high tide; however, these depths are much influenced by winds, and the greatest, is at low tide, 7½ feet, and at high tide, 15 feet.

1871 H 108 Many intelligent people from the interior of the country away from the sea, have never heard of 'bars' at the outlet of rivers, and when others speak of getting across or over the bar they naturally look round to see it; but they don't see it, because it is simply a ridge of quicksand which has been scooped out of the bed of the river by the strong running current and piled up on the edge of the deep water of the sea.

1874 KEASBEY 43 This is Volusia bar, a belt of sand drifted across the mouth of the river as it broadens into the lake.

See also OYSTER BAR; SAND-BAR.

BARRENS. A tract of land having little or no vegetation. DAE 1697. The quotations here refer to pine barrens. In contrast to those in the Carolinas, Florida barrens resemble prairies (1836). (A.) DA 1651.

1818 Y 32 In the spring, these islets [in ponds] speckling the barrens . . . have a singularly handsome appearance.

1827 W 39 Barrens are found on the seacoast, and on the ridges, between the large water courses.

1836 SSW 295 In the part of Florida I have travelled through, the barrens are monotonous enough, but differ from those in Carolina having, in some measure, prairie features. The growth is scattered, and the eye is often delighted with the extensive reach of verdurous plains, piny vistas, and glades, with here and there an undulating green mantled hill.

See also FAN-PALMETTO BARREN; PINE BARREN; PINE-BARREN LAND; SAND BARREN.

BASIN. Also, BASON. A natural hollow containing water (DAE 1729); an area having a depressed center (DAE 1821); the area drained by a river (DAE 1804). A landlocked harbor or bay. OED. The first meaning is applied to a sink (1791); extension occurs in the reference to a spring (1852), the pool of a spring (1827), and a lake forming the catchment area of a stream (1784). The 1822 and 1871 writers called the Everglades region a basin in the sense of a depressed, saturated area enclosed by higher lands. The main body of a bay (1832) as opposed to its embranchments, as well as a swelling or expansion in the course of a river (1819), is also thus designated.

1743 C II v From these Rocks . . . plentiful Streams of limpid Water . . .

are received into spacious Basons, formed naturally by the Rocks.
1778 U.S. Continental Congress, *Secret Journals* 97 The embargo on rice [should] be continued in force till such time as the vessels destined to form the blockade by water shall have arrived in the basin of St. Augustine.
1784 HUTCHINS 81 The eastern branch ends in a bason or lake at the bottom of a rising ground.
1791 B 203 In this place a group of rocky hills almost surrounds a large bason, which is the general receptacle of the water, draining from every part of the vast savanna, by lateral conduits, winding about, and one after another joining the main creek or general conductor, which at length delivers them into this sink.
1819 NVSM 133 The river St. John's is here extremely beautiful, at least a mile and a half in breadth, a little higher up it opens into an extensive basin.
1822 SIMMONS 25 It would thus appear, that below the St. John's, the peninsula consists of an immense basin, which, probably, forms the chief supply of the latter stream.
1825 GADSDEN 119 The route of the road surveyed is on the pine lands described as lying between the sand hills and second chain of minor lakes or ponds on the east, and the great basin of the St. John's.
1827 W 24 The basin is circular, fifty yards in diameter, of a bluish green colour, but perfectly transparent, and exceedingly deep.
1832 ASPNA IV. 211 The east bay joins the basin or main body of the bay at this point.
1837 W 28 Leaving Richmond bay, a circular basin.
1851 BYRNE 12 The swamp lands . . . occupy natural depressions or basins, which have been gradually filled up by deposites [*sic*] of vegetable *debris*.
1852 IJ 22 I asked him where the Spring was, at which he pointed to the great basin of water.

1871 H 136 The great basin known as the Everglades.
Attrib. with *spring*.
1843 FHQ XV. 58 The Basin spring, is two hundred or more yards in rear of the Salt spring, in circumference eighty or ninety yards, perfectly transparent, and of great depth.
See also FRESH-WATER BASIN (attrib.).

BAY. The OED gives the sense of an indentation of the sea into the land with a wide opening, to which the DAE (1612) adds the meaning of a wide-mouthed inlet. The term is used synonymously with *harbor* (1803) and *nook* (1837), but a bay within a bay is referred to as an *arm* or *prong* (1837). Extension of meaning occurs in the reference to the dilations in a river as bays or lakes (1793) (*Cf.* INLAND SEA). The distinction between *bay* and *gulf* is not always clear; but according to the OED, "a bay is wider in proportion to its amount of recession than a gulf; the latter term is applied to long landlocked portions of sea opening through a strait, which are never called bays." At any rate, the 1587, 1625, 1652, 1743, and 1778 quotations specifically refer to the Gulf of Mexico.

1563 RIBAULD 30 There appeared vnto vs about seuen leagues of on thys syde of the ryuer of May a great opening or Bay of some ryuer.
1587 L 2 And toward the West the Bay of Mexico.
1609 VRV 17 Hee pitched his campe on the sea side, hard vpon the Bay which went vp vnto the towne.
1625 PURCHAS 870 Thirteene leagues to the North, the *Bay of Charles*, by another name of *Iohn Ponce of Lyon*.
Ibid., 929 In a certaine great Bay in *Florida* (the which runs 300. leagues within the Land) they see Whales in

some season of the yeare, which come from the other Sea.

1652 HEYLIN 115, 116 All of them [*i.e.*, rivers] falling into the Bay of *Mexico...Panuca* lyeth...beyond the large and spacious Bay of the *Holy Ghost.*

1743 C II 21 These [plants]... are mostly found to abound in... small Bays of the Sea.

1743 FRLCSH iii *The Possession of Augustine would have made the great Bay of* Mexico *the Southern Boundary of the British Empire.*

1763 ASPPL I 36 [Extract from treaty of peace between Spain and England:] ... with Fort St. Augustine and the bay of Pensacola.

1773 MS. 175 Apalache is situated upon the Gulf of Awube[1?] now Apalache Bay or rather Gulf.

1778 *The Present State of the West-Indies, etc.* 3 But this Bay ... [is] improperly called, from one of its parts, the *Gulf* of *Mexico,* when it ought to be called the *West-Indian Sea,* which a simple neck of land separates from the great sea, to the East of it.

1791 B 90 On my doubling a long point of land, the river appeared surprisingly widened, forming a large bay, of an oval form, and several miles in extent.

1793 MAG I. 625 St. John's river ... pursues a northern course, in a broad, navigable stream, which in several places spreads into broad bays or lakes.

1803 E 210 Pensacola bay ... is justly considered one of the best harbours on the whole coast.

1813 MELISH 4 *Spiritu Santo,* or *Hillsborough Bay* ... is a capacious inlet.

1823 ASPM II. 1027 The bay ... is completely land-locked by the main land and the island of St. Rosa.

1823 ASPNA IV. 965 The salt ponds ... extend to a bay or inlet which makes into the eastern end of the island from the passage between it and the next key.

1837 W 19-20, 26 The western arm is called Escambia Bay ... East Bay is the third prong [of Pensacola bay] ... Gallivans or Delaware Bay is the nook formed east of Punta Longa or Cape Roman.

1869 FICSP 139 The rock ... slopes both toward the Bay [*sc.*, Florida bay] and the Everglades.

BAY-BUSH FLAT(S). A flat on which the predominating growth is bay shrubbery.

1825 GADSDEN 120 For the next six miles cypress swamps and saw-grass ponds, diversified occasionally with saw-palmetto and bay-bush flats.

BAY-GALL. The DAE (1775) defines a bay-gall as low-lying, spongy land overgrown principally with sweet bay. However, the specific interpretation here is as either a channel (1823) or a watercourse (1775) covered with a spongy soil mixed with vegetable fibre, or a miry thicket (1818) consisting of loblolly bay (a small evergreen tree of the Southern states; the black laurel) and gall bushes (a gallberry bush) enclosing the head of a watercourse. Prob. Southern or Southeastern.

1773 MS. 219, 277 Bay gall... Crossed a cypress bay gall [*sic*] issuing out of Do. [ditto] ponds.

1775 R 31-32 Bay and cypress galls ... intersect the pine lands, and are seldom of any breadth; the bay galls are properly water courses, covered with a spungy earth mixed with a kind of matted vegetation fibre; they are so very unstable, as to shake for a great extent round a person, who, standing on some part thereof, moves himself slightly up and down... the water standing in them is impregnated with acid.

1818 Y 29 The *Bay-Galls* are miry thickets encircling the heads and sheltering the currents of almost all the streams of Florida.—They are called Bay-Galls from the predominant growth of different kinds of Bay and Gall bushes which cover them forming a swampy, tangled thicket sometimes impenetrable.

1823 V 91 In the pine lands, the early courses of the creeks and streams are through two sorts of channels, *bay galls* and *cypress galls*. The *bay galls* are spongy, boggy, and treacherous to the foot, with a coat of matted vegetable fibres: the loblolly bays spread their roots, and the saw palmetto crawls on the ground, making them altogether unpleasant and even dangerous to cross: the water in these bay galls is strongly impregnated with pyroligneous acid.

1836 SSW 176 The smaller variety ... grows in what are called the Bay Galls.

1869 FICSP 30 [The] low flat, swampy regions ... are frequently studded with "bay galls."

Attrib. with *branch, swamp.*

1836 SSW 139 The flankers ... skipped along waist high through scrubby bushes, and rustling saw-palmettoes, over knotty bogs [*sic*] and bay gall branches.

1787 in SIEBERT II. 245 [The Witness] saw no swamp but a narrow slip of bay gall swamp.

See also CYPRESS GALL, GALL.

BAY HEAD. A bay-gall (*q.v.*).

1773 MS. 272 Passed 2 ponds a bay gall or head, running in a big swp.

BAY LAND. Land overgrown with bay trees; a bay-gall (*q.v.*).

1871 H 97-98 There are tens of thousands of acres of immensely rich bay lands in Wakulla county that are susceptible of easy drainage, the soil of which is from ten to twenty feet deep.

BAYOU. Although the NID gives six specific shades of meaning with many subdivisions, neither the DAE nor the records bear out any such complicated interpretation. The basic idea appears to be that of a small, sluggish tributary stream. DAE 1766. The Florida illustrations fall into two

groups: the one describing a sluggish branch or creek discharging through a delta (1818); and the other indicating an estuarial creek or inlet (1837; 1869), or a small bay, open cove, or harbor (1823; 1827). NID. The term is used once to designate an estuary of the sea (1837). It is probable that at least the second meaning (bay, inlet) is peculiar to the Gulf coast region of Florida; apparently the word is not used in this sense on the Atlantic coast of the state. Prob. Southern.

1818 Y 35 One mile and a half above where this bayou comes in, another, but not so large leaves the river on the east side and is connected by several small channels with a wide but short stream entering the sound eight miles east of the mouth of Apalachicola.

1823 STCW 38 A large bayou at the southwest penetrates within five rods of the Gulf.

1827 W 13-14 Bayou Chico ... is a pleasant, healthy, and safe harbour for small craft.

1837 ASPMA VII. 832 [We] drove them about two miles through several small hammocks and across two or three bayous or estuaries of the sea.

1837 W 20 Bayou Texar enters the bay one mile above Pensacola. It is four miles long, but narrow.

1869 BRINTON 106 This coast ... is an almost continuous belt of marsh, cut by innumerable creeks and bayous, extending from five to fifteen miles into the interior.

See also CREEK BAYOU (attrib.).

BAY POND. A pond in which bay trees grow.

1773 MS. 271 In low pine land ... a bay pond ¼ m. off.

1825 GADSDEN 120 Occasional ... grassy flats, spotted with cypress and bay ponds.

BAY SHORE. The coast of a bay. DAE 1823. Prob. Southern. DA 1732.

1834 ASPMA V. 462 One bastion front of the work rests immediately on the bay shore.

BAY SWAMP. A swampy tract overgrown with bay trees. DAE 1741. Prob. Southern. The detailed descriptions given herein indicate that a bay swamp is a low-lying area covered with shallow water and aquatic vegetation, chiefly the red bay (1743). One writer identifies this type of land as being the actual source of cypress-branches (1766), probably because of the pond-like nature of bay swamps; the same author also uses the term interchangeably with cypress swamp.

1743 C II. iv Particularly Pine-Lands are often intermixed with narrow Tracts of low Lands, called Bay-Swamps, which are not confined by steep Banks, but by their gradual Sinking seem little lower than the Pine-Land through which they run. In the middle of these Swamps the Water stands two or three Feet deep, shallowing gradually on each Side. Their Breadth is unequal, from a Quarter to half a Mile, more or less, extending in Length several Miles. On this wet Land grows a Variety of Evergreen Trees and Shrubs, most of them Aquaticks, as the *Alcea Floridana, Red Bay, Water-Tupelo,* etc.

1766 B 22, 34 Some ponds are a mile or two big . . . with a rivulet running out, and sometimes with a bay or cypress-swamp at the head . . . Bay-swamps are frequently found in the pine-lands, being the general heads of the cypress-branches.

1823 STCS 32 The road descended from the hammock into a bay swamp through which we waded nearly up to our saddle skirts for upward of a mile.

BEACH. The shore of the sea; the part of the shore lying between high- and low-water-mark. OED. The meaning is extended in the 1769 quotation to designate a sand bank thrown up by the sea.

1742 RCBH 32 Col. Vander Dussen . . . ordered the Regiment under Arms, and marched along the Beach towards the *Point.*

1769 STORK 10 Hallifax river . . . is separated from . . . [the sea] only by a sandy beach, in some parts a mile, in others two miles broad. This beach or bank seems to be formed by the sands; which, either by hurricanes, or in a course of ages, have been washed up by the sea.

1803 E 247 On the north east side of Matacombe, there is a beautiful beach, which has the appearance of whitish sand, but on examination is found to be broken shells, coral etc.

1823 ASPNA IV. 965 The beach of this and the neighboring islands, and the keys on the Florida reef, are composed of very fine, broken shells, and minute particles of the limestone rock and coral, almost as fine as sand, but not a grain of sand was discovered on any of them.

1827 W 6 Westward, the coast . . . exhibits a beach of sand, white as snow, and almost as hard as rock.

1873 S 10 The steamship Ladona drove ashore during the terrible gale of Aug. 17, 1871. She struck the beach in a bight twelve miles north of Canaveral light . . . She lay fifty feet from shore, and had dragged half a mile in the sand.

See also DESERT BEACH (attrib.); SAND BEACH; SEA BEACH; SHELL-BEACH.

BED. The bottom of a watercourse, or of any body of water. A layer or bed-like mass—here—of rocks (1823); the layer of earth into which plants sink their roots (1765). OED.

1765 B 9 These [pistia] by storms are broke from their natural beds and float down the river in great patches.

c. 1767 FHQ XII. 117 The bed of the river being about fifteen miles above the Fort.

1791 B 149 The bed of the river was nearer the level of the present surface of the earth.

1822 SIMMONS 37 [The] pure waters [of Lake Ware] . . . are so extremely clear, as to admit the Sun's rays to a considerable depth; and the light may, for some distance, be seen, playing upon its bed of silver sand.

1823 V 82 These falls are merely rapids over a bed of secondary limestone rocks.

1831 USCSD vol. 214 #136. 16 [After one mile the cut-off] enters into the serpentine bed of an old bayou.

1871 H 108 [A bar] is simply a ridge of quicksand . . . scooped out of the bed of the river.

See also MARL-BED; OYSTER BED; PEAT BED.

BEECH HAMMOCK. Also, BEACH HAMMOCK. Probably a hammock of beech trees.

1823 ASPPL III. 821 John B. Strong . . . presented his claim for six hundred acres . . . at a place known by the name of Beech Hammock.

1828 ASPPL VI. 69 A royal title . . . for 300 acres on Amelia island, at a place called Beiche Hammock.

1874 S 31 Somebody had fired the beach hammocks.

BEND. The common meaning given in the DAE (*c.* 1665) of a turn in the course of a stream is here extended to apply not only to an indentation in the coastline (1837) but also to a curve in the shore line of a lake (1842). Because some kind of a watercourse is usually associated with a swamp (*q.v.*) it is sometimes difficult to distinguish the latter from the former; however, the 1823 (p. 804) and 1825 examples appear to refer to a notable crook in the outline of the

swamp proper. The DAE (1789) also defines this term as a tract of land within a turn of a river (1823 [p. 772]; 1871).

1765 B 7 This rich swamp terminated at the bend of the river.

1773 MS. 323 This . . . I endeavour to shew more fully, however, because of the last Bend, or Course of the Florida Stream at this Place, where it enters . . . the New Bahama Channel.

1822 S 6 The lands included in the bend of the St. John's. [SIMMONS]

1823 ASPPL III. 772 Samuel Fairbanks presented his memorial for eighty acres of land, lying in St. Antonio's bend, on the margin of St. John's river.

Ibid., 804 The third contains five hundred acres, at the Big bend of Durbin's swamp.

1825 ASPPL IV. 638 Your memorialist claims title to a tract . . . situated . . . on the head of the north branch of Durbin's swamp, to the west of the part of said swamp called the Big Bend.

1831 ASPMA IV. 731 *Apalachicola river, Florida.*—An experiment was made this year to improve the navigation of this river, by cutting off the points forming some of the most difficult bends.

1837 W 140 In several deep bends of this coast, very good plantations might be cultivated.

1842 PREBLE 43 Paddled around the bend in the Lake.

1871 H 102 Mushy Bend is the name of a tract of fertile land on the Choctawhatchie river, some fifteen miles long by five in width.

1874 SAR 177 The largest number of budded trees in the county in one body is in what is appropriately called "Orange Bend," on the Ocklawaha river, between Lakes Eustis and Griffin.

See also MARSH BEND (attrib.).

BIGHT. Also, BITE. An inward bend in a coastline; spec., a bay (1823); a corner or recess in an inlet (1871). DAE 1640. (Also EDD.)

1775 R xx   South of Rio Seco is another point of rocks, and south of it a
small bite.

1823 V 53   The bight between cape
Sable and punta Largo, or Cape Ro-
mano, is called the bay of Juan Ponce de
Leon.

1871 S 31   Salt water fishes piled
themselves into the bight of the inlet.

1873 S 10   The steamship Ladona ...
struck the beach in a bight twelve miles
north of Canaveral light.

BITTER LAND.   Sour land; a gall. DAE
1837. Prob. local in Florida.

1827 W 53   The third kind of swamps
are those spongy tracts, where the waters continually ooze through the soil,
and finally collect in streams and pass
off. These are properly termed galls,
sometimes sour, sometimes bitter lands.

BLACKJACK RIDGE.   A sand ridge
overgrown with blackjack (a species
of oak trees). DA 1775.

1823 STCW 28   In some places black-
jack [sic] ridges are seen.

1837 W 126   The peninsula between
Pensacola Bay and St. Rosa Sound, is a
mixture of pine and black jack ridges.

1869 FICSP 28   [The impression that
much of the soil in Florida is worthless]
will not hold good ... [of] the "black
jack" ridges.

BLOWING SPRING.   A spring which
boils intermittently in such a way as
to produce a flapping sound. [?A
blowing cave. DA 1825.]

1852 IJ 35   There is another spring
called the blowing spring that will boil
up rapidly for two or three minutes then
sink down about two feet, remain quiet
about a minute, then the water becomes
agitated producing a sound like ducks
playing in the water, and it will then
boil up again. This is its constant practice.

BLUFF.   The DAE (1687) defines the
term generally as a steep bank or

shore, and also as a sharp rise in the
level of land (1796). Several more
specific meanings are given below as
follows: rising ground (1784); a spur
from the sand hills (1818); elevated
spots on the banks of a river which
are partially inundated at high tide
(1818); a palmetto grove (1874 1st
quotation); an island (1874 1st quotation). Note that in no case does the
height exceed 100 feet. (A.)

1742 RCBH Apx. 44   Colonel *Vander
Duffen* ... found ... a *fine Bluff* opposite to the mouth of the River St. *Sebastian's*.

1775 R Apx. lxxxiii   You will then open
a large red bluff on the main land in the
NE quarter.

1784 GME 97   There are on each side
of the river a number of rising grounds
or bluffs.

1796 G 12   Seven miles to the eastward of Boca Chica there is a *Small
Island* with a remarkable high bluff of
trees, which in most views appear *in
the shape of a saddle*.

1818 Y 34, 36   At its southern extremity, a Bluff comes in on the east side—a
barren spur from the sand-hills ... Below this point there are several places
dignified with the name of bluffs, but
they all are partially inundated at high
water except Old Woman's Bluff ... In
the winter and spring the banks of Apalachicola below Fort Gadsden are covered with water except in a few places,
called, though improperly, bluffs ...
These partially elevated spots seldom
extend more than a few hundred yards
and have generally a thick growth of
timber peculiar to southern rivers with
live-oak, white-oak, maple, white pine,
cypress, bay and cabbage palmetto.

1823 V 44   Immediately beyond the
mouth of this creek are the Turkey
bluffs, of rich yellow sand and forty feet
in height, extending a mile in length.

1869 BRINTON 54   About six miles
from the entrance the channel runs close

along the base of a hill or headland of moderate height, covered with pine, cedar, etc. This is *St. John's Bluff.*

1870 BILL 79 Passing Yellow Bluff, a small landing of trifling importance, at which the steamer halted.

1871 H 128 *Massacre Bluff,* where six shipwrecked sailors were killed by Indians, is a mound, covered with trees on the east bank.

1874 S 17 We soon passed Long Bluff, a grove of palmettoes half a mile in length ... Possum Bluff is a charming island, alive with opossums and alligators.

1874 SAR 58-59 The banks on which this most beautiful and variegated growth is found are precipitous and high, at some points rising from the water's edge as boldly and precipitously as a rock to the height of from ten to forty feet, at others looking as if they had been graded, one grade rising above another to the height of 100 feet. This is what is known as "The Bluff" of the lake.

Prec. by a qualifying term: a "broken" *bluff.*

1775 R Apx. lxxvi A high island, whose northern end is a broken bluff.

1796 G 25 The middle entrance of Boca Grande in Latitude 26 38 north, is known by a broken bluff with a grove of pine-trees standing very near the beach on the North end of the South island.

1818 Y 33 Some of the bluffs are high and broken—projecting from the steep sand-hills below the Flint.

Attrib. with *island, point, shore.*

1775 R. Apx. lvii The entrance of *Porto Puercos* is readily known by two bluff islands at its mouth.

1765 B 4 Arrived at squire Roll's a bluff point 17 foot high.

1862 FHQ XV. 87 All boats are brought close under the bluffs, the channel running close by the bluff shore.

See also CABBAGE-BLUFF; CLAY BLUFF; COCKLE BLUFF; PINE BLUFF; SAND BLUFF.

BLUFF LAND. Land that rises steeply. DAE 1666. Here, the land extends down to water. (A.)

1831 USCSD vol. 214 #136.16 The survey was accordingly commenced ... at a point where the bluff land makes down to the edge of the open water.

BOAT CHANNEL. A channel that is navigable for smaller vessels.

1837 W 23, 31-32 From this [sound] to Tampa Bay, there is an inland boat channel ... Helley's Keys are a range of sandy islands extending in front of Tocobagos, or St. Joseph's Bay. From Tocobagos to Tampa there is a boat channel behind these keys, but at some places it is very shoal at low tide.

BOG. A piece of wet, spongy ground, too soft to bear any heavy weight on its surface; a morass. DAE 1623. (Without pl.) Bog land, boggy soil (1827). OED. Note the unstable quality of this type of land (1815).

1609 VRV 19-20 They passed through a countrie full of bogges, where horses could not travell.

1744 KIMBER 22 We march'd thro' several Bogs and Swamps up to our Bellies.

c. 1767 FHQ XII. 119 The road to this place is frequently interrupted by boggs, ponds, etc.

1775 R 173 We have in these provinces no undrainable boggs.

1815 NWR 105 This is a very extensive swamp, and much of it a bog; so much so, that a little motion will make the mud and water quiver to a great distance.

1827 USCHED Vol. 217 #43.33 Immediately above the mound B, the river could not be navigated in a canoe, for it is a narrow rivulet, in the middle of wide bog.

1836 ASPMA VII. 143 The same difficulty also occurred in a palmetto swamp of considerable extent where horses could not be used on account of the bog.

1854 ESB 54 Some cavaliers ... wasted the strength of their horses in coursing deer and in racing through water and bogs.

See also CYPRESS BOG.

BOIL. The bubbling upheaval of water above the surface and in the center of a spring.

1852 IJ 23, 35 I did not perceive that the water was any colder in the boil than in any other part of the Spring. The boil is about four feet in diameter, it rises a foot above the level of the water and then gracefully rolls off ... In Fla ... there is a spring, the boil of which is so strong that a heavy man may jump from an elevation of ten feet into it and he will not sink below his waist, and then he will be thrown out of the water.

BOTTOM. (1) The ground or bed beneath a watercourse or body of water. OED. Spec., the bed of a dried-up lake (1837). (2) Low-lying land (1818), a valley, a dell; an alluvial hollow (1821; 1827). OED; EDD. DA 1750. *Cf.* INTERVAL.

(1) 1563 RIBAULD 11 We cast an Anker at tenne fadome water, the bottome of the Sea beynge playne wyth muche Ocias [*sic*].

1731 C I. 73 [These plants] are in great Plenty at the Bottom of the shallow Seas and Channels.

1765 B 9-10 The roots striking deep, often touch the muddy bottom [of the river].

1775 R 265 A bridge was built over ... [a creek] to the west of the town ... but the great depth of the water joined to the instability of the bottom did not suffer it to remain long.

1784 HUTCHINS 82 In one place off the East end of Rose island, out of sight of land, the bottom is of a coarse gravel, mixed with coral.

1796 G 19 There is not above 12 feet water within a mile of it [*i.e.*, *the shore*], the bottom solid rock.

1821 DARBY 12 The bottom of the gulf undulates so greatly, that ... the submarine inequalities are very much more considerable than are those of the adjoining shores.

1837 W 42 The bottom of all these channels is formed of the soft limestone; but it is usually covered with a white-wash of dissolved matter, about a foot thick.

Ibid., 133 When a sudden draught has withdrawn the waters [of Alligator Lake], millions of fish have been left to perish on the muddy bottom.

1869 BRINTON 106 The channels between them are usually shallow, with mud bottoms.

(2) 1744 KIMBER 21 Mounting the Sand-Hills [we] lay under Arms, in a Bottom, between two Ridges.

1812 FHQ IX. 67 The pine barren between this and the Saw Mill is handsome in consequence of its being broken by bottoms.

1818 Y 24 [These] brooks ... have narrow bottoms of very rich soil.

1821 F 156 It is not thus with the canes of ... hollows or bottoms.

1827 W 10 Residences on the low alluvial bottoms, and near the marshes, have usually, in autumn, been attended with agues and bilious fevers.

See also CANE BOTTOM; RIVER BOTTOM; SECOND BOTTOM.

BOTTOM LAND. A stretch of low-lying ground; a bottom. Usually in pl. DAE 1634. The 1803 and 1837 authors hardly distinguish this type of land from the bank of a river, and describe it as sometimes being inundated. (A.)

1803 E 233 As you ascend, the banks become more elevated, and some of them which may be called bottom land, are seldom overflown: these are remarkably rich, and extremely fertile.

1818 Y 102 Cotton and hemp will succeed beyond a doubt and indigo will on the bottom land where the stiff marl has but a little mixture of sand.

1827 W 9　The estuaries of large rivers, and rich bottom lands ... are usually unfavourable to health.

1837 W 125　The bottom lands on the Escambia River are very rich, but are subject to be overflown.

1870 BILL 189　In the rich hummock and bottom lands, a black mold, with a mixture of the sand, is seen.

See also RIVER-BOTTOM LAND (attrib.).

BOWL. A bowl-shaped natural basin. OED 1860. Spec., a well.

1869 BRINTON 104　The *Punch Bowl is the name given by the sailors to a curious natural well about one mile south of the mouth of the Miami and close to the shore. It is always filled with good sweet water.

BRAKE. An area covered with bushes, briers, reeds, etc.; a canebrake (1837). DAE 1757. (A.)

1836 SSW 141　Until sunset, we were practising double quick extensions trough [sic] pine barrens; forwarding and rallying skirmishes over bogs and brakes.

1837 W 128　The streams ... pass into brakes of reed cane.

See also CANEBRAKE; REED-BRAKE.

BRANCH. (1) A tributary of a creek or river. DAE 1642. When the 1803 author refers to the "main branch" of the St. Marys he actually means the river itself, or the principal channel thereof. Subsidiary streams large enough to be called rivers are twice spoken of under this designation (1784; 1827). The 1827 writer mentions an underground branch of a river. (2) A small stream; a brook. DAE 1663. (A.) (3) The meaning is extended to apply to both a lagoon (1766) and a bay which forms part of a larger bay. (4) An extension

from the main body of various land features; namely, an arm or wing of a cave (1827), cypress swamp (1766), marsh (1791), oak hills (1818), ridge (1823), and swamp (1777). OED.

(1)　1763 ROBERTS 12　This last is a branch of the *Apalachicola* river.

1784 HUTCHINS 81　Yellow Water [river], a branch of the East bay.

1787 in SIEBERT II. 194　[The Witness] Says That he had a Warrt. of Survey ... for 1000 Acres Situated on a Branch of the Six Mile Creek called little Trout Creek.

1791 B 106　This enchanting little forest is partly encircled by a deep creek, a branch of the river.

1803 E Apx. 139　The river St. Mary's is formed by the water draining out of the Okefonoke swamp along several marshes, or small swamps, which join into one, and form, or constitute the main branch or body of the river.

1823 ASPPL III. 801　William Drummond presented his memorial to this board, praying confirmation of title to five thousand seven hundred and sixty acres of land, lying on a creek called Buck branch, on the banks of the river St. Mary's.

1823 V 39　Its western branch or Smith's Creek heads in Graham's a wamp [sic].

1825 GADSDEN 120　Crosses near the Tomoka a small branch tributary to the same.

1827 W 16, 21　The Ocklockney river enters the west end, where a large branch passes off to the west, called Crooked river ... The eastern branch [of the Chapola] continues under ground several hundred yards.

Ibid., 82　There are three principal branches that [unite and form boggy creeks].

1871 H 132　Boats can be taken from a branch of Jupiter river across into the lake.

(2)　1818 Y 139　Cross a bad branch

in the first mile, and an open branch in the fourth, another open branch in the fifth—a thickety and miry branch in the seventh.

1825 ASPPL IV. 602 The marsh of a branch called the Sweet Water branch.

1832 USCHED vol. 219 #185.6 [The survey] is carried over the lowest ground to the Horse Shoe branch.

(3) 1766 B 17 Here several more large branches or lagoons branched eastward, and spread their numerous branches in the marshes.

1784 HUTCHINS 75 About eight miles from Rose island ... the bay turns more to the eastward, and is divided into two large branches or arms.

1827 W 11, 15 The north branch [of Pensacola bay] is called Yellow Water bay ... Ten miles from the entrance [of St. Andrew's bay], another branch extends westwardly thirty miles; this branch is in some places ten miles wide.

(4) 1766 B 26 This north side [of the lake] is generally a narrow cypress-swamp to the pines, widening a little in some branches.

1777 FHQ IX. 41 I ... [left] a small party in a branch of a Swamp.

1791 B 183 After crossing over this point or branch of the marshes, we entered a noble forest.

1818 Y 23 A wide branch of [oak hills] ... stretches up the Tallahassa creek.

1823 V 74 Branches of this ridge lie on both sides of the Amisura river.

1827 W 36-37 To the right of this last branch of the cave, the excavation has been examined about one hundred feet.

Attrib. with *creek*.

1823 ASPPL III. 793 One hundred and forty-five acres of land, situated about seven miles north of St. Augustine, on Red-house branch creek.

See also BAY-GALL (attrib.); CREEK BRANCH; CYPRESS-BRANCH; HEAD BRANCH; LAKE BRANCH (attrib.); LINE BRANCH; POND BRANCH (attrib.); SAVANNA BRANCH (attrib.); SPRING BRANCH; SWAMP BRANCH (attrib.).

BRANCH LAND. Probably land watered by a branch. Called "creek bottom" in DA 1870 under *branch* (attrib.).

1874 SAR 117 On Amelia Island ... are soils of calcarious sand that are adapted for the finest qualities of long staple cotton ... which the branch, fresh marsh and black rush lands attached to them are especially suitable for gardening.

BREAK. A sudden interruption in the terrain. DAE 1760. A gap in the shore line produced by the flooding of an inlet (1821). A round and sloping depression in the earth's surface; a small basin or hollow (1818).

1773 MS. 224 To Break in the Sand hills.

1818 Y 26-27 The dreariness [of the high pine flats] ... is at intervals relieved by the intervention of very deep and sudden breaks in the surface filled with the greatest variety of ever-green ... and sheltering springs of delightful water.

1821 F 98 The whole position and face of the break appeared to me to be from within.

1823 V 43 On Indian river some of the best hammocks in the Floridas are to be met with ... the occasioned breaks of pine bluffs are rather advantageous ... for settlements.

BREAKER. A reef or sand bank on which the waves break. *?Obs.* DAE 1722.

1741 GHDPOPW 190 The South Breakers, or Sand Banks help to form the Entrance of the Harbour.

1763 ROBERTS 24 At the entrance of this harbour are the North and South breakers, forming two channels.

1775 R Apx. xvi When you are on the outer breaker [of the shoal], land is scarce visible.

1796 G 21 The outermost breakers of

the shoal which surrounds it, are at 15 miles distance from the Cape.

1821 F 89 [St. Augustine harbor] is surrounded by breakers, which are not as dangerous as they appear to be.

BRIDGE. A natural bridge (*q.v.*).

c. 1767 FHQ XII. 119 [The] Chipouly ... is twenty three miles from the bridge.

1818 Y 42 There is a natural bridge over the river nearly three miles in extent ... The break from under the bridge on the south side is abrupt.

1827 W 37 A great road formerly crossed this bridge: it is now travelled by some persons, during the summer; in winter, the whole is overflowed.

1837 W 48 Twelve miles from the Gulf, it sinks under ground for three fourths of a mile. From this bridge to the sea, it is navigable for small vessels.

BRINK. The edge of the land bordering a piece of water: formerly denoting "bank, shore, brim" (1587 below); now esp. when this rises abruptly from the water (1836). OED. Bank by the side of a river (Dial. EDD).

1587 L 45L Hys wyfe accompanyed withall the women of the village came vnto the Ryuers brincke.

1836 SSW 264 If suddenly a hoarse-mouthed bloating bull frog, mounts the brink and bellows out 'Blood and Ounds,' the little frogs suddenly pop into their holes and cease their chirping.

BROOK. A small stream; a branch. DAE 1622.

1744 KIMBER 24 [At] *the Grove* ... there is a running Brook of the finest Water I ever drank.

c. 1767 FHQ XII. 117 The N.E. River takes its rise from some small brooks near Mikisuki.

1784 HUTCHINS 77 The town of Pensacola is surrounded by two pretty large brooks of water.

1821 F 178 Six mile Brook ... is a pretty little winding stream.

1837 W 49 Cantonment Brook is situated at the east side of [the mouth of the Hillsborough River].

See also FRESH-WATER BROOK.

BRUSHWOOD. Small growing trees and shrubs; esp., a thicket, underwood. OED.

1836 SSW 268 The troops ... could not penetrate ... the close brushwood of the branch ... [which was] filled with Indians.

1874 S 30 Umbrageous brushwood shut out all sunbeams.

BURROW. A hole made in the ground for a dwelling place by an animal (here, a gopher). OED. A similar long and very narrow passage constructed by a salamander chiefly for the purpose of locating edible roots. (1836).

1827 W 27 The Gopher ... delights in black jack ridges, which are easily penetrated with its burrows.

1836 SSW 163, 165 Met in the pine barrens ... the hillocks of the Salamanders ... Their burrows are exceedingly numerous in various places, and give an appearance to the plains similar to that produced by ploughing up the ground.

C

CABBAGE-BLUFF. A bluff overgrown with cabbage palmetto (trees).

1766 B 13 Set out from Cabbage-bluff, so called from the great number of palm or cabbage-trees growing there.

CABBAGE GROVE. A grove of cabbage palmettos.

1775 R Apx. xx 1½ miles further is a high cabbage grove.

CABBAGE HAMMOCK. A hammock covered with a growth of cabbage palmettos. DAE 1837. Prob. local in Florida.

1773 MS. 273 In Cabage Hammok—above Savannah runs gr. [great] way east.
1787 in SIEBERT II. 251 This tract had about 160 acres of it rich low Cabbage Cedar and Mulberry Hammock.
1823 ASPPL IV. 387 This deponent is also well acquainted with another tract of fifty acres of land, which is on Amelia island, at a place called Cabbage Hammock.

CABBAGE KNOLL. A knoll overgrown with cabbage palmettos.

1773 MS. 284, 285 A grt. boggy Savh. & cab. [cabbage] Knowl . . . In Savh. sur[rounde]d & interspersed with cabb. Knowls.

CABBAGE LAND. Land covered with cabbage palmettos. DAE 1837. Poss. local in Florida.

1773 MS. 227 Clear cabage Land-by the Spaniards called the Palmaro.
Ibid., 273, 284 In cabage Land—near Savh . . . In cab Land, mixed with pine.

CABBAGE POND. A pond around which cabbage palmettos cluster.

1773 MS. 282, 283 In low Pe. [Pine] Ld. [Land] scatt. Trees—Cabbage pond near . . . Cabage Pond near . . . On narrow neck—small cabage Pond near.

CABBAGE SWAMP. A swamp or low hammock (1822) overgrown with cabbage palmettos.

1821 F 78 [The meadow is] interspersed with clusters of small copped trees, surrounding cabbage swamps.
1822 SIMMONS 6 [The Diego Plains] are bordered on the west, by a Cabbage Swamp, or region of low hammock, which might be easily drained and reduced to cultivation.
1836 SSW 174 The situation had not much to recommend it, looking out . . . upon . . . [the] cabbage swamps that bounded the horizon.
1837 W 137 The north part of the county embraces the Cabbage Swamp

and Diego Plains, both containing superior land.
Attrib. with *tract*.
1823 ASPPL III. 739 Made a small hole on the Cabbage swamp tract, about three or four feet deep.

CABBAGE-TREE HUMMOCK. A hummock consisting chiefly of palmetto growth.

1842 PREBLE 37 Waded fifty yards farther and reached the dry land,—a wide plain dotted with cabbage-tree and pine hummocks.

CABBAGE-TREE ISLAND. An island covered with cabbage palmettos.

1796 G 28 The Kay of Bay Honda . . . is a very remarkable Kay, (*cabbage-tree Island*) having a great many cabbage-trees, and being the only one which has them in plenty.

CABBAGE-TREE LAND. An area on which the predominating growth is the cabbage palmetto.

1823 V 50 Over this are a number of islands and promontories, many of which are altogether of hammock growth, with mixtures of pine and cabbage tree land.

CANAL. A watercourse connecting other streams or bodies of water with each other.

1823 V 49 Rio Seco, unable to discharge itself over the dry inlet, has forced itself by a natural canal through a neck of high land into the Middle river.
1825 GADSDEN 119 The western base of [the chain of sand hills] . . . is washed by another succession of smaller lakes or saw-grass ponds and swamps, occasionally connected with each other by natural canals.

CANE BOTTOM. A stretch of low land, generally along a river, upon which cane is growing. DAE 1819. Poss. Southern.

1821 F vii [The tract] contains the richest cane bottoms.

CANEBRAKE. A stretch of land overgrown with canes; a thicket of canes (1823; 1874). DAE 1775. Southern. DA 1769.

1791 B 233 Now at once opens to view, perhaps, the most extensive Cane-break* that is to be seen on the face of the whole earth.
1821 F 147-48 Advancing into the country, are often found extensive plains of grass and cane brakes, on which vast herds of cattle were formerly raised; they are also well adapted to rice and sugar.
1823 STCW 22 We were unable to find where the waters emerged from out of the earth, on account of cane brakes and undergrowth, which rendered it absolutely impenetrable.
1837 W 130 The lands on the Appalachicola are very rich ... [and] interspersed with luxuriant cane brakes.
1874 S 17 Great dewy spider-webs reflecting all the colors of the rainbow swung from the canebrakes.

CANE HAMMOCK. A canebrake.

1821 F vii [The tract] contains the richest cane bottoms, and upland cane hammocks.

CANE LAND. Land upon which cane grows in abundance. DAE 1786. Prob. Southern.

1827 W 86 There are some very rich cane lands on the Appalachicola river.

CANE PASTURE. Pasture land overgrown with canes.

1773 MS. 281 In high Pe. [Pine] Ld. [Land] ... above Savh: near here cane Pasture.

CANE SWAMP. A stretch of swampy land overgrown with canes. DAE 1709. Prob. Southern.

1731 C I. 50 Their loud chattering Noise reverberates from the hollow

Rocks and deep Cane-Swamps.
1769 STORK 5 The abundance of cane-swamps are a strong indication of the goodness of the soil.
1874 S 17 The river ... was still fenced in by canes twenty or thirty feet high. From the top of the pilot house, as far as the eye could reach, we could see cane swamps stretched—north, south, east, and west. They were at least forty miles wide.

CAPE. A point of land jutting into a stream (1821; 1854) or body of water. DAE 1602. The projection may be in the form of a peninsula (East Florida peninsula 1771), promontory (1791), tongue of land (1874), or the elbow or pointed end of an island (1773; 1821 2nd quotation; and 1837). A bank of sand running into a river is also thus designated (1871). The sense is extended to denote the series of keys called the Martyres (1652), and also the shoal of a cape (1827).

1563 RIBAULD 11 A certayne poynte of Cape situate Vnder that Latitude of nine & twenty degrees & a half ... we haue named Cape Francois.
c. 1565 Hawkins voyage, in HAKLUYT (1589) 537 The 12 day in the morning we fell with the Islands upon the cape of Florida.
1589 DRAKE 42 The thirteenth of May ... proceeding about the Cape of FLORIDA, we never touched aniewhere.
1614 PURCHAS 647 Calos is neare the Cape of Florida.
1652 HEYLIN 117 Called from hence *Cabeca de los Martyres,* or the Cape of *Martyrs.*
1707 Archdale, *A New Description of ...Carolina,* in CARROLL II. 92-93 That part of the Continent which is called *Florida* ... begins at Cape Florida, in the Latitude of about 25, and runs *North East* to 36½.
1731 C I. 38 [The red birds] are com-

mon in all parts of *America,* from *New-England* to the *Capes* of *Florida.*

1763 ROBERTS 98 I took my departure for *St. Augustine,* doubling *Cape Florida.*

1771 VIAUD 256 ftn. [St. Augustin] another English settlement on the east coast of Cape Florida.

1773 MS. 300 Cape Florida, is the North Point of this Inlet.

1791 B 168 Successfully crossing the N. West bay . . . [I] came to . . . the West cape or promontory.

1796 G 22 That elbow, which is commonly termed Cape Florida.

1797 MAG under *Florida, Cape.* Florida, Cape, the southernmost point of land of the peninsula of East-Florida.

1821 F 82, 99 On approaching the capes you see *Lake George* . . . The last [inlet] is in the north end of the first island, whose south end De Brahm has thought proper to call Cape Florida, although it is by no means a cape, or head land.

1827 W 17 Cape St. Blass . . . stretches into the sea near twenty miles, in successive ridges: even at that distance, it is little more than seven fathoms deep.

1835 ASPMA VI. 534 There is a small cape upon the bay called Gadsden's Point.

1837 W 28 Punta Longa, or Cape Roman . . . is the south point of a large island.

1854 SMITH-F 18 [The Cacique] lives inland on the last cape of the river.

1871 H 131 *Cape Malabar* which appears on every map, and is supposed by geographers to be on the coast outside, is a low bank of white sand running from the west shore of the river into the stream a half a mile or so.

1874 S 22 An osprey had built its nest in a cypress tree upon this cape . . . The tongue of land was called Osprey Point. Attrib. with *land.*

1773 MS. 175, 176 ftn. (a) These two Vessels made this Cape Land on the day of St. Helene; one Jordan on board

of one of the two Vessels was the first, who spied the Mouth of Apalachicola Stream . . . Neither of these places are so near a Cape Land as Apalachicola.

See also SHOAL CAPE (attrib.).

CARRYING PLACE. A place where canoes, etc., have to be carried overland from one stream to another. DAE 1689. (A.)

1773 MS. 259 The Land on the . . . South & East Side [is laid out in private Properties] as far South as to the Head of St. Juan's Stream, to the carrying Place out of this into South Hillsborough Stream.

Ibid., 286 In [hilly pine land] . . . narrow ridge—carrying place 500 L [or S] wide.

CASCADE. A small waterfall. DAE 1738.

1825 FHQ III. 38-39 The thick foliage of the undergrowth . . . served to screen the view, though not the sound of a beautiful cascade.

CATTLE-FORD. A ford suitable for the crossing of cattle; a cowford.

1766 B 31 Rowed down to the Cattleford, below which is a marsh on both sides.

CATTLE RANGE. A sparsely settled region over which cattle graze. DAE 1640.

1818 Y 37 In the forks of some of the branches there is high pine barren and good cattle range.

1874 S 24 The pine woods of the great peninsula are a vast cattle range.

CAUSEWAY. A raised way across wet or marshy ground or across water. NID. Here, a natural bridge (*q.v.*).

1818 Y 43 There is a natural bridge over this creek covered with timber . . . It is not easy to account for those singular causeways which are found on all the Florida creeks.

CAVE. A hollow place opening more or less horizontally under the ground. OED.

1827 W 35 After proceeding about sixty yards, the cave is crossed by a stream twenty feet wide.

1837 W 149 Nearly allied to the sinks, are the subterranean Caves.

CAVERN. A subterranean or submarine cavity [in a spring]. OED.

1791 B 165 Just under my feet, was the inchanting and amazing crystal fountain, which incessantly threw up, from dark, rocky caverns below, tons of water every minute.

1827 W 35 The Arch cave ... descends gently, for three or four rods; the cavern then opens, to the extent of a hundred feet wide, and fifty feet high.

1837 W 11 [The springs] scarcely ever attain the size of mill streams, ere they are precipitated into the caverns of the earth.

CAVITY. A hollow place. OED. A subterranean void often connected with a watercourse. A hollow or conical depression in the surface of the earth (1791).

1766 B 19 Then the surrounding sand slips into the cavity ... [of the spring].

1791 B 204-05 But that which is most singular, and to me unaccountable, is the infundibuliform cavities, even on the top of these high hills, some twenty, thirty, and forty yards across, at their superficial rims exactly circular, as if struck with a compass, sloping gradually inwards to a point at bottom, forming an inverted cone, or like the upper wide part of a funnel.

1818 Y 43 The stream is [probably] engulphed in one of the many cavities peculiar to countries of secondary floetz formation.

1829 USCHED vol. 187 #147.4-5 It is owing to the numerous cavities of this rotten substratum, that the surface of the ground is seen interspersed with numberless inverted conic hollows.

CAY(O). Also KAY(O). A low, insular sand bank; a range of low-lying reefs or rocks. OED 1707. (KAY: DAE 1761.) The 1854 translator appears to be making some kind of a distinction between a *cay* and an *island*, but what he had in mind is not clear. Cf. *Key*. Prob. not used elsewhere in U.S.; also used in Spanish-American areas. The first group illustrates the *cay(o)* form; the second, the *kay(o)*.

(1) 1652 HEYLIN 117 The *Martyres*, called also the *Caios*, are three great Rocks rather then [sic] Ilands, covered with a white sand, and full of bushes.

1763 ROBERTS 21 To the north hereof are several small Cayos.

1796 G 7 ftn. The Spaniards give the name of *Cayos* to those low and flat islands which are so numerous on the Coasts of Florida and Cuba, whence the English word *Kay* or *Key*, and the French word *Caye*.

1821 F 104 Cayo Huesos, or West Key ... has a salt-pond, and some high ground.

1837 W 290 Above the Cayos or islets, the river [Caloosahatche] opens to four hundred yards in width.

1854 SMITH-F 14, 26 To the west of these islands is a great channel, which no navigator dares go through with a large vessel; because, as I have said, of some islands that are on the opposite side towards the sunset, which are without trees, and formed of sand. At some time they have been the foundations of cays, and must have been eaten away by the currents of the sea, which have left them thus bare, smooth and sandy ... The islands of the Martires, which have their confines on the west in certain *cayos* (keys), the Tortugas, formed of sand, and for this reason are not to be seen from a distance ... From the Lucayan word *cay* the Spaniards make "cayo," from which comes the English "key."

(2) 1773 MS. 244 This formerly supposed Island went by the Name of Kayo Larga, but since it is discovered by the Author to be part of the Continent, it is known by the Name of Istmus Larga.

1774 Barton in G 28 Off Matacumba lies a small Kay, called Frenchman's Kay; and on the North end of the Main Kay is good water.

1796 G 7 The Tortugas . . . consist of eleven small Islands, or *Kays*.

1803 E 244, 245 Came to an anchor on the west side of Kayo Ani, or Sandy Key, which is a small island . . . The soundings from Sandy Key, to Key Vaccas, were regular and generally . . . similar to that described between the Cedar Keys, and Kayo Anclote.

CEDAR HAMMOCK. A hammock consisting chiefly of cedar trees. DA 1901 under *cedar* (no def.).

1787 in SIEBERT II. 251 This tract had about 160 acres of it rich low Cabbage Cedar and Mulberry Hammock.

1828 ASPPL VI 64 Edward Wanton petitions . . . six hundred and fifty acres on Cedar Hammock . . . on said river St. John's.

CEDAR ISLAND. An island on which cedar is the predominating growth. Prob. Southern. DA 1633 under *cedar* (no def.).

1775 R 285 At the disemboguing of the river, out of the lake, lies a small cedar island.

CEDAR KEY. A key on which cedar trees grow. DAE 1774 (Romans q.) under *cedar* (no def.). Prob. local in Florida.

1803 E 243 We were in the great cove, or bay, between the Cedar Keys, and Kayo Anclote.

1837 W 31 Still farther south are the Cedar Keys, an extensive group jutting far into the Gulf. They are very rocky, and separated by innumerable salt creeks. The cedars and other trees on these islets are small and sparse.

CEDAR SWAMP. A swamp in which cedar is the prevailing growth. DAE 1636-7. (A.)

c. 1765 FHQ XIX. 113 Every here and there one finds a Cedar Swamp, and under the large trees is much Brush.

1787 in SIEBERT II. 181 The . . . Witness . . . Says . . . he was upon Mr. Edward's 500 Acre.tract of Land upon Cedar Swamp.

1824 ASPPL III Plate at end of vol. Cedar Pantano or Swamp.

1837 W 248 The Indians had gone back with their plunder, about three miles, to a cedar swamp.

1874 SAR 53 The cedar swamps of Florida are at the present time supplying . . . pencil manufactories on this continent.

Attrib. with *creek*.

1824 ASPPL IV. 362 Thence north towards the east, 200 chains, to a cypress upon the western shore of Cedar Swamp creek.

CHANNEL. (1) This term usually denotes a narrow piece of water, wider than a strait, connecting two larger pieces; here, a pass, passage, or sound. OED. (2) A watercourse. DAE 1622 [?]. Spec., a subterranean current (1823 p. 64), and a stream thinly covered with earth (1823 p. 91). Extended to apply to the principal branch of a river (1791; 1803). (3) The deep part of a stream or other stretch of water. DAE 1622 [?]. (4) The bed of a watercourse. OED.

(1) 1741 GHDPOPW 181 This Island . . . extends . . . ten Miles Southward along the Coast, leaving a Channel between it and the main Land.

1769 STORK 9 This island is . . . divided from the main land by a narrow channel, called Matanza river, though in reality a channel of the sea.

1773 MS. 244 48 Islands [border] ... upon Hawke Channel, which by a Ridge of Rocks and Sand Banks, (generally called the Martyrs, or Martiers,) is separated from the Florida Stream in the Outlet of the Gulf of Mexico.
1774 Barton in G 28 Between the two last Kays lies *Boca Grande*, a channel of 15 feet water, and a mile broad.
1776 NAWIG under *Florida, East.* These separations, in which are formed several channels for small vessels, were named by the Spaniards The Islands and Keys of the Martyrs.
1796 G 10 There is some difficulty arising from the channel or entrance across the Reef.
1821 F 104 The reef begins in latitude 25 34, and the channel between it and the islands will admit a vessel drawing sixteen feet water.
1823 V 122 At *key West* terminates what was formerly called by the British *Hawke channel*, but which is now known as the passage through the keys.
1823 STCW 40 The St. George channel or sound affords a passage for small vessels.
1837 W 40 On the English charts this pass is called Egmont Channel.
1856 USCHED vol. 893 Part I. 553 Between the westernmost chain [of keys] there run channels some four feet deep.
(2) 1743 C II. iii Most of the Coast of *Florida* and *Carolina*, for many Miles within Land, consists of low Islands and extensive Marshes, divided also by innumerable Creeks and narrow muddy Channels, thro' which only Boats, Canoes, and *Periagua's* can pass.
c. 1767 FHQ XII. 114 Two small rivers ... mix their waters at this point and become one channel, of about 900 feet broad running S. 9 miles.
1787 in SIEBERT II. 169 St. Mary's river Florida, was ... the best Channel for Ships of burthen to enter.
1791 B 96 I ... arrived at the desired place, having fortunately taken the right channel of the river, amongst a

multitude of others, occasioned by a number of low swampy islands.
1803 E 234 The most western [mouth of the river] ... is at this time the main channel.
1818 Y 35 Another [bayou] ... is connected by several small channels with a wide but short stream.
1823 V 64, 91 In times of high freshets, the space above the subterraneous channel is inundated ... In the pine lands, the early courses of the creeks and streams are through two sorts of channels, *bay galls* and *cypress galls.*
1825 GADSDEN 120 A grassy channel about 70 yards wide, with a rapid current from the lake.
1837 W 149 A deep channel of cold transparent water skirts the south side [of the cave] for some rods, it then breaks off into wells and finally disappears altogether.
1869 FICSP 116 In the time of high waters ... [Lake Harris] divides itself, a part of the waters running westwardly through Lake Dunham and Ocklawaha swamp into a channel emptying into Lake Panasoffka.
1871 H 126 *Sharpe's Creek*, a crooked channel with strong tide.
(3) 1563 RIBAULD 34 The channell & depth of this river of Seyne. is on the side of the medow that is in the Ile of May.
1587 L 61L Our generall went about to sound the Chanel of the Riuer to bring in his shippes.
1766 B 10 The river here is 200 yards broad, and 9 foot deep in the channel.
1784 GME 98 At the entrance into the harbour, are the north and south breakers, which form two channels, whose bars, or low tides, have eight feet water.
1822 SIMMONS 37 [The horse] I rode became so ungovernable, as soon as he found a foot-hold, that I was obliged to turn him off into the deep channel, and swim him the whole way.
1829 USCHED vol. 187 #147.14 The bay of Espiritu Santo has three main channels.

1852 WFH 8 [The] inner passage from St. Marys to the St. John's . . . is . . . in one spot difficult, from the hull of a sunken boat lying near the channel.
1871 H 131 The Narrows . . . is occasioned by oyster reefs on the east side of the river which have obstructed that part of the channel.
(4) 1818 Y 43-44 Immediately after [the stream is engulphed] it finds vent . . . and continues its course in a channel made by its own current.
1823 V 37 The water in its efforts to escape has already traced a channel towards the narrow sand bank which rises from the beach.
1831 USCSD vol. 214 #136.16 This cut-off has a straight channel for the first mile.
1837 W 13 When the waters of these Lagoons are greatly swelled . . . they burst their shelly barriers and open a deep channel into the ocean.

See also BOAT CHANNEL; RIVER CHANNEL; SHIP CHANNEL; TIDEWATER CHANNEL.

CHASM. A deep rent, cleft, or fissure in the rock; here, a natural well (1823), a cleft in the bottom of a spring (1856), or a fissure in a cave apparently caused by a watercourse (1837). OED.

1823 V 120 On . . . [the] east end [of Old Maticombe] are fine wells in the solid rock, said to have been cut by the Indians, but which appear to be natural chasms, similar to those found on many parts of the peninsula of Florida.
1837 W 150 The passage [in the cave] terminates in a narrow chasm, which appears to have been a watercourse.
1856 FHQ I. 35 At its bottom an immense horizontal chasm, with a dark portal.

CHOP(S) (OF A CHANNEL). The entrance into a channel. OED.

1775 R Apx. xxxv The way is to run boldly up to within pistol shot of the NE part of this small key, when you will find yourself at the chops of a channel which leads up to the watering place.

CLAYBANK. A bank of clay. DAE 1839. Cf. RED-CLAY LAND.

1837 W 146 [Florida is] a calcareous fragment of the Appalachian mountain, clothed with some sterile sand banks, some rich variegated clay banks, and some beautiful coralines.
Attrib. with creek.
1823 FHQ XIV. 84 After that there is the Conecuh, Yellow Water, Pea River, Clay Bank creek and the Choctawhatchie requiring to be ferried.

CLAY BLUFF. A bluff composed largely of clay. DAE 1804. (A.)

1837 W 19 [The banks of Perdido Bay] in many places, are formed of clay bluffs, proper for bricks.
1874 SAR 118 The clay bluffs along the St. Mary's river and the so-called sand hills in the northwestern corner of the county, form a third distinct body of agricultural lands.

CLAYHOLE. A water-hole in a clay-bed. OED. Sup. 1843 (American) under clay. Spec., a pond. Poss. local in Florida.

1836 BARR 9 On the night of the 27th, camped near a pond called the Clayhole.

CLEAR LAND. Land free from trees and undergrowth. DAE 1704 under clear.

1775 A 273 Soon afterwards, we came in sight of their camp in a little spot of clear land, surrounded by a thick cane-swamp.

CLEAR-WATER LAKE. A lake having transparent waters.

1874 SAR 145 Nothing is seen in this section but scrub and barren wastes except an occasional oasis and some clear-water lakes.

CLEAR-WATER POND. A pond consisting of limpid water.

1822 SIMMONS 40 Some of the lakes of which I have spoken, though fine sheets of water, are . . . surrounded by melancholy and monotonous forests of pine. The waters of all of them are remarkably clear; hence, they are termed in the country, "Clear Water Ponds."

1836 SSW 295 [The sheet of water] was one of the 'clear water ponds,' which make a distinguished feature in Florida scenery.

CLEFT. A fissure or crevice—here—in a cave. OED.

1837 W 150 To the right of this last branch of the cave, the clefts have been traced about one hundred feet.

CLIFF. A steep face of rock. DAE 1622. Possibly the 1784 reference is to a clay bluff. The OED gives as a special modern use the meaning of a perpendicular face of rock overhanging a river (1822), in which sense the 1819 writer uses the word synonymously with *bluff*. The term is also applied to vertically projecting rocks at the bottom of a spring (1823; 1856).

1763 ROBERTS 26 They fell in with a range of islands and rocks, to which the *Spaniards* gave the name of *Martyrs*, from a resemblance the cliffs bore, in their fancy, to men fixed upon stakes.

1775 R 282 This island [called *"Hobe"* by the Spaniards] is thirty-nine . . . miles long: at twenty-four miles from its north-end are several high cliffs of a blue stone.

1784 HUTCHINS 73 It would be difficult to ascertain the entrance [of Pensacola bay], were it not for a remarkable red cliff.

1819 NVSM 153 Upon a high cliff or bluff, on the southern side of the river.

1822 SIMMONS 28 The cliffs on the [St. Johns] river . . . appear as if stuck full of birds' eggs, half buried in the clay.

1823 STCW 44 The spring . . . presents to the eye a pale azure transluscent [*sic*] surface under which are seen myriads of fish . . . disappearing behind the cliffs of rock which project into the fountain.

1827 W 6 From Cape St. Blass to the Appalache river, a distance of sixty miles, the coast is composed of a yellowish brown sand, alternating with white cliffs and sometimes with salt marshes.

1856 FHQ I. 35 From one side of [the portal of Wakulla springs] . . . looms up a limestone cliff, the summit of which is itself nearly fifty feet beneath the spectator in a boat.

See also OYSTER CLIFT.

COAST. Also, COST. (1) The margin of the land next the sea, the seashore. OED. As the NID editors comment, the meaning is extended to include both the islands belonging to the coastal region (1822; 1823) and the adjacent waters (?*Obs.* 1569; 1589; 1609; 1625; 1743): both of these senses appear to coalesce in the 1837 quotation. The term is also applied to the bank of a river (1822 Simmons). *Obs.* OED. (2) The border of a country; borderland. (Chiefly pl.) *Obs.* OED. (3) A tract or region; a district. *Obs.* OED.

(1) 1563 RIBAULD 11 Thursdaye the laste of Apryll . . . we discouered . . . a faire Coast.

c. 1565 Hawkins voyage, in HAKLUYT (1589) 537 We went to the Northwest to fetch winde, and also to the coast of Florida to haue the helpe of the currant.

1569 HAWKINS, *A true declaration.* Facsimile ed. 11 [We] sought the coast of Floryda, where we found no place nor Hauen for our shippes, because of the shalonesse of the coast.

1587 L 2 On the *cost* toward the Cape, where commonly the Ships are cast away, there is more store of Siluer, then toward the North.

1589 DRAKE 47-48 We passed thus alongest the coast hard abord the shore, which is shallow for a league or two from the shore.

1609 VRV 13 The ships lost one another: and two of them fell on the coast of *Florida.*

Ibid., 179 It is a gentle coast, but it hath many sholdes.

1625 PURCHAS 869, 870 And in the Coast of *Florida,* which looketh to the West, are the *Tortoyses,* seuen or eight Ilands together . . . All the Coast on the West side vnto the Gouernment of *Panuco,* which is aboue 300. leagues, is called *The Gulfe of New Spaine.*

1652 HEYLIN 115 Others report that all the Gold and Silver which they have amongst them came from some ships which had been wracked upon those Coasts.

1731 C I. 72 40 Leagues from the Coast of *Florida.*

1743 C II. vi The coasts of *Florida* . . . with the Sounds, Inlets and lower Parts of the Rivers, have a muddy and soft Bottom.

1762 J 69 Upon the whole coast, for two hundred leagues, are several vast beds of oysters.

1796 G 14 The direction of the coast trenches still more to the northward.

1821 F 89 The stream between the Florida coast and the Bahama Islands being very narrow.

1822 ASPNA IV. 963 It may well be supposed that on a coast so dangerous as the Florida keys, the difficulties of navigation must be very numerous.

1822 SIMMONS 31 [The] banks, or rather coasts [of the St. Johns river], at present, exhibit an unbroken line of towering forests.

1823 V 81 The coast generally between Spirito Santo bay and Charlotte harbor is composed of flat islands in front of high forests of pine.

1827 W 89 On the Atlantic, the coast is level for a great distance inland.

1837 W 29 The coast is of the roughest reef rock, and covered, to some distance under water, with mangrove bushes.

1869 BRINTON 106 [The west] coast . . . is an almost continuous belt of marsh, cut by innumerable creeks and bayous, extending from five to fifteen miles into the interior.

(2) 1663 Charles II *Patent to Edward Earl of Clarendon,* in OLDMIXON I. 330 The King *granted them all that Territory . . . Southerly, as far as the River* San Mattaeo, *which borders on the Coast of* Florida.

1666 *A Brief Description of the Province of Carolina on the Coasts of Floreda.* [Title]

1708 OLDMIXON 329 In the Year 1622. several English Families flying from the Massacres of the Indians in *Virginia* and *New-England,* were driven on these Coasts.

(3) 1589 DRAKE 46-47 In this place called S. Avgvstine, we vnderstand the king did keepe . . . an hundred and fiftie more, seruing there for no other purpose, then to keepe all other nations from inhabiting any part of all that coast.

1625 PURCHAS 868 There are but two Fortresses in this Prouince with men in Garison, both in the Coast that looketh to the East.

See also DESERT COAST (attrib.); GULF COAST; SEACOAST.

COAST COUNTRY. An area or region bordering the sea.

1874 SAR 184 The country is more elevated and more undulating than any one would suppose it to be for a coast country.

COASTLAND. The land next the sea. NID under *coast.*

1874 SAR 170 [The] rivers . . . form a belt of fine coast lands about as wide as these rivers are long.

COAST-RIDGE. A ridge abutting upon the sea.

1869 BRINTON 41 Between the coast-ridge and Lake Okee-chobee the "Keys," ... are scattered through the Everglades.

COCKLE BANK. A bank found along the Gulf consisting of sand and cockle shells.

1818 Y 48 The cockle banks are elevated spots along the gulf shore, consisting of a mass of sand and shells heaped up by the sea at a very remote period and rendered escarped as at present by subsequent revolutions of tempest and current. Their great age is apparent from the depth of mould and vegetable detritus which they always exhibit and their original formation is plain from the irregular manner in which the sand and shells are heaped up together. Their growth is principally cedar and cabbage tree with great quantities of the cassino bush.

COCKLE BLUFF. A bluff composed of sand and cockle shells.

1818 Y 35 This is a point of pine land moderately high which probably extends from the interior and unites with the cockle-bluffs on the west side of the delta.

COCONUT HAMMOCK. A hammock of coconut trees.

1837 W Map Coconut Hammock.

COD (OF BAY). The inmost recess of a bay or inland sea. *Obs. Naut.* OED.

1770 WYNNE 347 Apalache ... river enters the Gulph of Mexico about one hundred miles from the cod of the Bay of Apalache, at the northwest end of the peninsula of Florida.

CONTINENT. (a) The North American continent. DAE 1648. That part of the continent which is called Florida (1660; 1775; 1821). (b) The mainland, as distinguished from islands, islets, or peninsulas (spec., Florida, 1745). *Obs.* OED.

(a)1660 LE BLANC, *The World Surveyed,* 355 In the year [1564] ... Captain Laudoniere ... built Fort *Caroline* upon the River *May,* and thence made some inroads upon the Continent. 1741 GHDPOPW 181 The Port is formed by an Island, and a long Point of Land divided from the Continent by a River.

(b)1745 OSBORNE 744 Not far from *Martyres* westward, lie the *Tortugas* dangerous islands, where the continent of *Florida* turns again almost directly north for near five degrees. 1771 VIAUD 63 I took notice that, instead of making towards the continent, he carried us from one island to another. 1775 R 289 These hills [about the bay of Juan Ponce de Leon] ... have apparently been the last retreats ... of the *Coloosa* savages, when ... the *Creeks,* drove them off the continent. 1821 F 100 From the tapering shape of the continent approaching to the meridional extremity, the ground becomes more strong. 1822 ASPPL III. 519 [Presque Isle is bounded] on the northwest by Grant's lake, the continent, and Keys and Sandwich gulf. 1837 W 37 The space between the Mattacumbe and the continent, is sprinkled over with small islets, called Lignum Vitae Keys.

COPPICE. A small wood or thicket consisting of underwood. OED. Spec., a dry cypress pond, or hammock (1836).

1587 L 32 I came home from the woods and coppises. 1771 VIAUD 219 A large hen-turkey ... ran into a coppice. 1836 SSW 143 The beautiful ... Horn Bush or Sandhill Rosemary, grew in coppices over the more gravelly and sandy spots of the barren.

Ibid., 299 A feature peculiar to these prairies is the coppices or dry ponds of cypress which constantly recur . . . with their regular angled boles . . . In some places, these highland islets or coppices may be called hammocks.

COPSE. A coppice or thicket of underwood; the underwood of a forest. OED.

1837 W 158 Large bodies of men were concealed at a short distance, behind a copse of woods.

1874 S 27 The grove and its copses were illuminated as with a Drummond light [*i.e.*, by fire].

COQUINA LAND. Land consisting chiefly of coquina rock (a soft stone consisting of marine shells bound together by calcareous cement).

1874 SAR 156, 165 A narrow strip of coquina land separates these waters from Indian river proper . . . It . . . includes 200 acres of what is known as the Segui hammock, a high ridge of coquina land lying but a few rods back from the river.

CORAL BANK. A submerged bank composed of coral.

1775 R Apx. xli The vessel . . . struck, and as it were dragged over a coral bank.

1796 G 9 There is a coral bank of 12 feet water at the distance of 5 leagues.

1803 E 253 Many of those islands and shoals have evidently had their origin from coral banks, which not only like those of oysters, are known to increase, but to surpass them greatly in magnitude.

1837 W 38 There are some coral banks near the mouth of the harbor [of Key West].

1856 USCHED vol. 893 Part I. 553 From the small key on which the signal stands there is a coral bank extending one mile in length up to the main key.

CORAL REEF. A reef or marine bank of coral rock. OED.

1831 AUDUBON 62 The great coral reef or wall lies about eight miles from these inhospitable isles.

1837 W 40 The Florida Keys are sheltered from the sea by a coral reef that extends near two hundred miles in length, and at a distance of from three to seven miles, forming a channel between it and the keys.

1874 SAR 170 The numerous channels [from the Withlacoochee to the Anclote] generally make their outlets to the Gulf through the coral reefs cut by the larger rivers.

CORNLAND. Land suitable for the cultivation of corn. OED. [*Obs.*?]

1765 B 7 In about 400 yards came to rising ground, pretty rich, and good corn-land, then to palmetto yet blackish soil.

1769 STORK 11-12 The trees and shrubs on the profitable corn and cotton land, are the cabbage tree, the arboreous grape vine, and spice bark trees, the hiccora, plumb, and papao.

COTTON ISLAND. An island suitable for growing cotton.

1823 V 36 Talbot and Fort George islands . . . are fine cotton islands.

COTTON LAND. Land suitable for raising cotton. DAE 1825. Prob. Southern.

1769 STORK 11-12 The trees and shrubs on the profitable corn and cotton land, are the cabbage tree, [etc.].

1852 WFH 37 There are large tracts of valuable cotton and sugar lands which will soon be taken up.

COUNTER-CURRENT. An opposite current. OED.

1796 G 23 Whenever any point of land projects beyond the general line of the coast, or where the shores approach nearer to each other, the central current is confined, and a counter-current on one or both sides is produced in-shore.

COUNTRY. (a) A region associated with a (not always) specified place or river. DAE 1676. (A.) (b) A district remote from towns or cities. DAE 1841. A wilderness (1803); the interior as opposed to the seacoast (1827).

(a) 1797 MAG under *Apalachy.* Apalachy *Country,* extends across Flint and Apalaches Rivers, in East-Florida.
1836 ASPMA VII. 292 The country around the mouth of the river is a low, flat marsh.
1837 W 24 The country around this extensive bay, is generally poor land.
1855 USCSED vol. 756 #76.6 [The grade between Santa Fe valley] and the termination of the broken country adjacent to Newnansville, 10 to 15 feet.
1870 BILL 128 Indian-River country some thirty miles eastward, is more frequented by [geese].
(b) 1795 GUTHRIE, *New System,* 988 The inland country towards the hills is extremely rich and fertile.
1803 E 214 Upon a report reaching some of their towns, that the Seminoles, and Euphales intended abusing us, and plundering our camp, a large body of them flew to our assistance, and offered to protect us through the country to the source of the St. Mary's.
1827 W 63 Mexican cotton . . . grows better in the country than on the seacoast.
1837 ASPMA VII. 875 The fifth day continued over a bad country of hammocks, cypress swamps, and boggy places.

See also BACK COUNTRY; COAST COUNTRY; COVE COUNTRY (attrib.); DESERT COUNTRY (attrib.); FARMING COUNTRY; GRAZING COUNTRY; LAKE COUNTRY; LIMESTONE COUNTRY; LOW COUNTRY; MARSH COUNTRY (attrib.); OPEN COUNTRY; PINE COUNTRY; PINE-BARREN COUNTRY (attrib.); PINE-WOOD(s) COUNTRY (attrib.); POND COUNTRY (attrib.); PRAIRIE COUNTRY; ROLLING COUNTRY; SAVANNA COUNTRY (attrib.); SEASHORE COUNTRY (attrib.); SWEET-WATER COUNTRY; TIMBERED COUNTRY; WAVING COUNTRY; WILD COUNTRY; WILDERNESS COUNTRY (attrib.).

COURSE. The path or direction taken by a moving stream (including subterranean [1837]). OED. Spec., applied to a pass or passage between islands (1818; 1832). The meaning is extended to apply to the line or direction of stationary forms, such as a chain of islands (1796), the coast itself (1821), a cave (1837), or a reef (1837).

1587 L 25 Hoping by this meane to discouer . . . the certayne course of the Riuer.
1763 ASPPL I. 35 To the source of St. Mary's thence, by the course of that river, to the Atlantic.
1775 R 34 [The St. John's River] then continues its course with a considerable current northward.
1791 B 110 We entered a narrow channel, which after a serpentine course, for some miles, rejoins the main river again.
1796 G 12 The general course of the chain of islands turns gradually to the northward of East from Cayo Hueso.
1818 Y 36 The west pass after leaving the other pursues a southwest course for six miles.
1821 F 99 About fifty miles north of the southern point of the main land, the coast changes its course from S. S. E. to directly south.
1832 USCSD vol. 214 #136.16 The passes into the sound above described, have different courses.
1837 W 42 During fair weather vessels of any size may sail very near to this reef along its whole course.
Ibid., 148, 149 The sink holes . . . mark the course of the subterranean rivers . . .

The course of the cave now bends to the north-west.

COVE. (1) A small bay, inlet, or recess in a shore. DAE 1616. Spec., a careening ground (1829 p. 18); a road (1796); a roadstead (1775). Extension of meaning occurs in the designation of a *creek* as a *cove* (1823; 1824). (2) With particular reference to a well-known low area on the Withlacoochee River west of Ocala (1837). In the sing. the term signifies a shallow lake containing hammock islands (1836 p. 146), or a swamp (1836 p. 258). In the pl. the reference is to the small bays or inlets formed by the islands and peninsulas of this region (1874). (3) Meadowland adjoining such an inlet. DAE 1637. Spec., a lawn. (A.)

(1)   1743 C II. 21   These [plants] . . . are mostly found to abound in quiet coves or small Bays of the Sea.

1765 B 8-9   Behind [the bluff is] . . . the cove of the great lake . . . which is supposed to be the extent of the real tides flowing.

1775 R Apx. xx   The coast forms here a small kind of cove, which makes a good road stead for small craft.

1796 G 20   The shore forms here a little cove, which makes a good road stead for small craft.

1823 ASPPL IV. 599   The boundaries of which said tract commence at a gum tree marked with a cross on the side of a cove or creek of the said river.

c. 1824 ASPPL IV. 341   The north [line] formed by a creek called Bayley's cove.

1829 USCHED vol. 187 #147.6, 18 Black creek, at its entrance into the St. John, presents a wide cove, across which stretches a bar . . . Within this bay are those of Escambia and Yellow-water, and the Spanish cove called Careening Ground.

(2)   1836 ASPMA VII. 146   The cove appeared to me, from the knowledge I had of it, to be a large shallow lake, about twenty-two or twenty-three miles in length, occupying a bend of the river, and communicating with the river by cypress swamps on its banks at many places. The breadth of the lake is generally from one to five miles, interspersed with islands of hammock growth and apparent fertility. The peculiar impracticability against military operations arises from the water being too shallow for boating, and the impossibility of passing to the islands, except on foot, through morasses of such depth that our troops, at the three points at which it was passed, were nowhere less than up to the middle.

Ibid., 258   And thus . . . enclose the Seminoles in their stronghold in the cove, or big swamp of the Withlacoochee.

1837 W 242   The Seminoles since the commencement of the war, have concentrated about the great cove of Ouithlacoochee.

1837 ASPMA VII. 387   Billy Omathla's wife . . . informed me that the Indians had not moved from the Wahoo swamp and the coves on the Wathlacoochee.

1874 SAR 173   The distance between the lake and river is about four miles, and they are frequently connected by saw-grass meadows. The islands and peninsulas thus formed are what are known as the "coves." These coves constitute some of the richest hammock lands in the State.

(3)   1791 B 203   We next passed over a level green lawn, a cove of the savanna.

Preceded by a qualifying term.

1823 V 43   Hammocks and a large entrance cove give it an handsome appearance.

Attrib. with *country, swamp*.

1836 ASPMA VII. 146   Not one [white man] of them had any knowledge of that cove country.

1837 ASPMA VII. 389-90, 406   To what extent was the *cove swamp* penetrated by General Scott in March or April, 1836.... [Gen Scott] hurried across the Withlacoochee and thence to Tampa Bay without devoting more than one day to ... the great and leading object of the campaign, namely an examination of the *Big Cove swamp.* Captain Drane testifies that that swamp, [is] from 15 to 20 miles in width.

See also EDDY COVE.

COWFORD. A shallow place in a stream where cattle may cross; a pass suited to the same purpose (1823).

1765 B 1 The river ... is sometimes brackish, but in wet [seasons] is drinkable to Cow-ford.

1773 MS. 260 Item, anno 1760 from said Barrier Gate to the Cow-ford upon St. Juan's Stream.

1821 F 78 The *Cowford,* so called from the number of cattle which crossed that part of the river.

1823 V 67 The Cowford or pass St. Nicholas, twenty eight miles from the bar, is distinguished by its narrowness, being scarcely one thousand yards across, contrasting with the other reaches of the stream which are very wide.

1827 W 21 The Chactawhatchee rises near the east line of Alabama; its general course is south and west, till it arrives at the Cow ford.

1837 W 124 Jacksonville ... is situate on the north side of St. Johns River, at the Cowford, thirty miles from the bar. [1869 BRINTON 56 Col. I. D. Hart ... built his cabin on the spot now known as the "Cow's Ford."]

CREEK. (1) An inlet of the sea or of a river. DAE 1619. Used interchangeably with *river* (1823 ASPPL), *cove* and *river* (c. 1824), and *bayou* (1828). (2) A stream tributary to a larger river; a small stream, a brook or rivulet. DAE 1638. (A.) Called a *branch* (1823) and a *run* (1824).

A large branch (1765 ASPPL). DA 1622.

(1) c. 1565 Hawkins voyage, in HAKLUYT (1589) 538 In the day time the captaine in the shippes pinnesse sayled along the shoare, went into euery creeke, speaking with diuers of the Floridians.

1587 L 24L I imbarked ... to sayle right toward the opening of the river: wherein we entred a good way up, and found a creake of a reasonable bignesse.

1609 VRV 18 And so they marched that day, and the day following, compassing great Creekes which came out of the Bay.

1766 B 33 Past by Trout-creek, 300 yards broad, salt to its head.

1773 MS. 254 Great and the two little Talbot Islands are cut off from the continent by great and little Talbot (Creeks of the Ocean) and by part of Fort St. George Creek.

1797 MAG under *Sebastian River,* St. Sebastian River, St. or *Spanish Admiral's Creek,* on the E. Coast of East-Florida.

1819 NVSM 133-34 The river St. John's ... opens into an extensive basin, from which are several branches called creeks, but which in England would acquire the dignity of rivers.

1823 ASPPL III. 782 Forty acres of land, lying in St. John's county, commencing on the left or western bank of the Ocklawaha creek or river.

1823 V 38 Passing the narrows the course of the creek or channel meanders through the extensive marshes to the junction of Hernandez's and Pellicer's creeks.

Ibid., 84 A small inlet called Indian creek near cape Florida.

c. 1824 ASPPL IV. 341 The north [line] formed by a creek called Bayley's cove; and the west the natural boundary of the said river.

1828 ASPNA III. 937 Which tract of eight hundred arpents is situated and bounded on the south side of a creek

known by the name of Bayou Grande,
about seven miles west-southwest from
Pensacola.
1854 ESB 54 They . . . compassed in
the march great creeks which come out
of the bay.
1871 H 126 *Sharpe's Creek*, a crooked
channel with strong tide, running from
the southeast side of the bay.
(2) 1731 C I. 2 The lower parts of
the Rivers and Creeks near the sea
abound most with these Eagles.
1742 RCBH Apx. 24 After passing
some creeks and over some hard marsh
in several Places.
1763 ROBERTS 12 Fifty miles lower
down the *Euchi* creek.
1765 ASPPL V. 764 From thence, still
in a straight line, to another creek or
great branch.
1765 B 5-6 [The] fountain . . . directly
formed a large deep creek 40 or 50
yards wide to the river, and deep
enough for a large boat to swim loaded
to its head.
1819 ASPPL IV. 170 tr. A tract or
round of land . . . which commences
from the creek known as Sweetwater
creek, on the river Apalachicola.
1823 ASPPL III. 819 Three hundred
acres of land, lying on the creek called
Coleson's branch, on the east of the
river St. John's.
1824 ASPPL IV. 394 tr. From a creek
which leaves said river and turns to the
west, which is called Gonzalez Mendez's
run.
1837 W 52 These three creeks drain
a branch of the glades, that approach
within twelve miles of Indian River.
Ibid., 126 The pine level . . . is watered by numerous springs that unite in
the Cold Water Creek, a branch of
Black Water [river].
1871 H 131 [Elbow] creek breaks
through the bank of the river.
    Preceded by a qualifying term.
1836 SSW 212 The moon . . . beams
fell brighter, and with softness upon the
winding marsh bound creek.
    Attrib. with *bayou, island, lake, swamp*.

1832 ASPNA IV. 206 Rocky Creek
bayou is just below the fourth [cove]
below Alaqua bayou.
1823 ASPPL III. 775 Two thousand
acres of land, lying on the neck of land
between St. John's river and Maxton's
creek, known as Maxton's creek island.
1837 ASPMA VII. Map 262 Pease
Creek Lake.
1823 ASPPL III. 790 Hibberson and
Yonge [pray] . . . confirmation of title to
two thousand acres of land, lying in two
tracts of one thousand acres each, on
Front creek swamp.
1830 ASPPL VI. 76 In 1816 George
Clarke certified that he had surveyed
one thousand acres of land on Trout
Creek Swamp.

    See also BRANCH CREEK (attrib.);
CEDAR-SWAMP CREEK (attrib.); CLAY-
BANK CREEK (attrib.); DRY CREEK; ELBOW
CREEK (attrib.); FRESH-WATER CREEK;
HAULOVER CREEK (attrib.); LAKE CREEK
(attrib.); NATURAL-BRIDGE CREEK
(attrib.); PINE-BARREN CREEK (attrib.);
POND CREEK (attrib.); SALT CREEK;
SPRING CREEK; SWIMMING CREEK.

CREEK BRANCH. A tributary creek.

1765 B 9 On the north side is a great
extent of clear marsh, producing tall
grass towards the head of the creek-
branches on both sides in the marsh,
many of which branches head in a great
cypress swamp.
1818 Y 140 Six and a half miles to Big
Creek branch of Apalachicola.

CROSSING. A place at which a river
or other stream is usually crossed.
DAE 1753. (A.)

1818 Y 43 [The course of Assilla
Creek] to the crossing of the lower
route is nearly south.
1837 W 229 The left [flank was or-
dered] . . . to pass by the upper crossing
of the Ocklawaha.

CROSSING PLACE. A crossing (*q.v.*).
DAE 1763. (A.)

c. 1767 FHQ XII. 120 At the crossing

place [the river] takes a subterraneous passage for about ten yards and then appears again forming a Natural Bridge. 1773 MS. 268　In Marsh on the crossing Place of above Gall.
1818 Y 43-44　The creek is thirty-five feet wide at the crossing place.
1823 STCS 28　An Indian ... said that he intended to take the boat from the lower crossing place on the Suwannee and go to St. Marks by water.
1827 USCHED vol. 217 #43.76　[The Indians] crossed St. Mary's about three miles below Ellicott's Mound, at what is called the Pine Log Crossing Place to this day, because a very tall tree would reach across that place.
1836 SSW 134　The Indian name for it is "Tiketa" or the crossing place, as it is fordable in one part.

CURRENT.　(1a) A stream, or the moving portion of a body of water. OED. With the exception of the 1796, 1821, 1822, and 1827 examples, all of these quotations probably refer to the Gulf Stream. (b) With specific reference to the Gulf Stream. (2) The flow or flux of a stream; esp. the swiftest part of it. OED. Spec., the motion of the tide extending inland into the freshwater rivers (1823).

(1a)　c. 1565 Hawkins voyage, in HAKLUYT (1589) 538　We felt little or none till we fell with the cape, and then felt such a currant, that bearing all sailes against the same, yet were driuen backe againe a great pace.
c. 1583 Sir Humfrey Gilbert's voyage to Newfoundland in HAKLUYT (1589) 682　We were assured to haue commodity of the current, which from the cape of Florida setteth Northward.
1613 PURCHAS 642　It runneth out into the Sea with a long point of land, as if it would ... set barres to that swift current which there runneth out.
1741 GHDPOPW 8　The Current rushes with such Violence through it [the Gulf of Florida] and sets so strong-

ly toward the Coast of *Florida* which is very shallow and without any Harbour, that ... ships run great danger of being cast away.
1775 R Apx. xliv　As you come round [Isaac Rock] ... you immediately get into ... the current of the *Gulph.*
1796 G 14　To the westward of Cayo Hueso there is a general current to the south-westward along the Reef.
1803 E 265　The difference [in temperature] in this case, does not appear to depend upon the depth of the water, but upon the current setting rapidly from a warmer into a colder climate.
1821 F 107　The writer, in a voyage made in 1803, in the ship Rufus King, drifted among these keys, which he cannot but consider the more dangerous, as the currents baffle all calculation.
1822 SIMMONS 28　From this place, to its head, the current [*sc.*, St. Johns river] is lined by an aquatic plant.
1827 W 6　The Tortugas shoals throw the currents of the gulf so far out to sea, that they scarcely strike the western coast of Florida until they reach Cape St. Blass.
(b)　1769 STORK vi　When vessels ... fall into the stream of the gulph of Florida, they are carried forcibly to the northwards by the strength of that ... current.
1796 G 22　Between the Island of Cuba and the main land, it forms that remarkable Current called The Stream of the Gulf of Florida.
1822 ASPNA IV. 964.　That rapid current denominated the gulf stream sweeps the Florida reef with incredible velocity.
(2)　1609 VRV 29　Hee came to a River with a great current.
1766 B 16　It is difficult to find the main river, but by the strong current.
1773 MS. 335　This Eddy takes its Current in an opposite direction.
1818 Y 35　The current [of the bayou] is gentler than that of the river.
1823 V 82, 84　In dry seasons the tide rises high in the fresh water rivers

being perceptible some distance from the sea ... The current of the tide is very rapid ... The rapid current of the gulf stream sweeping close along this part of the Florida coast has the effect of closing the bars of the inlets.

1829 USCHED vol. 187 #147.13 There is a constant swell on the bar ... added to the shifting of the bar and to the strong current from the river.

1837 W 291 A small stream of water from the interior, entered the creek with a rapid and forcable [sic] current.

1873 FHQ XIV. 270 The Silver Run ... flows with a current of clear white water into the Ochlawaha.

See also COUNTER-CURRENT; EDDY CURRENT.

CUT. A natural water channel; a bayou. DAE 1708. An inlet. (Spec., 1823. All quotes., ? except 1855). OED. The OED editors classify the latter usage as *local*. ("1890 M. Townsend *U.S.* 137 *Cut*, used on the eastern shore of Florida as synonymous with inlet." OED II. 1287.) Prob. *obs.* in England.

1775 R Apx. xxvi Give *Fools Cape* and *Bear Cut* a good birth.

1823 V 117 The inlet at the north end called *Bear Cut.*

1837 W 34 Bear Cut on the east, is a mile wide, and six feet deep.

1855 USCSED vol. 756 #76.5 Starting from the harbor of Fernandina, the line would continue on Amelia Island till convenient to cross the inland passage at a point known as *Kingsley's Cut.*

CUT-OFF. A sluggish stream connecting two rivers DAE 1817. (A.) DA 1814. Chiefly S.

1773 MS. 252 [Title of map] Plan of Nassau Inlet & of the Stream as far N.W. as the cut-off situated in Latde. 30°, 13′ 24″.

1824 ASPPL IV. 451 The said John Tanner, in the spring of the year 1821, settled on the east side of the river

Apalachicola, near the Cut-off in that river.

1831 USCSD vol. 214 #136.16 The examinations were commenced at the natural cut-off from the Appalachicola river to the Chipola. This cut-off has a straight channel for the first mile, where it enters into the serpentine bed of an old bayou, which it follows to the latter stream. Its length is about five miles, and its breadth varies from 60 to 100 yards.

CYPRESS. A shortened form of *cypress swamp.*

1837 ASPMA VII. 874-75 After we cleared the opening we came to a piece of low cypress, the bottom very soft and about a mile over.

CYPRESS BOG. A bog overgrown with cypress trees.

1837 FHQ VII. 93 The advance guard met two Indians, who retreated to a Cypress bog. Our lines were immediately extended around it, but the soil was so marshy that it could not be entered by horsemen. At several points, horse and rider disappeared beneath the surface. Even in the trail we were following, the water came to the skirts of the saddle, sometimes for the distance of half a mile. Several men being ordered to dismount and enter the bog, overgrown with cypress trees and tall grass. . . .

CYPRESS-BRANCH. A branch flowing through a cypress swamp.

1766 B 34 Bay-swamps are ... the general heads of the cypress-branches.

CYPRESS GALL. A piece of poor land or swamp on which cypress trees grow. DAE 1775. Poss. Southern. A cypress gall is lower than a glade, and differs from a bay-gall chiefly in having a firm, sandy bottom and non-vitriolic water. According to Romans (1775) the galls are actually watercourses covered with a thin layer of earth; moreover, Vignoles (1823) refers to galls as channels. Cypress galls, as explained by Williams (1827), are pine-barren swamps overgrown with cypress trees.

1773 MS. 272   A bigg [*sic*] bay & Cyp. [cypress] gall near.

1775 R 32-33   The cypress galls differ from these [bay galls], in being a firm sandy soil, in having no vitriolic taste in the water, and very seldom vent [*i.e.*, have an outlet] . . . the cypress they produce, is a dwarf kind . . . there is no undergrowth here, but in some dry seasons some tolerable grass.

1818 Y 27   This district . . . consists of large isolated tracts perfectly level and surrounded by either glades or cypress and bay-galls, which are a little lower than the other and receiving nearly all the falling water leave the palmetto part commonly firm and dry.

1823 V 91   In the pine lands, the early courses of the creeks and streams are through two sorts of channels, *bay galls* and *cypress galls* . . . The *cypress galls* have firm sandy bottoms, and are only troublesome from the multitude of the sprouting knees.

1827 W 52   Pine barren swamps . . . are natural basins, containing the waters of the surrounding country. These swamps, when covered with small coast cypress trees and knees, are usually, but improperly, termed cypress galls.

See also GALL; BAY-GALL. *Cf.* CYPRESS SWAMP.

CYPRESS GROVE. A grove consisting of cypress trees.

1744 KIMBER 24   On the other Side, a most delicious Grove of Cypress . . . extends its leafy Honours.

1786 in SIEBERT II. 38   A settled plantation known by the name of Cypress Grove.

1842 PREBLE 40   At sundown landed and pitched our tents under a cypress grove.

CYPRESS HAMMOCK. A hammock composed chiefly of cypress trees.

1773 MS. 282   On the Edge of great Savh.—a cypress Hammok near.

CYPRESS ISLAND. An island on which cypress trees grow.

1869 BRINTON 88   The [Oklawaha] river is divided into numerous branches, separated by wet cypress islands.

CYPRESS POND. A pond in which cypress trees grow. DAE 1800. DA 1708. Prob. Southern.

1773 MS. 268   In high Pe. [pine] Ld. [land] . . . Cypress Pond near.

1787 in SIEBERT II. 240   The remainder pine land and large Cypress ponds.

1825   GADSDEN   120   Scattering growth of dwarf pine trees, occasionally spotted with cypress ponds and swamps.

1874 SAR 118-19   The balance of the lands of Nassau county are pine barrens . . . interspersed with numerous "bay-galls," cypress ponds, [etc.].

CYPRESS SAVANNA. A savanna upon which cypresses grow.

1773 MS. 271   A Cypress Savh. near a Branch . . . a Cypres Savanh. near.

CYPRESS SINK. A watery depression overgrown with cypress trees.

1869 FICSP 63   The first and most widely distributed means, for restoring and invigorating the fertility of the soil, whenever exhausted, is furnished by the swamps and lagoons and cypress sinks that may be found in all sections.

CYPRESS SWAMP. A swamp in which cypress trees grow. DAE 1666. DA 1641. Prob. Southern. Possibly identical with *cypress gall*. Cypress swamps are generally said to be isolated, and located near the heads of rivers (1823) or smaller streams (1871). Except for the characteristic growth this type of swamp closely resembles a bay-gall (1871).

1773 MS. 309 The third kind is called Cypress Swamp: its Soil is richer and blacker than that of the Maple; has also a Mixture of some white sand, but is not overgrown with Canes . . . The young Trees . . . are rather in a very sandy Soil; but from thence to the center the Soil increases in Richness; the Rain Waters are so well sheltered by the Trees, that they hardly dry up in these Swamps, unless in the hottest Seasons. 1786 in SIEBERT II. 44 This Tract . . . was all Pine barren Land Except 20 or 30 Acres which were Cypress & Oak Swamps.

1818 Y 30 The cypress swamps differ from the Bay-Galls in the absence of that soft spongy soil which renders the latter so dangerous and in its growth which is principally cypress with a mixture of evergreens and a less tangled and impenetrable undergrowth—[sic] The soil is however nearly the same, with perhaps a greater proportion of white clay. They have about as great an elevation and consequently about as much water as the other swamps, and are generally dry in summer.

1823 V 90 *Cypress swamps* are mostly near the heads of rivers, and in a continued state of inundation; little or no underbrush, but only crowds of the cypress shoots or *knees,* which point up like small pyramids.

1856 FHQ I. 35 Wakulla Fountain . . . wells up in the very heart of a dense cypress swamp.

1871 H 27 Isolated swamps from which the branches and creeks have their starting point, are called "cypress swamps," "cypress ponds," or "bay galls," according to the growth of the trees they sustain.

Attrib. with *land.*

1787 in SIEBERT II. 203-04 The said Tract comprised eight hundred and Seventy five Acres of rich Cypress swamp Land, fit for rice.

D

DALE. A valley. "In literary English chiefly poetical, and the phrases, *hill and dale. . . .*" OED.

1784 GME 97 Perhaps there is no country more beautifully diversified with hills and dales . . . than that which borders on the low lands upon this river. 1836 SSW 152 We . . . discovered at the edge of a gentle dale, two settlements enclosed by fences.

DAM. A bank or barrier of earth thrown up by gales and the action of the Gulf Stream so as to close an inlet.

1871 S 31 Heavy eastern gales, combined with the action of the gulf stream, sometimes shut the inlet. About fifteen years ago a storm closed the gap. The ocean had done its work well, and the dam remained intact . . . One day a north wind . . . began to back up the water in the inlet . . . A high neap tide followed. As it began to fall, a thread of fresh water found its way over the sandy barrier. Within twenty minutes the dam was burst, and the pent-up waters were roaring and rushing to the sea.

DEAD WATER. Water in which no current is perceptible. DAE 1848. Here, either the meeting place of a river and the opposing currents of its tributary creeks (1822), or a lake having no regular outlet (1874).

1822 SIMMONS 29 The *bonnet leaf,* a species of lotus, also abounds in the dead water formed by the meeting currents of the river and the creeks, that fall into it.

1874 S 21 Lake Okechobee . . . is simply a vast platter of dead water, situated near the centre of an immense marsh. It has no outlet except in the rainy season. Then its waters rise until they pour over the encircling marshes into the Everglades.

DELL. A deep natural hollow or vale of no great extent, the sides usually clothed with trees or foliage. OED. A narrow valley. EDD.

1827 W 38 The Wakully rises gently from a retired dell, in a low level country; surrounded by deep embowering groves.

1830 FHQ XXIII. 221 Beyond the grove, there was a "bosky dell."

1870 BILL 116 Then a dell appears, festooned with climbing and o'er-arching growths.

DELTA. Alluvial land of a more or less triangular shape formed at or near the mouth of a river. DAE—1802 is the earliest date pertaining especially to the Mississippi; elsewhere, 1818. (A.) Here, with reference to either the Apalachicola or Suwannee River. The 1827 and 1837 author refers specifically to the alluvium forming the delta; and the 1829 writer notes the very unstable nature of a delta.

1818 Y 35 The delta of the Apalachicola proper commences one mile and a half above Fort Gadsden where a very large bayou leaves the river on the west side and by the accession of several others in its course, becomes, at the point of their reunion, larger than the main stream.

1827 W 22 [The Apalachicola] has carried a considerable Delta into the bay of the same name, which it enters among numerous low marshy islands.

1829 USCHED vol. 187 #147.9 At the approach of the Gulf, the [Suwannee] river exhibits the appearances of a marshy delta, through which run to the sea numerous outlets. The depth, and even the course of the latter, experience frequent and sudden changes, caused by the storms from the sea, and the flood from the stream.

1837 W 23, 47 The Wakasasse Bay is formed by the delta of the Suwanne

River . . . The Appalachicola enters the bay, through several mouths, and has thrown into the bay a great extent of marshy delta.

DESERT. (1) A desolate, barren region. OED. It is impossible to tell whether the 1609 quotation belongs under (1) or (2). (2) Any wild, uninhabited region, including forest land. *Obs.* OED. Spec., a swamp (1819); a forested area destroyed by fire (1823).

(1) 1609 VRV 32 He . . . travelled two daies through a desert.

1769 STORK i Its broad sandy beach has a disadvantageous appearance to ships sailing near the coast . . . The several concurrent accounts of the unhealthiness and infertility of West-Florida, whether true or false, have had no little effect in creating an opinion, that the whole of Florida ceded to Great-Britain, is little better than a sandy desert.

1775 R 35 Mr. Rolle . . . made an odd attempt towards settling and making an estate in as complete a sandy desart as can be found.

(2) 1819 NVSM 142 The warlike Indians of the Creeks and Seminoles have a religious veneration for this immense desert [*sc.*, Okeefenokee swamp].

1822 ASPPL III. 521 An association of patriotic and enterprising citizens . . . respectfully beg leave of Congress to be permitted . . . to transplant themselves on the wild deserts of South East Florida.

1823 V 78 No end appears to this very remarkable desert [*i.e.*, a forest devastated by fire thirty years previously].

1837 W 164 [The Spaniards] had come from Ocala, one hundred and thirty miles, eighty of which were a perfect desert.

Attrib. with *beach, coast, country, plain, waste.*

1836 SSW 307 Yon pale gold streak of

desert beach ... laces the blue mantle of the waters.

1816 ALLEN 10   We were cast upon a desert coast.

1763 ROBERTS 38   After two days journey through a desart country, he arrived at *Caliquen*.

1771 VIAUD 162   Before us [stretched] a desert plain.

1791 B 218   The backs of the ridges ... presented to view on every side, the most dreary, solitary, desert waste I had ever beheld.

DESERT ISLAND.   A barren island.

1744 KIMBER 9 ftn.   *St. George's*, and *Talbot's* ... are two other small desert Islands to the South, opposite to *St. Wan's*.

1771 VIAUD 69-70   Behold us now a second time left on a desart island ... The island produced neither root or fruit, of any kind, to sustain us.

1817 Grant in V 150   "All the vacant lands ... to the south by the gulf of Mexico, including the desert islands on the coast."

1821 ASPPL V. 724 tr.   The Brigadier count of Pumonrostro ... requests ... all the waste lands ... by the Gulf of Mexico, including the desert island [*las yslas desiertas*] on the coast.

DISMAL SWAMP.   An especially gloomy, lonely, forbidding swamp. DAE. *c.* 1656. (A.)

1829 USCHED vol. 187 #147.7   St. Mary's river takes its rise out of the extensive swamps which are on the Georgia line, and stretch between the head branches of St. Mary's and Suwannee rivers. These swamps, called emphatically dismal swamps, are generally covered with a thick growth of bay trees, vines, and undergrowth; at some places short bay bushes, at other sedge grass, are the only growth.

DITCH.   Any watercourse or channel. OED. Esp. one that is narrow (1874).

1731 C I. 70   This Plant grows in Ditches and shady moist Places.

1827 W 55   Virginian Gratiola ... [grow in] ditches.

1874 S 28   The lagoon [of the Everglades] became a ditch barely the width of the boat. This ditch was as crooked as a ram's horn, and was intersected by hundreds of similar ditches. All were lined with stunted bushes, choked by reeds and sawgrass.

DIVIDE.   High land forming a watershed between two streams. DAE 1806 [?]. (A.)

1855 USCSED vol. 756 #76.5   Crossing [the Nassau river] ... the divide is reached separating the waters of the St. Mary's and Black creek. This divide, by a gentle ascent, leads to the Alachua trail ridge, which being crossed, we are immediately upon the divide between New and Sampson rivers, which continues to the valley of the Santa Fe river.

DIVIDING RIDGE.   A ridge that forms a divide or watershed. DAE 1788. Also referred to as a *backbone* (1869); not necessarily the highest portion of land in a region (1829). (A.)

1812 FHQ IX. 69   The land over which we travelled is very barren owing to its being so elevated being a kind of dividing ridge between the branches of the Scambia, Yellow and Cold Water Rivers.

1818 Y 131   No change in the face of the country until ascending the dividing ridge between the gulf and Atlantic waters.

1829 USCHED vol. 187 #147.38   The dividing point of the Florida ridge is near the 76th mile, about four miles west of the Ocklawaha swamp; its elevation above the Gulf has proved to be but 87 feet. However, on the western side of the ridge, the country between the 26th and 41st miles is higher than the top of the dividing ridge, near the

76th mile; on this distance of about 15 miles, the greatest elevation is 153 feet above the Gulf. This elevated ground presents no features of a ridge; but is rather formed of isolated hills.

1869 FICSP 116 Lake Harris is situated upon the dividing ridge or "backbone" between the Gulf and the Atlantic.

DOCK. A cove or recess in a coast where boats may anchor. DAE 1622. Spec., a harbor.

1830 ASPNA IV. 966 This harbor is in fact a natural dock, as easy of access and as safe when in as can be desired.

DOUBLE-LAND. Under *double* the OED gives this as a *Nautical* term and quotes as follows: "1867 SMYTH *Sailor's Word-bk., Double-land,* that appearance of a coast when the sea-line is bounded by parallel ranges of hills, rising inland one above the other." Nevertheless, the probability is that the reference given below pertains not to elevation, but rather to a coastline consisting of a long, narrow strip or neck of land paralleling the mainland yet separated from the latter by an arm of the sea, so that what appears is not merely one line of shore but two.

1775 R 288 From Hobé to the latitude 25:44, the coast is all double land, or narrow necks between the sea.

DOWN. An open expanse of elevated land; upland. OED. Here, an everglade—poss. an individualism.

1791 B 173 After leaving the rivulet, we passed over a wet, hard, level glade or down.

DRAIN. (1) A small stream or branch. DAE 1751. (A.) DA 1719. The synonymous use of the term with *marsh* may be the result of the fact that these streams are sometimes "quite dry."

(2) A natural watercourse which drains a tract of country. OED. Spec., a watershed (1871).

(1) 1803 E 279, ftn. The water [*sc.,* St. Mary's] issues along several small marshes or drains* which soon unite in one . . . This [Okefonoke] swamp . . . is watered by a vast number of small streams and drains . . .* These drains are sometimes quite dry.

(2) 1791 B 197 We were under the necessity to fording creeks or rivulets, which are the conduits or drains of the shallow, boggy ponds or morasses just under the hills.

1823 V 63 The little Suwanee or little St. John's river heads in the celebrated Oke-fin-o-cau swamp, and is almost the only drain that large tract of low land has.

1829 USCHED vol. 187 #147.7 Nassau River is the drain of the low grounds extending between St. Mary's river and the St. John.

1837 W 50 Dry Creek . . . terminates in a drain from the Glades.

1871 H 49 The Chipola river . . . flows south, nearly through the centre of the county, and empties into the Apalachicola river, or what is known as the "Dead Lakes." This [*sic*] the main drain or water shed of the county.

DROWNED LAND. Land subject to frequent inundations. DAE 1752. (A.)

1837 W Map Drowned Land [connecting Chapola River with Appalachicola River].

DRY CREEK. The bed of a stream which runs only after a rain. DAE 1807. (A.)

1837 W 130 Dry Creek, and Hard Labor, are the only two streams that convey currents through the pine barren.

1837 W 50 Except Dry Creek, or Sable Creek as it is sometimes called, there is no river below the Swallow River. This creek throws up at its mouth high banks of sand, and is doubtless very rapid in high freshets.

E

EDDY. A current of water running contrary to the main current. NID. A circular motion in water, a small whirlpool. OED.

1769 STORK vi   When vessels, in their way to Europe, double the capes of Florida, they are under a necessity of keeping near to the shore, in order to take the benefit of the eddies and land breezes.

1773 MS. 335   Within the aforesaid Line [of the Gulf Stream] is an eddy quite smooth, changing gradually, as it approaches Hawke Channel and Islands from the Stream's deep blue, to a beautiful Sea-green, and at last into a milk-white.

1803 E 260   The stream in its progress from the Florida Keys, forms three large eddies on the coast: the first is south of Cape Carnaveral.

1821 DARBY 7   Here the current turns ...leaving a species of indraught or eddy, between the current and the Florida and Carolina shores.

1871 S 31   [At Jupiter Inlet] the tide sets in with wonderful force. The current is very strong, and the banks and flats inside are quickly flooded. Immense eddies are formed.

EDDY COVE. A small, sheltered inlet (of a river) containing a whirlpool or eddy.

1791 B 228   It is in the eddy coves, under the points and turnings of the river, where the surface of the waters for some acres is covered with the leaves of the Nymphea, Pistia, and other amphibious herbs and grass.

EDDY CURRENT. An eddy.

c. 1590 White voyage in HAKLUYT (1600) 291   From the Cape [of Florida] to Virginia all along the shore are none but eddie currents, setting to the South and Southwest.

1803 E 261   Such vessels as are sail-ing to the southward between the coast and stream, will frequently be benefitted by the eddy currents setting southerly.

1821 F 111   On approaching the Florida side, the eddy currents and tides setting through the different channels in the reefs and inlets are very variable, and frequently enter a greater distance into the gulf than mariners are aware of.

EDDY WATER. Eddying water; here, found close to shore.

1791 B 93   [Floating islands] are first produced on, or close to, the shore, in eddy water.

1803 E 264   The difference which I generally found between the water in the Stream, and the eddy water on the coast, was about seven degrees.

ELBOW. (1) A sharp bend in the course of a river. OED. A crooked channel (1871). (2) An outward projection or corner of land; here, a cape. OED.

(1)   1823 V 68   The stream [sc., St. Johns] after passing the Devil's Elbow widens again ... [and passes] Buffalo bluff.

1871 H 129   The crooked channel among the reefs is called "Devil's Elbow."

(2)   1796 G 22   When it gets past that elbow, which is commonly termed Cape Florida, it is opposed by the Islands and banks of Bahama.

1797 *American Gazetteer* under *Georges, St.*   Cape St. George's lies about 6 leagues to the eastward of Cape Blaize, being an elbow of the largest of St. George's islands.

Attrib. with *creek.*

1837 W 52   Elbow Creek enters just above the south point of Merritt's Island.

ESTUARY. (1) An inlet or creek through which the tide enters; an arm of the sea indenting the land (1823 p. 56). OED. A bayou (1837). (2) The tidal mouth of a great river (or rivers

[1829]), where the tide meets the current of fresh waters. OED.

(1) 1823 V 55, 56 The estuary at the head of the Bay of Appalachie receives two small rivers, at the junction of which is placed the small fortification of St. Marks . . . St. Andrew's bay . . . is a deep estuary.
1837 ASPMA VII. 832 [We] drove them . . . across two or three bayous or estuaries of the sea.
1874 S 27 After sailing down this estuary to its confluence with the ocean at Jupiter.
(2) 1827 W 9 The estuaries of large rivers, and rich bottom lands . . . are usually unfavourable to health.
1829 USCHED vol. 187 #147.18 *Pensacola Bay*—This fine bay is the estuary of the Yellow-water, Middle, and Escambia river.

EVERGLADE(S). A low, marshy region, mostly under water and overgrown with tall grass, cane, etc. In these records always in the pl. (except when used as an attributive) and with reference to the well-known extensive low region in southern Florida. DAE 1823. ("Further north similar tracts, in the region bordering on the sea, are called *dismals* or *pocosins*." CD.)

The origin of this term is unknown,[1] and with regard to this problem the OED editors comment as follows: "The formation is irregular, and the intended etymological sense uncertain; perh. *ever* was used to mean 'interminable.' " In my opinion the latter remark is correct. In the first place, English-speaking people apparently referred to the Everglades long before they knew what it consisted of. When Roberts (1763) men-

tioned the "great *Laguna del Espiritu Santo*" he was probably using a collective term for the entire lower southern portion of the peninsula. However, all of the authoritative writers, including De Brahm (1773), Romans (1775), Vignoles (1823), and Williams (1837) profess either a partial or total ignorance of the region. As late as 1821, Forbes tells us (p. 96) that even "the Indians represent [the southern points] as impenetrable; and the [British] surveyors, wreckers, and coasters, had not the means of exploring beyond the borders of the sea coast, and the mouths of rivers." In fact, although Preble (1842) maintained that the Everglades had been traversed by expeditions of the Army and Navy before the battle of Lake Okeechobee (1837), no eye-witness account of an actual crossing prior to his has come to light.

Secondly, the use of *glade* to denote an everglade occurred in Florida as far back as 1744. Whether or not this usage originated in the South cannot be stated with certainty; but, excepting (perhaps) the 1789 (Morse) and 1804 (Clark) quotations in the DAE, this interpretation of the term appears to be confined to the South. Evidently, from 1644 Americans have used the word to designate moist, swampy areas north of the Florida border. It is not surprising, then, to find that one writer (Young) who crossed into West Florida with General Andrew Jackson in 1818 described a similar terrain as *glade* (*q.v.*) or *wet glade* (*q.v.*). Moreover, it is by no means impossible that other explorers, coming after the

[1]My recent conclusions on the origin and formation of the term *Everglades* were published in the February, 1953, issue of *American Speech*. The first known usage of the word is treated here.

transfer of the territory to the United States in 1821, should first apply to the more southerly region—having a similar but also a more extensive and complex terrain—the designation of *Glade*.

Although one possibility is that prior to 1823 both *Everglades* and *Glade* had been used orally with reference to the now well-known tract in Florida, still there is no record that either term was applied to this area before that date. The probable reasons for this fact are as follows: (1) The British never explored—and therefore never attempted to describe —this area during their possession of the territory, 1763-1783; and (2) there was very little activity in Florida on the part of English writers during the Spanish rule, 1783-1821. On the basis of these reasons, and also the fact that three observing writers— Darby (1821), Forbes (1821), and Simmons (1822)—never use either term, one might conjecture that *Everglades* was developed from *Glade* between 1821 and 1823. The earliest writer to use *Ever Glades* (Vignoles, 1823) also refers to this region as the *Eternal Glades*, the *Glade*, the *Great Glade* (*cf.* 1871 quotation below), and, "as it is emphatically termed, the Never Glade." If *Never Glade* (which occurs only once) is not a misprint, in this case it may have been used sarcastically. Another author (Williams, 1837) also calls this area "the interminable glades." Why the plural *Everglades* prevailed is not indicated. However, it may be that *Glade* was not considered sufficiently specific; and *Great Glade* and *Eternal Glades* might have been too awkward for everyday speech. Undoubtedly, the apparently perpetual extent of the area accounts for the "Ever" element of the term.

Another etymological theory is that *Everglades* is a translation of a native Indian term. For this explanation the present writer is indebted to Mrs. Alberta Johnson, corresponding secretary of the Florida Historical Society, who wrote as follows in a letter dated April 25, 1950:

In Document 242, Buckingham Smith's report to the Senate on a survey of the Everglades is a "Memoranda from S. R. Mallory, Collector of Customs at Key West, to B. Smith, dated at Key West, Sept. 1847: The Ever Glades extending from Jupiter Inlet on the east to the Caloosahatchee on the west, and from thirty to fifty miles wide, are no more than their Indian name Pay-hay-okee, denotes, viz: 'Grassy Water.'" Pay-hai-o-kee appears on a military map of 1839, although during the Seminole War, 1835-1842, *Everglades* is commonly used. Darby, 1821, and Simmons, 1822, do not name the area. John Lee Williams, in his *Territory of Florida*, 1837, says: "The back country presents a singular alternation of savannas, hammocks, lagoons and grass ponds, called altogether the Everglades." The dictionary definition of the word is, "A region of low, spongy land, usually flooded with water, and covered with tall grass, used specially of the marshes of southern Florida." Apparently Vignoles was the first to designate that area as Everglades and its several forms, perhaps a truer translation of the Indian "Pay-hai-okee." We have a War Dept. map, 1847, filed with an Engineer's Report, with "Pah-hay-o-kee, or Grass Water, Known As The Everglades." I have searched everything in the library that even mentioned Everglades, and now believe the origin to be the Indian term, and this does not seem to be used until after 1821, at least on maps.

Regarding the place name, Pahokee, which is the modern form of *Pay-hai-o-kee*, William A. Read says on pp. 27-28 of his *Florida Place-Names of Indian Origin* (Baton Rouge: Louisiana State University Press, 1934): "This name is composed of *pahi*, 'grass,' and *oki*, 'water' —'grass water'—a term applied by the Seminoles to the Everglades . . . On the Taylor War Map, 1839, the name of the Everglades is recorded as *Pay-hai-o-kee or Grass Water*."

It is difficult to account for the formation of the word. One possible explanation is that *Everglades* might have been formed on the analogy of *evergreen* or such quasi-adjectival uses of *ever* as Shakespeare's "A never writer, to an ever reader."

In detail, the Everglades are described as overflowed country (1836), submerged flats (1825), and also as a vast basin (under *glade* 1871) filled with marshes and wet savannas intersected by lakes and lagoons—all together forming a labyrinth (1837). It is said that certain parts of the Everglades are devoid of vegetation (1842), and also that it has an outer margin consisting of prairie which has been formed by receding waters (1869). Specifically, under *glade*, the region is called a "grass meadow" or "grassy lake" (1871).

The Tanner *Map of Florida* (1823) is not, as the DAE and DA indicate, the first published reference to the term. (The Tanner citation in the OED is dated 1827.) The notation on this map reads, "Entered according to Act of Congress, the 20th day of August 1823." Furthermore, on page 17 of the "Geographical Memoir" of Tanner's *New American Atlas* (which includes the map just mentioned) is found the following: "Map of the Territory of Florida. I am indebted for nearly all the materials I possess for this territory, to Charles Vignoles, Esq., who politely and very liberally furnished me with all the original maps and notes from which he had constructed his excellent map of Florida." Tanner signs this memoir (p. 18) and dates it "Sept. 10, 1823." That the Vignoles *Map of Florida* (1823) was printed before Tanner's is evident for several reasons: At the bottom of the former's map occur the words, "Entered according to Act of Congress 17th day of March 1823, by H. S. Tanner"; and on April 26, 1823, the St. Augustine *East Florida Herald* advertised that "19 MAPS OF FLORIDA, by *C Vignoles*, engraved in a handsome style by Mr. Tanner, of Philadelphia, are expected here in a few days," the same journal notifying the public on June 21st of that year that these maps were on sale at the office of the Herald. The Vignoles and Tanner maps of Florida seem to be identical; apparently, the wording on both of them is exactly the same. The full *Everglades* quotation (see 1822 below) is absolutely the same on both maps. On another part of both maps the words "Boca Ratone or Dry River Inlet now (1822) shut" are found, and two other similar "(1822)" references are also given. For the reasons given above, the first illustrations in the OED, DAE, and DA entries of *everglade* should be corrected from "1823 Tanner *Map Florida* . . ." to "1822 (1823) Vignoles *Map Florida*. . . ."

1822 (1823) V *Map of Florida* Extensive inundated Region, covered with Pine and Hummock Islands, of all sizes, and generally called THE EVER GLADES.

1823 V 52　Beyond a boundless savanna . . . mingling at length with the Ever Glades.

1825 GADSDEN 119　An attempt to penetrate by the everglades proved unsuccessful; the whole surface of the earth was covered with water from four and five inches to two and three feet in some places . . . The everglades, or submerged flats of the cape, [are] spotted with small islands of pine, palmetto, etc.

1836 ASPMA VI. 442　The rivers there all heading in the "everglades," (the overflowed country so called).

1837 W 150-51　That part of the peninsula of Florida that lies south of the 28th degree of north latitude, declines towards the centre in form of a dish, the border of which is raised towards the coast. Near Cape Florida, this border is from twelve to twenty miles from the sea beach. It is formed of the same calcareous rock which skirts the Gulf of Mexico as far west as the Appalache River. This vast basin is filled with marshes, wet savannas, intersected by extensive lakes and lagoons, forming a labyrinth which taken together, is called the Everglades. It is very little known.

1842 PREBLE 34　Passed through open Everglades, no bushes.

1868 FICSP 139　The border and outer margin of the Everglades is prairie, of from one-fourth to one mile in breadth, and comprises some of the finest and richest land in America, having once been a portion of the Everglades, and formed by the receding of the waters.

1871 H 136　The most prominent feature of South Florida is the great basin known as the Everglades, or Great Glade . . . The region known as Miami lies on the east of this great grass lake.

Attrib. in sing. form with *morass*.

1823 V 53　[The Delaware river] heads in lake Macaco, or at all events in large lagoons in the recesses of the Ever Glade morass.

See also GLADE; PINE GLADE; WET GLADE.

F

FALL.　(1a) A sudden or steep descent in the course of a stream. DAE. 1634. (b) Also in plural with singular sense. DAE. 1815. (A.) (2) A series or succession of such descents, or one broken up into several parts; a cascade; a rapid. Usually pl. DAE. 1608. (3) A slope or declivity. OED.

(1a)　1766 B 14　The [river] . . . had some fall.

1818 Y 44　Sixty feet below [the ford], there is a considerable fall.

1836 ASPMA VI. 995　[The steamboat Minerva] was greatly delayed by a fall of the Chattahoochee.

(b)　1821 F 100　In the river Manatee is a considerable fall of rocks fourteen miles from its mouth. Above these falls the banks are very steep.

1827 W 24　The Histahatchee . . . is navigable nine miles, to the falls.

1836 ASPMA VII. 147　The instruction given to Major Read was to select a site for a post as high up the river as the obstruction or falls—twelve miles from the mouth [of the Withlacoochee].

(2)　1823 V 82　These falls [*sc.*, Haffia] are merely rapids over a bed of secondary limestone rocks.

1837 W 10　Here a ledge of rocks surrounds the Appalache Bay . . . forming falls and rapids.

(3)　1829 USCHED vol. 187 #147.32　The fall from the pond to this point is as much as 166 feet, on a distance of but 12⅛ miles.

1871 H 92　Turnbull swamp . . . needs draining to render it arable, and there is sufficient fall to allow of this, as is amply proved by some of Turnbull's old canals, which still discharge the waters of the swamps into the river.

FAN-PALMETTO BARREN. A barren upon which the principal growth is cabbage palmetto.

1836 SSW 159 Our road lay through a sandy pine and fan palmetto barren.

FARMING COUNTRY. Farming land.

1837 W 45 These waters generally, rise from fine springs on the borders of a good farming country, called the Pine Level.

1843 FHQ XV. 59 This is the finest farming country I have ever seen.

FARMING LAND. Land suitable for farming. DAE 1751. (A.)

1837 W 133, 138 In the northern part there are detached spots of good farming land ... The last mentioned swamps contain several sections of good farming land within 4 miles of St. Augustine.

FAST GROUND. Fast land.

1765 B 8 But between it and the common fast ground is a great swamp.

FAST LAND. Upland; land not subject to overflow or flooding. DAE 1681.

1791 B 129 I snapped my piece, but it flashed, on which they both turned about and galloped off, plunging through the water and swamp, never halting, as I suppose, until they reached fast land, as I could hear them leaping and plunging a long time.

1856 USCHED vol. 893 Part I. 553 Johnson's key ... is the only one in the vicinity that has any considerable amount of fast land on it.

FEEDER. A stream which flows into another body of water. OED.

1874 S 16 The fountain of the St. John's is at the head of some one of the intricate marshy feeders that crawl into this lake [Washington].

FIELD. (1) Open land as opposed to woodland; a stretch of open land; a plain. *Obs.* OED. (2) A floating field.

(1) 1609 VRV 178-79 There groweth another plant in the open field, which beareth a fruit like vnto strawberries, close to the ground.

1682 *The Present State of Carolina* 3 Carolina is part of the Main in *America*, and so much celebrated by Mounsier *Laudonere*, that he entitles it *Florida*, because of her florid, and fragrant fields.

1827 W 44 Cockspur [grow in] ... old sandy uncultivated fields.

1836 SSW 188 Saw in the sandy fields Cactus opuntia, Prickly Pear.

1837 W 165 Rivulets of charming water meandered through the fields.

(2) 1842 PREBLE 38 Followed [the inlet] out, pushing through fields of broad-leaved lilies and spatter-docks.

See also FLOATING FIELD.

FIRM GROUND. Firm land (1).

1837 ASPMA VII. 161 As the head of the right column approached firm ground, received a sharp discharge of rifles from the enemy.

1874 S 22 They were fortunate, however, in finding firm ground on the shore of the lake.

FIRM LAND. (1) Dry land, solid earth. *Obs.* OED under *firm.* (2) The mainland (as opposed to an island), a "continent." *Obs.* OED under *firm.*

(1) 1791 B 176 We arrived on a delightful, level, green meadow, as usual, which continued about a mile, when we reached the firm land.

1823 V 83 The interior of the southern extremity of the Florida peninsula, appears to have scattered over it many tracts of firm land in the form of islands and promontories.

(2) 1582 HAKLUYT *Diuers voyages* ... (n.p.). Iohn Baptista Ramusius in his Preface to the thirde volume of the navigations, writeth thus of Sebastian Gabot. It is not throughly [*sic*] knowne whether [New France] ... doe ioyne with the firme lande of Florida and *nova Hispania.*

1625 PURCHAS 868 *Florida* ... is a firme Land of a good climate.

FLAG-GRASS POND. A pond in which
flag grass abounds.

1825 GADSDEN 120 The last seven
miles . . . spotted with saw and flag grass
ponds.

FLAT. (1) Chiefly pl. A shallow or
shoal; a low-lying tract of land covered usually or periodically with
water as by the tide. DAE 1634.
Spec., a savanna (1870); the keys
known as the Martyrs. All of the
references are to salt-water areas, except one (1825). (2) Low land sufficiently free from overflowing to be
valuable as pasture or farm land.
DAE 1651. Possibly the 1825 quotation belongs under (1). (3) A tract of
elevated level land. DAE 1733. (A.)

(1) 1587 L 38 Fifteene yeares past,
three shippes . . . were cast away ouer
against a place named Calos vppon the
flates which are called The Martyrs.

1796 G 15 But that large space [be-
tween Key Largo and the mainland] is
almost one continued flat, with some
small channels of 5 or 6 feet water.

1823 V 42 On the main or western
side [of Merritt's island] is the proper
channel: the eastern branch is shallow
and its upper end spread with flats and
mangrove islands.

1825 GADSDEN 119 For two days
my party waded through these submerged flats [in the Everglades], and
with the greatest difficulty could a spot
be found sufficiently extensive and free
from water, for dry it was not, on which
to pitch our tents . . . We had to elevate
our blankets from the water, which
flowed beneath our bodies, with sticks,
palmetto leaves, etc.

1830 ASPNA IV 966 This harbor is
. . . completely walled in by the keys
and flats.

1836 SSW 159 They passed the night
in the open flats on the Matanza.

1870 BILL 75 Passing the headlands,
an open flat, or savanna, appears, in

width perhaps five miles, extending
however, many miles up along the coast
as far as the eye can reach. The river
crosses, in a westerly direction, this low
tract, much resembling the Jersey flats
between Newark and New York.

1871 S 31 The current [at Jupiter in-
let] is very strong, and the banks and
flats inside are quickly flooded.

1874 S 18 The clinker-built boat was
drawn over the shallow flat along the
shore.

(2) 1818 Y 25 The transitions from
both the sandy and fertile hills are
sometimes suddenly into the flats.

1825 GADSDEN 120 Occasional
swells of saw-palmetto lands . . . interspersed with grassy flats, spotted with
cypress and bay ponds.

(3) 1815 NWR 106 The ridge dividing their waters has high flats of
light land.

See also BAY-BUSH FLAT; FLAT-LAND;
FLAT PINELAND; FLATWOODS; MARSH
FLAT (attrib.); MUD FLAT; PALMETTO
FLAT; PINE FLAT; SALT FLAT; SAND
FLAT; SAW-PALMETTO FLAT.

FLAT-LAND. Land that is almost or
completely level. DAE 1735.

1818 Y 26 Of the flat-land in Florida,
there are four stages: 1. The high pine
flats. 2. The low flats with palmetto—
3. The Savannas, and 4. The marshes
of the sea shore.

1825 ASPIA II. 636 Somewhere about
that point on Gadsden's survey which is
denominated "flat lands filled with
ponds."

FLAT PINELAND. Pineland that is
practically or absolutely level.

1823 V 87 The *flat pine lands* are of
themselves of two kinds: the one sort
covered with a thick and luxuriant
growth of berry bushes, dwarf bays and
laurels, with grass only in patches, and
the pine trees sparsely scattered over
the ground: the other kind has little or
no undergrowth: being thickly covered
with savannas and cypress ponds and

galls, it is often overflown from them and on the least fall of rain becomes drowned; the herbage however is generally plentiful.

FLATWOODS. Pl. Level, low-lying areas of timberland, usually having poor natural drainage. DAE 1849. Originally, probably sand islands surrounded by marshes and lagoons (1874). (A.) DA 1841.

1869 FICSP 28 [The impression that much of the soil of Florida is nearly worthless] will not hold good even of ... the low "flatwoods."

1874 SAR 32 There is another species of pine land called by the natives "flatwoods."

Ibid., 118 The latter, sand islands of an older formation among the marshes and lagoons that early surrounded them, and from which the present flat-woods arose.

FLOATING FIELD. A drift of vegetation.

1791 B 106 The cape opposite to us was a vast cypress swamp, environed by a border of grassy marshes, which were projected farther into the lake, by floating fields of the bright green Pistia stratiotes.

FLOATING ISLAND. A detached mass of vegetation. "Formerly found in western rivers." DAE 1807. (A.) Spec., a floating island which has sunk (1874). *Cf.* ISLAND (4).

1791 B 88-89 [Pistia stratiotes] associates in large communities, or floating islands, some of them a quarter of a mile in extent, and are impelled to and fro, as the wind and current may direct. They are first produced on, or close to, the shore, in eddy water, where they gradually spread themselves into the river, forming most delightful green plains, several miles in length, and in some places a quarter of a mile in breadth.

1837 W 96 Pistia ... floats on the surface, the roots hanging like threads in the water, and often forming floating islands.

1869 FICSP 113-14 The soil upon which ... [the water flags] grow is not attached to the bottom of the river, but ... the water flows underneath their foundation. These were evidently floating islands, which have by means of roots, etc., become netted to the main land. The floating islands are formed sometimes in the river and sometimes in the lakes, whence they are carried into the river by the winds and currents. Sometimes the bonnet roots are detached from the bottom and rising to the surface eventually form an island by attracting and gathering the floating grass and mud, but usually a considerable portion of the soil becomes suddenly detached from the bottom by some cause unknown, and rises to the surface and is soon covered by a rank growth of flags or careless weed.

1874 S 17 We passed several floating islands. They are formed by the dead roots of the smart weed and other swampy vegetation torn up by the wind, and hurled upon the shore. A soil is formed, birds drop acorns upon the mass, and little trees make their appearance. A second wind sends the whole thing out on the lake, where it floats subject to every breeze. One of these islands was sunk in the channel between Lakes Poinsett and Winder, in the memorable gale of August, 1871 ... Its dead trees still appear above the water at the mouth of the river. Sometimes Indians and white hunters set these islands on fire. The blaze generates a gale, and the burning islands are driven across the lake. Some of the islands are over a half mile in circumference.

FLOATING PLAIN. A floating island (*q.v.*).

1791 B 89 In great storms of wind and rain, when the river is suddenly raised, large masses of these floating plains are broken loose, and driven from the shores, into the wide water, where they have the appearance of islets.

FORD. A place in a river where a man or animal may cross by wading. DAE c. 1650.

1818 Y 44 The ford which is shallow is based on a rough lime-stone rock.
1821 F 79 The *Cattle Ford* ... has below it a marsh on both sides, with high oak banks.
1823 V 63 In communicating between Pensacola and St. Augustine ... the fords and ferries are scarcely ever practicable.
1836 SSW 134 The guard house was opposite to this ford.

See also CATTLE-FORD; COWFORD.

FOREST. (1) A tract of land covered with woods and undergrowth. DAE 1673. Spec., an oak forest (1786; 1828); open forest (*q.v.*) (1791). (2) A wild uncultivated waste, a wilderness. *Obs.* OED.

(1) 1563 RIBAULD 19 The countrey theraboutes ... is the fairest ... of all the worlde, aboundynge in ... forestes.
1587 L 63 The forrest or woode continueth and stretcheth foorth beyond it.
1652 HEYLIN 115 The Woods and Forrests full of the largest Okes.
1731 C I. 31 The Indians chuse to sow no more than will serve them for that term, retiring ... into the deep recesses of the forests.
1786 in SIEBERT II. 38 A Villa known by the name of Oak Forest.
1791 B 160-61 The open forests ... stood at a considerable distance from each other, through which appeared at N.W. an almost unlimited plain.
1797 MAG under *Cuscowilla.* The lake is terminated on one side by extensive forests, consisting of orange groves.
1821 F vii [The saw-mill seats are] surrounded with forests that have never been touched.

1827 W 22 Thirty miles below this spring, an arm of the Appalachicola has lately burst into the Chapola, and formed a lake twenty miles in length, and seven wide, in which the forests are yet standing.
1828 ASPPL VI. 62 On the petition of John Bunch. 2,160 acres of land were granted by Governor White in 1804, at Oak Forest, in Mosquito.
1837 W 36 New Mattacumbe ... has a broken rocky surface, but is clothed with a forest of hardwoods, vines and plants.
1869 FICSP 34 There are, however, thousands of acres of rich hammock land within a mile of the river, which are as yet unbroken forest.
(2) 1775 A 457 Our rulers ought not to allow so mischievous and dangerous a body as the Muskohge to ingross this vast forest, mostly for wild beasts.
1873 FHQ XIV. 257 East Florida still remains for the most part a forest.

See also HAMMOCK FOREST (attrib.); MANGROVE FOREST; PINE FOREST.

FOREST LAND. Land covered by forest growth. DAE 1685.

1869 FICSP 28 [The impression that much of the soil of Florida is nearly worthless] will not hold good even of the forest lands.

FORK(S). (1a) The point of juncture of two or more streams; also, the area surrounding such a point. Usually pl. DAE 1645. Note the fork of a swamp and branch (1823). (b) The tract of land lying between two streams that come together. Sometimes pl. DAE 1692. Note the fork of a swamp 1828). DA 1674, *in the fork(s).* (c) One or other of the streams that come together; a tributary of a main stream. DAE 1697. (A.–all three senses.)

(1a) 1763 ROBERTS 12 On the forks of [*Euchi* creek] ... is a village of the same name.

1773 MS. 216   To the North, beginning at the Fork of the Apalachicola
Stream, which branches two Rivers,
Flint & Chatahutchee.
1812 FHQ IX. 70   We advanced near
the Scambia from the fork.
c. 1819 ASPMA I. 733   The Americans
are at the forks of the river Appalachicola.
1823 ASPPL III. 807   Five hundred
acres of land, lying on a fork made of
Durbin's swamp, and a branch made of
Julinton creek.
(b)   1818 Y 37   In the forks of some
of the branches there is high pine
barren.
1828 ASPPL VI. 108   This land lies on
the public road leading from Jacksonville to Camp Pinckney, in the fork of
Mill's Swamp, near the mouth of Alligator Creek, in the county of Nassau.
1837 W 140   In the forks between this
river and the Ocklawaha, the sand hills
and ridges rise to a considera[b]le
height.
(c)   1769 STORK 12   About 950
acres of land . . . are situated on the
northernmost fork of the river.
1818 Y 38   The main fork of Okalokina
before the junction [with] Little river
also runs through an extensive body of
good land.
1823 ASPPL III. 801   Five thousand
acres, lying on the great fork of Nassau
river.

FOUNTAIN.   (1) A spring or source of
water issuing from the earth and collecting in a basin; also, the head
spring or source of a stream or river.
Arch. OED. Spec., with reference to
subterranean streams. (2) An oceanic
spring. See quotation. *Cf.* SPRING.

(1)   1765 B 5-6   Out of the head of
which [cove] arose a prodigious large
fountain of clear water of loathsome
taste.
1766 B 14   I believe, that [the sea-
shells] . . . reach all under this whole
low country . . . and support the superior

soil, under which the prodigious sul-
phureous and saline fountains run.
1775 R 285   The large river in Charlotte harbour, by direction of its course
. . . might, perhaps, spring from the
same fountain.
1791 B 145   This creek, which is
formed instantly by this admirable
fountain, is wide and deep enough for
a sloop to sail up into the bason.
1793 AUG I. 625-26   Near Long Lake
. . . which communicates with St. John's
river by a small creek, is a vast fountain
of warm or rather hot mineral water,
issuing from a high bank on the river.
It boils up with great force, forming
immediately a vast circular bason, capacious enough for several shallops to
ride in.
1822 SIMMONS 29   The stream is
perfectly straight for the greatest part
of its course, but forms a short curve
near its fountain [*i.e.*, Silver Spring].
1823 STCW 24   This fountain, although equally large, is not by any
means so clear and beautiful as the
head of the Wakully.
1856 FHQ I. 35   Wakulla Fountain . . .
is the fountain-head of a river.
(2)   1837 W 149   An account of an
extraordinary fountain, bursting from
the Atlantic coast, about nine miles
south of St. Augustine, and from one
to two miles from the east shore of
Anastasia Island, has been published on
the authority of Captain Sisson . . . Persons . . . [have] alledged that they had
not only sailed across it, but had drawn
from the fountain buckets of tolerable
drinking water . . . On approaching the
place, says my informant, the sea appeared to be ruffled with short waves,
as though rocks lay beneath the surface,
and the color assumed a yellowish cast,
which led him to fear that they were
approaching a shoal: as the wind was
light, he ordered the lead to be cast,
and found from seven to eight fathoms
quite across the rippling space, that in
some places boiled and whirled, at intervals, in a very singular manner. The

whole space agitated was, perhaps, six rods across, and the water was considerably deeper here than on the adjacent coast.

FREESTONE SPRING. A spring whose waters contain little or no dissolved substance such as calcium, magnesium, etc.

1874 SAR 81 The supply of drinking water is ample and abundant, being obtained from the numerous freestone springs which gush out on all sides from the base of the hill on which the town [*sc.*, Quincy] is located.

FRESH LAKE. A fresh-water lake.

1775 R 33 There are ... good fresh springs in most parts of this country, as well as salt and fresh lakes.

FRESH MARSH. A fresh-water marsh. *Obs.* DAE 1638. Spec., quicksand covered with thin soil (1827).

1787 in SIEBERT II. 240 1000 acres ... lying between the Musquito river and the Sea forming a Neck of land about 400 acres good rich high land and fresh marsh.
1823 V 69 From Alexander's creek upwards the St. John's meanders through extensive fresh marshes, dotted with islets of orange and live oak growth.
1827 W 61 Some of the fresh marshes, on the contrary, are merely quicksands, covered with a very thin soil, and are of course quite barren.

FRESH MARSHLAND. Fresh-water marshland.

1874 SAR 117 The branch, fresh marsh and black rush lands attached to [the calcareous soils on Amelia Island] ... are especially suitable for gardening.

FRESH POND. A fresh-water pond. Prob. Southern.

1773 MS. 224, 226 Back of the Beach are Shrubs Palmetoes, cabbage, and fresh Ponds ... To fresh pond surrounded with marshes.

1827 W 27 Some [alligators] ... however, live in fresh ponds, forty miles inland.

FRESH RIVER. A fresh-water river. *Obs.* DAE 1637. (A.)

c. 1565 Hawkins voyage, in HAKLUYT (1589) 542 But for the foule of the fresh riuers, these two [*i.e.*, the "Flemengo" and the "Egript"] I noted to bee chiefe.
1731 C I. 78 These Birds frequent fresh Rivers and Ponds in the upper Parts of the Country, remote from the Sea.
1773 MS. (307) The Modern Indians, living only upon fresh Rivers, and far off from the Sea, grind the purple or blue Spot out of the Oysters.
1821 F 98 I saw the colour of the water near the very bank to be that of our fresh rivers in this climate.

FRESH SPRING. A fresh-water spring. Prob. Southern.

1775 R 33 These are ... good fresh springs in most parts of this country.

FRESH WATER. Spring-water as distinguished from rain-water. EDD.

1821 F 100 To the southward of this river, is a large body of marsh, through which several rivulets of fine water empty themselves into the ground, back of the keys, which begin here. A man may at this place stand with one foot in fresh, and the other in salt water; nay, when the tide is out, fresh water boils up through the sand.
1823 V 37-38 The planters have also resolved to dig across the beach and complete the opening of the [Matanzas] inlet, the fresh waters having destroyed their oyster banks.
1837 W 70 [River Flies and Spring Flies] confine themselves to fresh water.
Attrib. with *basin, well.*
1870 BILL 77 [The St. Johns is] fed by and flowing out of that vast fresh-water basin formed by the everglades [*sic*] and savannas.

1823 V 52 At Cape Sable or punta Tancha there are actually three capes, at the middle one of which are fresh water wells.

FRESH-WATER BROOK. A brook the water of which is fresh rather than salt. Prob. Southern.

1587 L 24L It is inuironed with an infinite number of brooks of fresh water.
1784 HUTCHINS 85 On the North side of the bay are two or three small fresh water brooks.
1823 ASPPL III. 786 Beginning at the entrance of Fresh Water brook.

FRESH-WATER CREEK. A creek the water of which is fresh. DA 1741. Poss. Southern.

1787 in SIEBERT II. 243 This tract ... had a fresh water creek.
1823 V 48 Jupiter creek ... as well as Fresh-water creek near the bar, have some connexion with the fresh water lake which approaches within four miles of Jupiter.
1837 W 143 Below Cape Florida, the coast declines again into sandy pine lands, for several miles, until Fresh Water Creek enters the Gulf.
1871 H 91 Elbow creek ... empties into the Indian river nearly opposite the south end of Merritt's island, and is ... fresh water.

FRESH-WATER KEY. A key located off the estuary of a river and thus at least partially surrounded by fresh water.

1837 W 31 The N.E. part of Waka-sasse Bay is filled with islets called the Fresh Water Keys, being situated in front of the estuaries of the Suwanne and Wakasasse Rivers.

FRESH-WATER LAKE. A lake the water of which is fresh rather than salt. DAE 1789. (OED 1774 under *fresh-water*.)

1587 L 39L One of these two declared ... that in the midway there was an Iland situate in a great lake of fresh water, named Sarrope, about fiue leagues in bignesse.
1762 J 69 In fresh water-lakes, and rivers, is a sort of shell-fish between a muscle, and a pearl oyster, in some of which are found pearls.
1825 GADSDEN 119 A chain of inlets or sounds and fresh water lakes extend north and south for the greater part of the distance.
1837 W 61 Fresh Water Lake lies parrallel and near to the southern Atlantic coast.

FRESH-WATER MARSH. A marsh or swamp containing fresh as opposed to salt water. DAE 1754. Poss. Southern.

1765 letter in STORK Apx. 33 When that [lake] is crossed, the country, as far as you can see, on both sides of the river, is a fresh water marsh.
1769 STORK 11 From latitude 26, 40, to 27, there is a branch of Hillsborough river terminating in fresh water marsh.
1775 R 30 Marshes ... are of four kinds, two in the salt, and two in the fresh water.
1786 in SIEBERT II. 58 The Rice Swamp which was cultivated and planted in 1779 ... was a fresh water Marsh.
1823 V 91 The *fresh water marshes* are of two kinds, *hard* and *soft*.

FRESH-WATER MARSHLAND. Fresh-water marsh.

1769 STORK 11 The fresh water marsh land, [consists] of 9386 acres.

FRESH-WATER POND. A pond consisting of fresh as opposed to salt water; spec., a fresh-water lake (1825). Prob. Southern.

1742 RCBH Apx. 16 The Land is mostly fine *Savannas* with fresh Water Ponds.
1784 HUTCHINS 84 The country between them is low and marshy, and full of fresh water ponds.
1823 ASPNA I. 1119 Nearly one-half

of the island is occupied by salt and fresh water ponds.

1825 GADSDEN 120 The ocean on the east, and sand hills and [a] chain of fresh water ponds or lakes on the west.

1827 W 18 Abundance of water fowls cover the fresh water ponds, which are found in all the valleys.

FRESH-WATER RIVER. A river unaffected by salt water. DAE 1645. (A.)

1763 ROBERTS 12 In the year 1717 the *French* erected Fort *Crevecoeur*, about a mile to the northward of the fresh water river [a branch of the APALACHICOLA river].

1787 in SIEBERT II. 242 The river was a fresh water river with little fall of tide and liable to overflow in gales of wind.

1803 E 252 Fresh Water River is said to be no more than the outlet to a large lake.

1823 V 81-82 In dry seasons the tide rises high in the fresh water rivers being perceptible at some distance from the sea.

FRESH-WATER RIVULET (RUN). A small fresh-water stream. *Fresh-water run* is prob. Southern.

1773 MS. 259 The several fresh water Runs and Rivulets pour into the Stream [*sc.*, St. Johns] so much fresh water, that their moving Weight forces the standing salt water, swelled up the Stream by Easterly Winds to contract in separate Places.

FRESH-WATER SPRING. A spring the water of which is fresh rather than salt.

1773 MS. 298 Out of this long bluff [illeg.] . . . a fresh water Spring.

FRESH-WATER SWAMP. A swamp containing fresh water.

1796 G 18 [On the north side of Kay Vaccas] there are several fresh water swamps, and natural reservoirs among the rock.

1873 S 6 [The alligator hole] is situated in a fresh water swamp.

FRESH-WATER TIDE-SWAMP. Probably a swamp connected with the ocean by a fresh-water stream which is affected by the rising and falling of the tide. (*Cf. tide-swamp* in DA, 1796, no def.)

1787 in SIEBERT II. 169 About three hundred acres . . . were fresh water tide Swamp on Clay foundation, equal to the Lands of Savanna river . . . fresh water, tide Swamp . . . timbered with tupelow, Ash, and large Cypress trees.

See also TIDE-RIVER SWAMP.

G

GALL. The CD defines *gall* as a low spot (in the southern U.S.), "as near the mouth of a river, where the soil under the matted surface has been washed away, or is in such a condition that nothing will grow on it"; and the EDD states that a gall is wet, spongy land (generally in pl.), "a barren or unfertile spot in a field, through which springs of water constantly ooze up." These definitions would apply in Florida, excepting that the soil there may be fertile. It is not unlikely that the word is derived from the fact that gall bushes grow on this type of land (*cf.* BAY-GALL, 1818 quotation); however, there may be some connection with the concept of "bitterness," since the waters are usually impregnated with acid, so that of all swamps this type has the coldest soil. Strictly speaking, galls are watercourses thinly covered with earth. (DAE 1823—no def.)

1773 MS. 218 Crossed a run in a Small gall.

1827 W 53 The third kind of swamps are those spongy tracts, where the waters continually ooze through the soil, and finally collect in streams and pass off. These are properly termed galls, sometimes sour, sometimes bitter lands. They are the coldest soils we have, and the waters arising through them are frequently impregnated with sulphur, vitriol, and iron. When their foundation is alluvial matter, it is usually very thin, like quagmire: the land may be shaken for acres in extent. When the base is sand, it is always a lively quicksand, very dangerous for cattle. These galls are usually covered with titi and other andromedas, loblolly and other laurels, vaccinums and vines.

See also BAY-GALL; CYPRESS GALL.

GAP. (1) An opening in a range of hills; a pass or notch. DAE 1750. (Also, EDD.) Spec., a notch in the forest line (1784). (2) The place where a stream has forced a passage through the coast. ("A break or opening . . . " CD.)

(1) 1775 R Apx. lxviii The pitch of the cape is known by the appearance of a gap in the land about 1½ or 2 leagues to the eastward of it.

1784 HUTCHINS 86, 87 The peninsula between St. Joseph's and Cape Blaise is a narrow slip of land, in some places not above a quarter of a mile broad. The gaps here and there upon it, and the water in the bay appearing through them from the mast-head . . . make it easily known . . . There is also a remarkable gap among the trees between the sea and the bottom of St. Joseph's bay, where is a narrow isthmus not above 5 or 600 yards broad.

(2) 1823 V 46 The Gap [near St. Lucie river] sixteen miles from the bar is remarkable, giving at sea the appearance of an inlet.

1837 W 43 A few years since, the high waters of St. Lucia River, forced a passage through the coast at the place called the Gap, on the old charts.

1871 S 31 About fifteen years ago a storm closed the gap [?at Jupiter inlet].

GARDEN. A natural grove.

1869 FICSP 107 In the primeval woods on the banks are vast gardens of the sour wild oranges.

GATEWAY. A passage for navigation. NID. Spec., a narrows; the mouth of a lake, *i.e.*, the place of entry of a river into a lake.

1871 H 131 About fifteen miles south of St. Sebastian, the river banks ahead seem to approach each other, and leave a narrow gate way for the river. This is The Narrows.

1874 KEASBEY 50 As we sail into the broad lake we gaze back . . . and seek to peer again into the narrow gateway of green from which we had just emerged.

GLADE. (1) A natural opening or clearing in a forest. DAE 1661. (2a) A tract of low, swampy land, sometimes inundated and often overgrown with grass; an everglade. DAE 1789. Poss. Southern. Spec., a wet down (1791); a savanna or wet glade (1818). Note how closely the 1818 description approximates those given a few years later to the extensive region in southern Florida. (b) The name of a particular area of this sort. DAE 1724. DA 1644. The *Everglades* (*q.v.*) called also the *glades,* the *Great Glade* (1823; 1871), the *Never Glade,* the *Eternal Glades;* also referred to once as the "interminable glades" (1837). *Cf.* CYPRESS GALL.

(1) 1743 C II. ii In woods of pine trees are frequently seen Glades or Openings, occasioned by the Fall of Trees, which lie prostrate one Way, by which is formed a straight and regular

Avenue an hundred Feet wide, more or less, and some Miles long. These are likewise the Effects of violent Gusts of Wind.

1827 W 106 In the valleys, there is a much heavier growth of timber, and frequently deep cane-brakes. There are, also, frequently to be met with, grassy ponds, surrounded by glades, which afford excellent pasture.

1836 SSW 187 When our troops thought that they had cut off their escape in front, a glimpse of them was seen far through the distant glades before them.

(2a) 1744 KIMBER 13 [The Wood's] only Vacuities were some few Glades, made by the Entrance of a Creek.

1791 B 155 After leaving the rivulet we passed over a wet, hard, level glade or down.

1818 Y 28, 30 The glades or Savannas are tracts a little lower than the palmetto land, and in winter are covered with water from a few inches to several feet in depth. They extend, with great variation of length and breadth through the whole country, sometimes forming long and narrow vistas through the pineland covered with luxuriant and nutritious herbage and in places, spreading into ponds or lakes many miles in extent only dry in the warmest seasons ... The traveler ... finds the change from the open glades to the tangled and equally inundated Bay-Galls of little benefit.

(b) 1823 V 49, 50, 53 The inland communication from New river to cape Florida, is from the head of New river to the head of the Rio Ratones through the Glade ... The Potomac river ... is ... connected with the *Great Glade* ... [p. 50] The Glade, or as it is emphatically termed, the *Never Glade,* appears to occupy almost the whole interior from about the parallel of Jupiter inlet to cape Florida, thence round to cape Sable to which point it approaches very near, and northwardly as far as the Delaware river discharging into Char-

lotte bay: its general appearance is a flat sandy surface mixed in the large stones and rocks, with from six inches to two feet of water lying upon it, in which is a growth of saw and other water grasses, so thick as to impede the passage of boats where there is no current ... Cape Sable creek ... heads like all the other Streams in the Eternal Glades.

1837 W 143, 151 This prairie usually terminates in cypress swamps, and those in the interminable glades ... On reaching the level of the glades, a vast grass meadow is expanded, apparently as boundless as the ocean; you then pass on the winding lagoons from six to twelve miles westwardly and the grass, by degrees, disappears and you are left in an unexplored grassy lake to which you can discover no bounds. It probably extends near to the eastern shore of the Gulf. The grassy borders of this lake is usually covered with water during the winter season, not so deep however, as to hide the grass which is very thick and tall. During the summer, the ground is often dry and hard for ten miles from the timbered land.

1871 H 136 The most prominent feature of South Florida is the great basin known as the Everglades, or Great Glade.

1874 S 27 [The traveller] must draw his boat over an arm of land completely encircling the lake and cutting it off from the glades.

See also EVERGLADE(s); PINE GLADE; WET GLADE.

GLEN. A secluded and narrow valley (in Florida, between hills). NID.

1825 FHQ III. 39 [The cascade] was formed by the rivulet above described, falling over a ledge of rocks into a deep glen.

GRASS KNOLL. A knoll overgrown with grass.

1836 SSW 70-71 The small islands or keys, appeared to be covered with Mangrove—others were nothing more than grass knowls.

GRASS LAKE. A lake in which grass grows; here, the Everglades.

1871 H 136 The region known as Miami lies on the east of this great grass lake.

GRASSLAND. Land producing grass. DAE 1682.

1871 H 136 These intervale lands [or savannas] . . . are natural grass lands.

GRASS MARSH. A marsh overgrown with grass.

1823 STCW 25 We encamped on a pleasant key near the shore of the grass marsh.
1855 USCSED vol. 756 #76.5 The remainder of the route . . . may be described as over a country gradually sloping to the Gulf . . . sprinkled with small cypress ponds and open grass marshes, varying in extent from 50 to 300 yards.

GRASS MEADOW. A meadow.

1823 STCW 39 On the left grass meadows extended to the north and west, as far as the eye can reach. The shores are sprinkled with beautiful keys.

GRASS PLAIN. A plain overgrown with grass. DAE 1826. (A.)

1837 W 300 At four miles from the mouth, a grass plain rises gradually from the west side to the height of fifteen feet, and skirted on the west with hammock land.

GRASS POINT. A point of land overgrown with grass.

1823 STCW 44 We came to anchor behind the grass point.

GRASS POND. A pond in which grass grows. DA 1837 (no def.).

1773 MS. 229 Grass Pond in a shrubby Land.
1837 W 135 From the Allachua uplands, the country descends westward,

. . . and is diversified by a variety of grass ponds and swamps.

1871 H 90 An apparent exception to this rule prevails in the case of cypress and grass ponds in the interior.

See also FLAG-GRASS POND.

GRASS PRAIRIE. A prairie or savanna overgrown with grass. DAE 1826. (A.)

1837 W Map Grass Prairie with clumps of Trees.
1842 PREBLE 43 Marched across a fine grass prairie for a couple of miles.

GRASS SAVANNA. An everglade.

1837 W 140, 142 McDougals swamp commences, where Turnbulls ends, there is only a narrow grass savanna, that separates them . . . West of Delespines tract, an extensive grass savanna . . . Occasionally cabbage hammocks of considerable extent, rise in the midst of these glades.

GRAZING COUNTRY. A country or region suitable for grazing. DAE 1789.

1822 SIMMONS 40 [The verdure on the dry edges] renders the districts that . . . [the ponds] occupy, the finest grazing country in the world.
1827 W 84 On the whole, the eastern part of Walton county is a pleasant and excellent grazing country.

GRAZING-GROUND(S). An area suitable for grazing. Here (and in the DAE 1835 quotation under *grazing*), always pl.

1822 SIMMONS 5-6 Even the extensive pine barrens . . . are not without their utility, as they afford excellent grazing grounds for cattle.
1874 SAR 96 Those once flourishing and famous plantations are now common grazing-grounds.

GRAZING LAND. Land suitable for grazing. DAE 1789.

1827 W 81 There are some savannas of a good moist grazing land.

1837 W 129 The hammocks on the north side of the main body of the bay [of St. Andrews] . . . will afford excellent farms, for ten or twelve miles, with good grazing lands in the rear.

GRAZING TRACT. Grazing country.

1837 W 134 This county is a fine grazing tract both for cattle and hogs.

GROUND. (1) The solid bottom or earth underlying the sea (or other water— *obs.*). Naut. OED. It is not certain that the 1586 quotation belongs under (1). (2) Any definite portion of the earth's surface. NID. Note the attempts of John Bartram (who also used the term *hammock*—see also the DAE) (1765, 1766) to describe hammock land as "declining ground," "middle ground," and "middling ground" (*cf.* "middling land" under LAND). All of the examples (except 1743) under (2) are preceded by specifying terms.

(1) 1589 DRAKE 43, 44 In the night the Lieutenant generall tooke a little rowing Skiffe . . . and went to viewe what gard the enemie kept, as also to take knowledge of the ground. 1742 RCBH Apx. 20 The *General, I,* and major *Heron,* went . . . to reconnoitre the *Point* of the *Bar* . . . We returned after viewing the Ground. 1764 FHQ XIX. 407 The sloop beating with such violence against the ground, that each stroke was expected to prove the last. 1775 R Apx. xii The bottom [of the rivers St. *Mary's* and *Nassau*] is a sand ground. 1796 G 15 The usual method of navigation in the channel between the Reef and the Kays, is always to come to an anchor in the night, where it is clear ground . . . The Reef from Cayo Sombrero is in general very broken ground as far as the West end of Matacumbe. 1803 E 254 It will likewise be necessary on coming to an anchor . . . every night while on the reef, to look out for clear ground. 1831 AUDUBON 62 The whole ground around them [*sc.,* Tortugas] is densely covered with corals, sea-fans, and other productions of the deep. (2) 1589 DRAKE 46 Wee assayed to go to the towne, but could not by reason of some riuers and broken ground which was betweene the two places. 1731 C I. 21 [The white oak] grows . . . most on high barren Ground amongst Pine Trees. 1741 GHDPOPW 184 Being prevented [from marching] by the Rivers and broken Ground in the Way, they embarked again on the River. 1742 RCBH Apx. 16 The *Indians* followed them upon their Track, but they . . . got into such *thickety* Ground, that they could not overtake them. 1743 FRLCSH 26 Besides his *Want of Plank,* and the Badness of the Ground, or more truly *Marsh,* on that Point, the Water is accounted a Mile over. 1763 ROBERTS 19 The whole shore upon which the current . . . sets is particularly low, flat, broken ground. 1765 ASPPL V. 757 If any person . . . shall take up any stony or rocky grounds, not fit for culture or pasture . . . the patentee shall be at liberty to withdraw his stock . . . in proportion to such cultivation and improvement as shall be made . . . upon the swampy or sunken grounds and marshes which shall be included in the same patent. 1765 B 2-3 The lowish or middle ground between the swamp and pine land is generally sand mixed with black mould, formed from the rotting of the fallen leaves from the thick brush and tall trees, which generally grow plentifully in this kind of ground . . . the middling ground being generally 300 yards broad to the higher land, some little swamps bordering the small rivulets. 1766 B 23 Whether they [*sc.,* Indians] planted the intermediate declining

grounds [*i.e.*, between the low, swamp-and-marsh land and the pinelands] I can't say, as large trees of cedar, celtes, and palms, with many other kinds, grow on most of them.
1803 E 275   Our journey . . . was extremely disagreeable owing to . . . the wet marshy ground on which we encamped.
1817 ASPPL IV. 200   With a prolongation of its lateral lines to and on the bay, as far as the pebbly ground, or where the bank of sand terminates.
1829 ASPPL V. 661 tr.   Of the first description are . . . places where the corporation meet, sandy beaches or grounds [arenales] which are on the banks of rivers.
1830 ASPPL VI. 549   It appears that, in crossing the Escambia bay, owing to the great width and bad ground, there was a mistake made of about half a mile.
1831 ASPNA IV. 101   Those [live oak trees] that grow in the marshy ground are straighter than those on a firmer soil.
1837 W 38   The west end of the island however is solid ground, based on a limestone rock over which the zoophite has spread a few feet of coralines, and the thick forests have on the top of both a rich soil.
Ibid., 220   During their retreat the cart-horse received three balls and on reaching a spot of dry ground he fell dead.
    See also (1) ANCHORAGE GROUND; ANCHORING-GROUND; HOLDING GROUND; MIDDLE GROUND; WRECKING GROUND. (2)   FAST GROUND; FIRM GROUND; GRAZING-GROUND; LOW GROUND; MARSH GROUND; MEADOW GROUND; PALMETTO GROUND; PASTURE GROUND; PRAIRIE GROUND (attrib.); RISING GROUND; SAVANNA GROUND (attrib.); SCRUB GROUND (attrib.); SOUR GROUND; SUMMIT GROUND (attrib.).

GROVE.   A small wood. OED. Spec., an orange grove; a hammock (1775, 1837).

1587 L 62L   Hee had seene a litle groue betwene the riuer & the fort.
1609 VRV 47   The most of it groues of wild Pine-trees.
1744 KIMBER 24   We arrive[d], at twelve at Noon, scorch'd to Death, and in great Want of Water, to a Place call'd *the Grove,* which truly merits that name.
1766 B 29   Here is a grove of orange-trees.
1773 MS. 309   There are also on the same soil very small groves consisting of nothing else than sour and bitter sweet Orange Trees.
1775 R Apx. lxxvi   The northern most entrance is likewise remarkable for a singular hommock of pine trees, or a grove standing very near the beach.
1796 G 25   The middle entrance of Boca Grande in Latitude 26° 38′ north, is known by a broken bluff with a grove of pine-trees.
1823 V 75   In this lake [Ware] is a beautiful island abounding with groves of the bitter-sweet or Seville orange.
1837 W 11   The hammocks present groves of live oak.
1870 BILL 195-96   Three [varieties of orange] . . . are. found growing wild, in irregular groves, along the principal rivers and streams . . . It is a beautiful sight to wander through these natural groves laden with such beautiful globes of gold.
    See also CABBAGE GROVE; CYPRESS GROVE; LIME GROVE; LIVE-OAK GROVE; MAPLE GROVE; OAK GROVE; OPEN GROVE; ORANGE GROVE; PINE GROVE; SOUR GROVE; WILD-ORANGE GROVE.

GULF.   (1a) A portion of the sea extending into the land. NID. Spec., the Gulf of Florida (now called the Straits of Florida, and formerly referred to as the Straits of Bahama); also ellipt. for the Gulf of Florida (1821). The term is used once to designate a comparatively small *bay* (1773). (b) A partially landlocked

sea. NID. Here, with particular reference to the Gulf (or "bay") of
Mexico. (For the distinction between
bay and *gulf*, *v. bay*.) This body of
water is called "the Southern Gulf"
once (1827). The meaning is extended
to apply to both seas on each side
of the Florida peninsula (1821). (2)
A gully. This is an extension of the
meaning of an abyss or deep chasm
given by all the dictionaries.
(1a)   1665 letter, in J Apx. 105   To
pass the gulph of *Florida* is for them
impossible, *should they lose the* Havana.
1741 GHDPOPW 179   San Agustin . . .
is situated on the Eastern Coast of
Florida; about seventy Leagues from
the Mouth of the Gulf of that name (or
Channel of *Bahama*).
1773 MS. 176 ftn. (a)   The Stream
Jordan; some will have it in the Gulf of
Pensacola.
1775 R Apx. xliii   Many people talk
about going southward thro' the *Gulph
of Florida* by keeping upon soundings
outside the reef.
1793 AUG Map I. 532   Gulf of Florida
or New Bahama Channel.
1796 G 7   Then . . . steer N.N.E. for
the Florida Gulf.
1797 MAG under *Bahama*   The *Strait
of Bahama*, or *Gulf of Florida*, lies between the coast of Florida and this
island.
Ibid., under *Florida, Gulf of*   Florida,
Gulf of, is the channel between the
peninsula of Florida and the Bahama
islands, N. of the island of Cuba; and
through which the Gulf Stream finds a
passage.
1821 F 105   Few vessels can come
through the gulf without seeing this
place . . . Sound Point, or Cape Florida,
being just north of it.
1837 W 34   Sandwich Gulf spreads in
a sheet six miles wide.
(b)   1652 HEYLIN 116   The Peninsula [is] . . . well known by three goodly
Bays . . . all opening into the Gulf of
Mexico, or the Bay of *New Spain*.

1672 LEDERER, John, *The Discoveries
of John Lederer* 23   I . . . think that the
Indian Ocean does stretch an Arm or
Bay from *California* into the Continent
as far as the *Apalataean* Mountains, an-
swerable to the Gulfs of Florida and
Mexico on this side.
1708 OLDMIXON 326   For several
years [the Spaniards] . . . search'd no
further than that Part of the Continent
which lies opposite to the Gulph of
New Spain.
1745 OSBORNE 744   From cape
Francis . . . to *Martyres* (coming up
from the gulph of Mexico to the north-
east parts of Florida) is near six degrees.
1763 ROBERTS 18   *La Sonda* is a
very large bank, that extends on the
west side of the peninsula into the gulf
of Mexico.
1775 A Apx. 457   Pensacola harbour
would be then serviceable also in a
time of war with Spain, being in the
gulph of Florida, and near to Cuba.
1797 MAG under *Florida Keys*   Florida
Keys, or *Martyr's Islands*, a number of
rocks and sand banks, bounded W. by
the gulf of Mexico, E. by that of Florida.
1821 F 112   This situation is melio-
rated in winter by the proximity of a
gulf on each side [of the Florida pen-
insula].
1823 V 77-78   Extending between the
Amasura river and the Mexican gulf is
a remarkable tract.
1827 W 9   West Florida is peculiarly
blessed. Her climate is temperate, both
from its latitude and from exposure to
the mild sea breezes of the Southern
gulf.
(2)   1823 STCW 23   On our return
we examined a deep gulf which had
been scooped out by a [mill] stream
entering the earth.
1827 W 79   A pleasant mill stream, the
collected waters of several fine springs,
winds along the eastern border of the
city [Tallahassee], until it falls, fifteen

or sixteen feet, into a gulf, scooped out by its own current.

GULF COAST. That part of the Florida coastline which borders the Gulf of Mexico. DA 1889 (no spec. ref. to Florida).

1832 USCSD vol. 214 #136.16 The easy approach to the bay from sea, is another great advantage over most of the harbors of the gulf coast.
1834 ASPMA VI. 455 On the Indian boundary, running parallel with the gulf coast, there are no settlements.
1869 FICSP 54 Perhaps no part of the United States can furnish a more exciting or agreeable winter hunting ground than Indian River and the Gulf coast.
1871 H 98 Mosquitoes are numerous only on the gulf coast.

GULF SHORE. The margin of land abutting upon the Gulf. This usage may be restricted to the area west of Tallahassee, and may also be obsolete.

1818 Y 48 The cockle banks are elevated spots along the gulf shore.
1823 STCW 28 These two great rivers with the Gulf shore, enclose a triangle of land.

GULF STREAM. A well-known oceanic current which originates in the Gulf of Mexico. DAE 1774. Here, that part of the current which runs along the Florida coast. DA 1769.

1743 FRLCSH iii The possession of Augustine ... must have expos'd their Galleons ... to further Difficulties and Obstructions in their Passage thro' the Gulf Stream, in Time of War.
1773 MS. map foll. 320 South of this Line the Current of the Florida Gulf Stream sets allways Northwardly.
1775 R Apx. xix Here the gulph stream comes very near the beach; the color of the water changes from a muddy green, to a beautiful saxon blue.

1796 G 20 From New Inlet to Coopers Hill the Gulf stream comes very near the beach.
1823 V 84 The rapid current of the gulf stream sweeping close along this part of the Florida coast has the effect of closing the bars of the inlets.
1836 ASPNA IV. 964 That rapid current denominated the gulf stream sweeps the Florida reef with incredible velocity.
1871 S 31 Heavy eastern gales, combined with the action of the gulf stream, sometimes shut the inlet.
    Cf. OCEAN-RIVER; STREAM.

GULLY. A ravine or small gorge worn by the action of water. DAE 1637.

1766 B 30 [The stream] ... gushed out over the rocks, where it had worn a deep narrow gully 8 or 10 foot deep.
1775 R 5 The gullies and hollows as well as the lower grounds of this town were ... filled with loggs.
1836 ASPMA VII. 291 [We passed] about two miles through a thick swamp and hammock, intersected with gullies.

GUM SWAMP. "In the south-eastern U.S., a swamp, or more commonly an area in a large swamp, in which the black-gum, or sour-gum ... or any other species of *Nyssa*, is the dominant tree." CD. Prob. the same as TUPELO SWAMP (*q.v.*). The one quotation listed in the OED under *gum* (1816) refers to North Carolina. Note OAK AND GUM SWAMP in the section on "Limitation" in the *Introduction*. Prob. Southeastern. DA 1743.

1773 MS. 264 In gum swamp.

GUT. A narrow passage or stream. DAE 1667. A channel; here, a pass between islands (1796). OED.

1773 MS. 274 In high Pe. [pine] Ld. [land] a boggy gut ahead.
1796 G 27 In almost every gut, among the many Islands in this Bay [*sc.*, Chatham], you will find it as much as 4

stout men can do to stem the current with a boat.

GUTTER. A channel which carries off surface water; a brook; here, a creek. DAE 1645.

1743 C II. iii　These Creeks, or rather Gutters, run very intricately through the Marshes.

H

HAMMOCK. Also, HAMMOK, HAMOC, HOMMOC. (The origin of *hammock* or *hummock* is obscure.) (1a) A tract of land having a deep, fertile soil and usually well wooded. DAE 1683. (A.) DA 1637 (= hummock). Although this type of land may consist of upland (1821 p. 95) or a ridge (1874 p. 165), the term is usually applied to any wooded (1836 SSW p. 18) level area (1821 p. 92). The 1827 author describes the soil of this type of land as being composed of white sand on which streams have cast vegetation which in turn has become humus. Hammocks are also identified with river bottom (1869 BRINTON); and the other 1869 writer says that the former are low, wet lands that never require draining. At any rate, hammocks usually have both a watery nucleus and a forested exterior (generally oak and hickory land) (1823), and are always thickly timbered and densely overgrown with shrubbery (1874). For other details see (2) below. (b) With reference to a particular area north of Tampa Bay known as the Big Hammock. (c) Preceded by a designating term: *back hammock; black hammock, grey and black hammock; detached hammock; dry hammock; high and low hammock; light and* *heavy hammock; prime hammock; wet hammock; wild hammock.* (2) Short for *hammock land.* The NID points out that the soil in this type of land has a greater depth and contains more humus than that of the flatwoods or pinelands. Though *hammock* is used synonymously with *swamp* (under [1] 1813), the former is distinguished by being higher than the latter, and also in having a shrubby undergrowth (1869). In detail, a hammock differs from a swamp in being drier; having a stiffer soil of loam and red clay, sand, and lime; but is timbered, like a swamp, with oak, magnolia and beech (1871). *Cf.* HUMMOCK.

(1a)　1773 MS. 309　The next Species of high Land differs very little in Soil from the midling Pine Land, and produces live and red Oak Hickery Nut, and wild Mulberry Trees; but this kind of Land is only met with in Groves (:by the Americans called Hammoks:) not exceeding one hundred Acres of Land. 1804 ASPPL IV. 160　Thence along the same path ... to the extremity of the hammock on the river Wakhulla. 1813 FHQ IX. 273　These hammocks or swamps are extensive tracts of fertile land covered with thick shrubbery. 1818 Y 41　In the extensive hammock which [lies] northeastwardly from its head there are hundreds of sinks with the purest water at their bottoms. 1821 F 92, 95　There is in the rear of the town an extremely valuable hammock of level land ... having an excellent assortment of timber ... A few spots of hammock, or upland, are found on this island. 1822 SIMMONS 5 ftn.　According to Noah Webster, *hommoc* is the proper orthography of this word. 1823 V 38　The grounds planted by Mr. Hernandez, are the northern point of a long narrow hammock called Graham's swamp.

Ibid., 75 The hammocks . . . in general surround the large lakes and savannas, though also found scattered over the whole face of the country like islets: within them however a pond or lake is generally found, and often their size is regulated by the extent of this watery nucleus. On the exterior of the hammocks the black oak and hickory land is disposed and gradually spreads to the pine ridges.
1825 ASPIA II. 629 There are interspersed through the country small light sandy hammocks.
1827 W 7 Where the tide or the streams have thrown upon [the white sand] . . . fossil or vegetable remains; these form hammocks.
1836 ASPMA VII. 137 These hammocks [east of the Suwanee] constitute so impenetrable a thicket as that an Indian who gets perhaps ten feet in them is not to be seen afterwards, and cannot be overtaken.
1836 SSW 18 *Hammock* is used generally for any thick wooded place.
Ibid., 299 In some places, these highland islets or coppices may be called hammocks, and with the cypress you see united clumps of tall and flourishing Bay trees . . . Occasionally the trail was crossed by larger and more extensive hammocks or swamps, consisting of a variety of forest trees and shrubs.
1837 W 33 [Caloosa Island] is diversified with thick groves of heavy timbered hammocks.
1852 IJ 34 The Hamocks [errata: "hammocks"] are as sandy as the Pine lands.
1869 FICSP 30-31 These hammocks are, as is generally supposed, low, wet lands; they never require ditching or draining.
1869 BRINTON 42 The hammocks are rich river bottoms, densely timbered.
1871 H 63 The hammocks are from a light to a dark gray color.
1874 SAR 95 The hammocks are very thickly timbered, the trees are large, the shrubbery is dense, and it requires

much labor to open roads through them.
Ibid., 165 [The tract] includes 200 acres of what is known as the Segui hammock, a high ridge of coquina land.
(b) 1822 SIMMONS 43 Forty miles further still, to the southwest, the Big Hammock commences, which is said to be forty miles in length, by six and seven in width, and extends to within twelves miles of Tampa Bay.
1826 ASPIA II. 689 The Big Hammock is much lower than the adjoining land, which is poor, pine, sandy hills, wholly unfit for cultivation. There is a large pond in the centre of this hammock, with several drains; in the wet season it is the greater part under water; in the dry season, there is no water except in this large pond. The soil, from its growth of timber, would induce a passing observer to believe it very fertile; but I found, on examining the land in many places, that it is a light mould two or three inches deep, based on white sand, and would, if cultivated, in three years become a bed of sand.
1869 BRINTON 95 Otter Creek . . . is on the western border of the dense Gulf hammock.
1869 FICSP 34 The Gulf hammock in Levy County, comprises perhaps the largest body of rich land in Florida.
(c) Preceded by designating term.
1874 SAR 165 The Segui hammock [lies] . . . but a few rods back from the river . . . In the back hammocks there are a vast number of wild orange trees.
1823 STCS 34 On this side of Little River it is a black hammock, in some places low, but not too much so for cultivation.
1869 FICSP 95 LANDS . . . Hammock —Grey and black.
1837 W 131 There are many rich hammocks, on the borders of the Appalache Bay, and the streams, that fall into it. There are also detached hammocks that are surrounded by fine lands.
1871 H 44 There are many small detached [*i.e.,* not bordering water] hammocks, around this large body of land.

1837 W 67 The Rattlesnake ... is occasionally found in the islands and dry hammocks of Florida.

1821 F 146 Those denominated high and low *hammock,* are most esteemed for the more valuable productions, such as cotton, sugar and corn.

1874 SAR 164 Fourth case. That of Mr. Fowler, on the west side of the Halifax, four miles south of Port Orange, on light and heavy hammock, pine, savanna, and marsh land.

Ibid., 212 Light hammock and pine land should be completely cleared.

1787 in SIEBERT II. 241 The next was prime hamoc the next an inferior hammock and the next Pine barren.

1829 USCHED vol. 187 #147.7 St. Mary's river flows generally through narrow strips of wet hammocks.

1871 H 100 In this county ... there are now many thousands on thousands of acres of wild hammock suited to [the production of tobacco].

(2) 1787, in SIEBERT II. 246 The land was hammock.

1821 F 109 The land is of the best quality, having a large proportion of hammock.

1823 V 45 Upon the beach side near the narrows are occasional pieces of good hammock.

1869 FICSP 29 Whenever ... the land is not so low as to be called swamp, and produces an undergrowth of shrubbery, it is called hammock.

1871 H 49 Hammock dry; soil loam, with red clay, sand and lime, in various proportions; timbered as the swamp, except the gum and bay; these lands are stiff; [locale: Jackson county.]

Attrib. with *forest, ridge.*

1874 SAR 210 A dense hammock forest, cutting off all circulation, has directly an opposite effect [*i.e.,* it lowers the temperature].

1873 S 11 About three years ago a farmer ... found a fine hammock ridge three miles south of the Hotel [at New Smyrna] and preempted it.

See also BEECH HAMMOCK; CABBAGE

HAMMOCK; CANE HAMMOCK; CEDAR HAMMOCK; COCONUT HAMMOCK; CYPRESS HAMMOCK; HAMMOCK ISLAND; HAMMOCK LAND; HAMMOCK SAVANNA; HIGH HAMMOCK; HIGH-HAMMOCK LAND; LIVE-OAK HAMMOCK; LOW HAMMOCK; MARL HAMMOCK; MULBERRY HAMMOCK; OAK HAMMOCK; PALMETTO HAMMOCK; PALM HAMMOCK; PINE HAMMOCK; REDBAY HAMMOCK; SCRUB HAMMOCK; SHELL HAMMOCK.

HAMMOCK ISLAND. An island consisting of hammock land.

1837 W 21 The sound behind Hammock Island affords shelter for vessels drawing 18 feet water.

1869 FICSP 114 North-east of the lake [Griffin] the country mainly consists of prairie or saw grass marsh, interspersed with rich hammock islands.

HAMMOCK LAND. Land embraced in or composing a hammock. DAE 1775. Poss. Southern. Note that this type of land is differentiated from savanna land by being wooded (according to the 1821 writer), and from pineland in having underbrush (1869). Spec., the "light" (*i.e.,* high, sandy and light in color) type of hammock land (1787; 1837), as opposed to the "heavy," low, and dark gray. "Also hammocky land," DA 1776.

1773 MS. 300 The Channel lays on the west side near the Hammock Land.

1778 in SIEBERT II. 42 There were 200 Acres of Hamock Land fit for Corn & Indigo.

1787 in SIEBERT II. 245 The plantation lay upon the river ... [and] was light hammock land but produced good crops.

1818 Y 31 The fertile upland is called *hammock land ... Hammock land ...* is always appropriated to two kinds of soil—the one high with growth of oak, hickory and thicket—the other, low, but dry, with a growth of bay, oak, large magnolia, beech, laurel, etc., with a variety of vines and other undergrowth. The high hammock is almost always fertile. The low has often too much sand.

1821 DARBY 10 This species forms in most instances an interval between the pine tracts and the marshes or savannahs, and indeed in no respect differs from the latter, except in being covered with wood. The hammock land ... of all the southern section of the United States, yields, next to river alluvion, the best arable soil.

1829 ASPNA III. 943 On the tract purchased from Judge Breckenridge ... one-fourth of the whole may be considered what is commonly denominated hammock land, the soil from 12 to 18 inches deep, consisting of decomposed vegetable substances and oyster shells, intermixed with the fine white sand, forming by nature so large a portion of the soil of Florida, particularly that bordering on the Gulf of Mexico.

1831 ASPNA IV. 102 The soil over which I have gone on the coast is only good in what is called hammock land; it is extremely rich, fertile, and light, of a dark color. [Context: live-oak hammocks.]

1836 SSW 175 The high and low hammock lands, which consist of a growth of live-oak, hickory, magnolia, red bay, and palmetto or cabbage trees, with an alluvium of mixed vegetable mould and loam, based upon clay and rotten limestone, are the most valuable lands in Florida, for sugar, cotton and corn.

1837 W 108 [Sea Island Cotton] ought never to be cultivated on lands that will produce either sugar or tobacco, but to be confined to light hammock lands, within the range of the sea-breezes.

1851 BYRNE 14 On nearly all the numerous rivers of the country, extensive bodies of first rate hammock, prairie, and swamp land.

1869 FICSP 29 The characteristic of hammock land as distinguished from pine is in the fact of its being covered with a growth of underbrush, while ... pine lands are open.

1874 SAR 146 In the midst of our wet season you can travel ... on or near this chain of hammock lands, on any of our public highways, without getting your horse's fetlocks wet.

See also HIGH-HAMMOCK LAND.

HAMMOCK SAVANNA. A savanna comprising hammock growth.

1823 V 90 The *hammock savannas* have a more fertile soil; fossil broken shells, are embedded in the mould which is rich and black, and of some depth: the clay is often within a foot of the surface of the earth.

HARBOR. A haven or port where ships may lie in safety. DAE 1622. Spec., a bay (1827). Note the detailed description of an inner and an outer harbor in the 1829 report.

1609 VRV 39 Sometimes they fought with the Indians, which passed along the harbour in their canoes.

1741 *Introduction to Report on Gen. Oglethorpe's Expedition to St. Augustine,* in CARROL II. 351-2 Col. Moore ... proceeded in the Vessels directly to the Bar of *St. Augustine* Harbour.

1762 AG I. 22 The chief harbour betwixt them also, and indeed the best upon all this coast of the gulph of Mexico, is Pensacola.

1769 STORK 7 The harbour of St. Augustine ... would be one of the best in America, were it not for its bar.

1773 MS. 300 This Harbour is formed by Grenville Stream issuing out of South Hillsborough Stream.

1796 G 9 There is good anchorage ... particularly in a small but snug harbour near Bush Kay, which is entirely sheltered from the sea by a large Reef of rocks, and a flat shoal within them, about ½ a mile broad.

1821 F 89 The harbour [of St. Augustine] ... is formed by a neck of land, on the north, and a point of Anastatia Island on the south.

1827 W 11 Pensacola bay ... is by far the best harbour on the Gulf of Mexico.

(1829) ASPNA IV. 962 The islands forming the Tortugas enclose an outer and an inner harbor; the first of which, besides affording a safe anchorage at all seasons of the year, is sufficiently capacious to ride in security all the navies of Europe; and that there is within this harbor another, still more secure, uniting sufficient depth of water for ships of the largest class, to a narrow entrance, not more than 120 yards wide, affording easy ingress and egress, and such as to be entered or departed from at all times, let the wind be from what quarter of the compass it may.

1854 ESB 57 They found the harbor stretching inland seven or eight leagues.

HARD MARSH. A marsh having a soil too solid for water to disunite the particles thereof. According to Romans (1775) this type of marsh consists of a marly clay. DAE 1737 (no def.). Prob. Southern.

1742 RCBH Apx. 24 [We passed] some creeks and over some hard marsh.

1775 R 30 The hard ones are made up of a kind of marly clay, which in dry seasons is almost burned up ... Hard marshes in general are such, whose soil has too much solidity, for the water to disunite its particles by penetrating them.

1787 in SIEBERT II. 240 1000 acres on new river about 500 of which is good high swamp and hard marsh.

1823 V 91 *Hard marsh* is made up of a kind of marly clay whose soil has too much solidity for the water to disunite its particles: and therefore, being also generally higher above the water, may be with little trouble adapted to proper cultivation.

HARDWOOD LAND. Land upon which hardwood trees grow. DAE *c.* 1817. (A.)

1870 BILL 190 The term "hummock" land ... is now applied to nearly all the hardwood lands in the State.

HAULOVER. A portage or place over which small boats have to be hauled or carried. *Obs.*[?] DAE 1837. Spec., a narrow isthmus (1823). (A.)

1773 MS 229 To hall over in the River 250 Links wide near the River Swamp.

1787 in SIEBERT II. 240 1000 acres on the neck of land the hall [*i.e.*, haul] over between the Musquito and Indian rivers.

1823 V 41 Half way down on the western side it is separated from Indian river by a narrow isthmus which is only 1980 feet wide, called the Haulover, across which canoes and boats are continually hauled.

1842 PREBLE 40 Passed both haulovers with little trouble.

1871 H 132 Lang, who until 1868 lived alone on an island in that lake, knows of a short haulover, where boats can be taken from a branch of Jupiter river across into the lake [*sc.*, Worth].

Attrib. with *creek, isthmus.*

1823 V 39 Haul-over Creek and Tomoca river form the head of Halifax river or Mosquito north lagoon.

1823 V 146 Thence in a similar way to Mosquito south lagoon to the Haulover isthmus.

HAVEN. A recess or inlet of the sea, or the mouth of a river, affording good anchorage and a safe station for ships. OED.

1563 RIBAULD 23 Our shippes ... lay aboue six leagues from the hauen to the sea.

1625 PURCHAS 868-69 Saint *Augustin* ... is the principall, because the hauen is good.

1745 OSBORNE 745 At *St. Joseph*

begins a great inlet ... in the middle of which lies *Ante,* a safe haven.

1773 MS. 175 In 1539 Ferdinando Soto ... landed the 31st of May in the Haven of Tampo, or Spiritu Santo.

1797 MAG under *Charlotte* Charlotte *Haven,* lies at the mouth of Charlotte R. in E. Florida.

1836 SSW 306 We steered for the blue haven that lay temptingly before us.

HEAD. (1) The source of a river or stream. OED. Spec., the source of a cove (1836). (2a) A projecting point of the coast; a cape, headland, promontory. OED. (b) A projecting point of a rock or sand bank. OED. It may be that the one quotation belongs under (2a). (3) A submerged rock or reef.

(1) 1587 L 40 I sent my two barkes to discouer along the riuer and vp toward the head thereof.

1708 OLDMIXON I 329 In the Year 1622. several English Families ... settled in the Province of *Mallica,* near the Head of the River of *May.*

1742 RCBH 22 Three Miles from the Head of a Creek.

1775 A Apx. 457 They carried their cypress bark canoes from the head of St. John's black river.

1827 W 82 The springs ... interlock with the heads of Shoal river and Uche creek.

1836 ASPMA VII. 146 What was the impression ... of headquarters as to the column having scoured the cove to its head?

(2a) 1563 RIBAULD 1 A certaine long coast of the West India, from the head of the land called Laflorida.

1587 L 2 The Cape thereof is as it were a long head of lande stretching out into the Sea an hundred leagues, and runneth directly towarde the South.

1773 MS. 333 The [Gulf] Stream ... by reason of its sudden change in its

Procession on the Promontory ... strikes more or less force on the narrow Head of the said Promontory.

(b) 1625 PURCHAS 869 Beginning on the West side, is called the *Point of the Martyres,* and to the East, the *Head of the Martyres.*

(3) 1796 G 21 There are some heads of rocks under water.

1823 V 117 From the transparency of the blue water he will see all the heads and shoals a good way off.

Attrib. with *lagoon, lake.*

1823 V 76-77 The Ocklawaha river takes its rise in lake Eustis, which like the head lagoon of St. John's river, is formed by the accumulation of waters from the great southern marshes.

1823 V 41 The head of this N.W. branch of Indian river and the head lake of St. John's river, approach each other very near heading in the same savanna or marsh.

Ibid., 67 The elder Bartram fifty years since, pursued the same route and arrived at the identical head lake, which terminated Captain Le Conte's expedition.

HEAD BRANCH. A branch flowing into a larger stream at or near its head. DAE 1792. DAE 1643.

1818 Y 37 *New River.* This stream rises opposite to and interlocks with the head branches of Big-log creek of Apalachicola.

1829 USCHED vol. 187 #147.37 [The line] crosses ... the main head branch of Hillsborough river, near the 21st mile.

1837 W 51 The distance from its head branches to Jupiter Narrows is about one hundred miles.

HEADLAND. A point of land projecting into water; a cape or promontory. OED. A bluff (1869).

1763 ROBERTS 23 The head-land, or cape, called *Cabo del Canaveral.*

1796 G 26 Chatham Bay, lies between Punta Largo, and Cape Sable, or Punta

Tancha, (as the Spaniards call it) the Southernmost head-land of Florida.

1822 SIMMONS 30 Orange groves [are] ... generally situated on the high headlands that point into the stream.

1869 BRINTON 54 About six miles from the entrance the channel runs close along the base of a hill or headland of moderate height, covered with pine, cedar, etc. This is *St. John's Bluff.

HEAD SPRING. A spring that forms or helps to form the source of a river. DAE 1765.

1766 B 24 We landed to search the head springs.

1823 STCS 34 We passed some ponds which are said to be connected with the sources of the Wachulla lying above its head spring.

1827 W 88 This high ground furnishes the head springs of all the rivers that fall into the Appalachee bay, within the county of Leon.

HEADSTREAM. A stream which is the source, or one of the sources, of a river. NID.

1837 W 54 The head streams are numerous.

HEADWATER(S). The streams from the sources of a river. Usually pl. OED.

1797 MAG under *Talassee Tallassee* ... a tract of land bounded by East-Florida on the south, from which the head water of St. Mary's river partly separates it.

1822 SIMMONS 10 By a canal of not more than six miles, the head waters of the north River may be connected through Pable Creek, with the St. John's.

1836 ASPMA VII. 142 By a lake which he described to be the headwater of Pease creek, and thence round the headwaters of the Ocklawaha.

1874 SAR 102 Nearly all of [the streams] ... towards the headwaters, are bordered on both sides by ... "virgin forest."

HICKORY HILL. A hill on which the principal growth is hickory.

1823 ASPPL III. 807 Two hundred acres of land, lying on St. Mary's river, two miles below Camp Pinckney, at a place called *Cattle Hickory Hill.*

1827 W 85 Hickory hill may cover four sections of land ... Both these hills [sc., Oak and Hickory] derive their names from the timber which predominates on them.

1837 W 128 Washington County is about fifty-four miles long, from Hickory Hill to St. Joseph's Bay on the south.

HICKORY LAND. Land upon which hickory is the prevailing growth. DAE 1674. Prob. Southern.

1743 C II. iii *Hiccory-Lands* ... This Land is of most Use, in general producing the best Grain, Pulse, Roots, and Herbage, and is not liable to Inundation; on it are also found the best Kinds of Oak for Timber, and *Hiccory*, an excellent Wood for Burning. This Land is generally light and sandy, with a mixture of Loam.

1773 MS. 266 Hickery Land.

1851 BYRNE 13 The "first rate pine, oak, and hickory" lands are found in pretty extensive bodies in many parts of the State.

HIGH HAMMOCK. (a) Hammock land which is higher than low hammock and characterized by having an undulating surface and a growth of live oak, hickory, mulberry, etc. This type of land is very productive of corn, sugar, and cotton. (b) Elliptical for *high-hammock land.*

(a) 1818 Y 31 *Hammock land* ... is always appropriated to two kinds of soil—the one high with growth of oak, hickory and thicket ... The high hammock is almost always fertile.

1823 V 88-89 The *high hammocks* are if possible more dense in their growth than the others, but the coat of

vegetable matter is thin, and the white sand lies within a foot or eighteen inches of the surface: they are said to be notwithstanding very productive for years, without any manure.
1832 ASPNA IV. 223 The growth of the high hammock is principally live oak, mulberry, red bay, stopper mastic, ironwood, wild fig, and palmetto; and it produces corn, sugar, and cotton in great perfection.
1836 SSW 175 The sugar lands were extensive and fine, being what is called "high hammock."
1851 BYRNE 13 High hammocks are the lands in greatest repute in East Florida. These differ from low hammocks in occupying higher ground, and in generally presenting an undulating surface. They are formed of a fine vegetable mould, mixed with a sandy loam in many places two feet deep, and resting in most cases on a substratum of clay and lime.
1869 FICSP 29 Then there is the high and light hammock.
1874 SAR 146 The greatest portion of this is that quality known as "high hammock," which, with the exception of wild-orange grove lands . . . has always been regarded as being the richest lands in the South.
(b) 1851 BYRNE 14 [A] great part of which is first rate land of the different denominations of high hammock . . . and pine.

HIGH-HAMMOCK LAND. Land consisting of high hammock.

1818 Y 24 But the fertile hills, called *high-hammock-land*, have a very mixed growth of forest trees, and are generally covered with a various growth of vines, shrubs and bushes.

HIGHLAND. Elevated land. Usually pl. DAE 1733. Spec., a plain or pine barren as opposed to a swamp or lowland (1769).

1769 STORK 5 The tract of land between them consists of plains covered with pines; these plains are called in America, pine-barrens, or highlands, in contradistinction to the swamps and lowlands.
1775 R 274 Imagine then to yourself a country gradually rising into a ridge of highland.
1823 ASPM II. 1027 In the rear of the town, at the distance of about half a mile, the highlands are presented, upon which military works may be constructed to advantage.
Attrib. with *forest, islet.*
1791 B 90 On the West side it was . . . invested with a swamp of Cypress, the trees so lofty, as to preclude the sight of the high-land forests, beyond them.
1836 SSW 299 In some places, these highland islets or coppices may be called hammocks.

HIGH SWAMP. Swamp land which is elevated to some degree. Since the description of the terrain is very similar to that of *hammock* (1), it is possible that this is another term for the same type of land.

1787 in SIEBERT II. 240, 242, 252 1000 acres on new river about 500 of which is good high swamp . . . The high swamp required no draining . . . The greatest part however was high Swamp, very fit for the growth of Sugar, Cotton, Indico [*sic.*], hemp, [etc.].

HILL. A natural elevation of the earth's surface rising more or less steeply above the surrounding country. DAE 1636. Spec., a mount (1796); a bluff (1828); a mountain [there are no real mountains in Florida] (1837). *Obs.* OED. *Cf.* MOUNTAIN.

1563 RIBAULD 23 We espyed on the south syde of the Ryuer a place verye fitte for that purpose, vppon a lytle hyll compassed with Cypres.
1587 L 22 I determined to search out the qualities of the Hill.

1743 C II. iii Strong Winds set on the Shore . . . raising innumerable Hills of loose Sand.
1763 ROBERTS 21 [A cayo] *Las Tetas,* so named from two hills on it, lies in the latitude of 25 deg. 45 min.
1796 G 20 The hill is sometimes called the Bald Mount.
1828 ASPNA III. 940 To the foot of the hill called Drunkard's bluff.
1837 ASPMA VII. 828 The Thlawhatkee, (White mountains,) an elevated range of hills not mentioned by any geographer, nor described in any account of Florida which I have seen, was passed on the 24th.
1871 H 104 The greatest elevation is *Orange Hill.* East of this is *Oak Hill;* about ten miles southward are *Mossy Hill,* and *Mud Hill* near the head of Holmes' Valley.

See also HICKORY HILL; OAK HILL; OYSTER HILL; PINE HILL; SAND HILL; SEA-SAND HILL; SPRUCE HILL; UPLAND HILL (attrib.).

HILLOCK. (1) A little hill. OED. (2) A small mound or heap of earth—here, thrown up by a salamander. OED.
(1) 1796 G 17 The most remarkable among them are [*sic*] the small Kay called The Paps, from the Three hillocks upon it.
1821 DARBY 9 The [lime] stone appears in every degree of induration, from solid building-stone, to loose hillocks of sea-shells.
(2) 1836 SSW 163, 165-66 Met in the pine barrens, and among these sand hills . . . the hillocks of the Salamanders . . . Over their burrows hillocks of loose earth are raised resembling in some respects those thrown up by the shrew mole and something like large ant hills— the mounds are of various dimensions from the diameter of a few inches only to that of several yards—the quantity of earth thrown up consequently varies from a pint to 2 or 3 bushels; the earth is loose and naturalists describe it as

having the appearance of being emptied out of a flower pot—no hole is to be discovered under this mass of loose soil, but if it be carefully removed, it is seen that the earth has been broken in a circle of an inch and a half in diameter, within which space the ground is loose, but still without any distinct opening.

See also SAND HILLOCK.

HOLD(E). Elliptical for *holding ground. Obs.*

1563 RIBAULD 12-13 The holde . . . was so good, that one cable & one anker held vs fast.

HOLDING GROUND. A bottom in which an anchor will hold. OED under *holding.*

1827 W 13 They all anchored in water from twenty-five to thirty-six feet, in good holding ground of soft mud.
1833 ASPNA IV. 805 Pensacola [harbor has] . . . a very good anchorage in it, in a good holding ground.
1855 USCSED vol. 756 #76.4 Cedar Keys . . . is easy of access, holding ground good.

HOLE. (1) A small pond. Poss. Southern. (2a) A small bay or opening in the coast. DAE 1639. (A.) (b) An inlet or creek ASPPL—here, a cove STCW. DAE 1639. (A.) (3) A deep place in water. OED. Spec., a spring (1852). (4) A hollow place or cavity —here, in the earth (1821), or rock (1773; 1827); a cave (1837). OED.
(1) 1743 C II. 72 By the continued running of the Water, a small Pond or Hole is usually made before the Mouth of the Spring.
1775 R 275 We next met with very great holes, fifty or sixty feet deep, and thirty or forty feet in diameter at the surface, in the highest part of the pine ridges, which afford some good water to the thirsty traveller.
1823 V 74 Over this portion of the country as in many parts of West Flor-

ida nature has scattered a number of wells, holes and ponds of all sizes and various depths.

1837 W 65   During the warm season they spend the night in holes of fresh water near the coast.

(2a)   1829 USCHED vol. 187 #147.12 The place called the Spanish Hole, 3 miles within the Outer bar, is the best to lie at anchor; the depth is 12 feet at high water.

1837 W 23   The shoals off South Cape break the seas so that . . . [ships] may enter the Spanish Hole.

(b)   1823 ASPPL III. 821   On the east side of St. John's river and head of Pottsburg creek, known by the name of *Tiger Hole*.

1823 STCW 40   We . . . ran into a deep hole about two miles from our last anchoring place, where we continued till the next morning. We named this cove Alligator Cove.

(3)   1771   VIAUD   81   [Wading ashore] we . . . had the good fortune to recover our footing again; for we had only fallen into a hole.

1852 IJ 22   The next morning my cousin accompanied me to the Spring, he stopped at what I took to be an enormous hole of water. I asked him where the Spring was, at which he pointed to the great basin of water.

(4)   1773 MS. (319)   Prawns . . . Spawn in the holes of the coral Rocks.

1821 F 172   The *Gouffre* . . . digs a hole in the ground.

1827 W 36   Many large holes, in the rock above, are filled with bats.

1837 W 149   The passage now turns north east, and opens into a hole one hundred feet in length.

See also ALLIGATOR HOLE; CLAYHOLE; POTHOLE; SINK HOLE; TURTLE HOLE.

HOLLOW.   (1) A valley, ravine, or gap. DAE 1649. (2) A round and sloping depression in the earth's surface. DAE 1702. Spec., a bottom (1821); a sink (1829).

(1)   1775 R 5   The gullies and hollows as well as the lower grounds of this town were . . . filled with loggs.

1812 FHQ IX. 68   The Pine Barren this day truly barren & very much broken with hollows and reedy branches.

1818 Y 27   Some of those singular hollows are one hundred feet in depth and of such steep declivity as to be almost inaccessible. They are the springheads of several creeks which enter the Apalachicola.

(2)   1743 C II. iii   Strong winds set on the shore . . . raising innumerable Hills of loose Sand further within Land, in the Hollows of which, when the water subsides, are frequently left infinite Variety of Shells, etc.

1791 B 177   When we ascend the top of the hills, we perceive the ground to be uneven, by round swelling points and corresponding hollows.

1821 F 156   It is not thus with the canes of marshy lands and hollows or bottoms.

1829 USCHED vol. 187 #147.4-5 The ground is . . . interspersed with numberless inverted conic hollows, called *sinks*.

1852 IJ 24   There is a hollow, which the road crosses, that bears the impress of having been submerged.

HUMMOCK.   A tract of land somewhat higher than an adjacent marsh, swamp, creek, etc., and usually well wooded. "Often with special reference to Florida." DAE 1635. (A.) Described as "rising" (1744). The term is used synonymously with *bluff* (1774), *grove* (1775; 1791), and *hill* (1796). The 1784 writer distinguishes the white sandy hummock from the red (*i.e.*, red clay). Cf. HAMMOCK. DA 1589.

1744 KIMBER 21   [The land] was only, here and there, diversify'd with rising Hummocks of Trees and leafy Thickets.

1774 Barton in G 28 To Kay Three Hummocks (*Saddle Bluff*).
1775 R Apx. lxxvi The northernmost entrance is likewise remarkable for a singular hommock of pine trees, or a grove standing very near the beach.
1784 HUTCHINS 82, 83 Rose island ... is very remarkable for its white sandy hummocks ... Between the bays of St. Rosa, and St. Andrews, ... There are likewise some red hummocks as well as white.
1791 B 187 We then entered a hommock or dark grove, consisting of various kinds of trees.
1796 G 21 About 8 leagues N. by W. ½ W. from Hillsborough inlet are the small hills called by Spaniards the *Tortolas,* and by us the Hummocks.

See also CABBAGE-TREE HUMMOCK; LIVE-OAK HUMMOCK; PINE HUMMOCK.

HUMMOCK LAND. Hammock land. DAE 1812. Prob. Southern.

1870 BILL 190 The term "hummock" land—the Indian name for elevated tracts lying above the low or wet lands —is now applied to nearly all the hardwood lands in the State.

I

INDIGO LAND. Also INDICO LAND. Land suitable for growing the indigo plant. (*Indico* is *obs.*)

1787 in SIEBERT II. 248 The 200 acre tract ... was tolerable good Indico [*sic*] land.

INLAND PASSAGE. A passage separated from, or remote from, the sea. Spec., a sound (1827).

1793 AUG 626 Indian river rises a short distance from the sea coast ... forming a kind of inland passage for many miles along the coast.
1825 GADSDEN 122 The communication to Cape Florida may be extended hereafter, either by opening and im-

proving the inland passage by the lakes and sounds.
1827 W 16 St. George sound, between the island and the main, is a pleasant inland passage.
1828 ASPMA IV. 16 An appropriation was also made for deepening the inland passage between the St. John's, in Florida, and the St. Mary's, in Georgia.
1829 USCHED vol. 187 #147.7 Nassau River ... is connected with St. Mary's river and the St. John, by an inland water communication, called Inland Passage, which runs parallel to the coast between the main and the Islands of Amelia, Talbot, and Fort George.
1837 W 134 There is a safe inland passage from the St. Johns to Savanna.
1855 USCSED vol. 756 #76.5 The line would continue on Amelia Island till convenient to cross the inland passage.

INLAND SEA. A large lake entirely or —here—nearly severed from the ocean. OED under *inland. Cf.* BAY, LAKE.

1874 KEASBEY 102-03 The stream widens out a few miles up, forming Lake George, a shallow inland sea, sixteen miles in length.

INLAND SWAMP. A swamp which is unconnected with tides or navigation; spec., a back swamp (1775). DAE 1802 (no def.). Prob. Southern.

1775 R 29 The back or inland swamps answer in situation to what are called the meadows or savannahs (among the pine lands).
1783 in SIEBERT II. 288 Inland Swamp.
1827 W 54 Sambucus ... deep inland swamps.

Attrib. with *land.*

1874 SAR 21 There are hundreds of thousands of acres of river and inland swamp lands densely covered with a growth of water oak, [etc.].

INLET. A narrow opening by which the water penetrates into the land; a small arm of the sea, an indentation in the seacoast or the bank of a lake or river; a creek. OED. Spec., a bay (1813; 1823 ASPNA); a nook (1871); an opening into the Reef (1796) or a river (1837 p. 27). Note that the inlets on the Atlantic sometimes shift their channels (1773), and that one of them, Jupiter inlet, occasionally closes altogether (1823; 1837 p. 52-53).

1743 CADOGAN 17 [Gen. Oglethorpe applied] to *Vanderdussen* at *St. John's* for 100 men to assist in keeping Possession of that Shore and Inlet.
1745 OSBORNE 745 At *St. Joseph* begins a great inlet of the sea for more than twenty leagues to the north latitude, and more than forty-four to the western longitude.
1773 MS. 342 The Inlets upon this Coast are all subject to the Inconvenience of having their Bars shifted by E, N, and N.E. gales.
1796 G 17 Rodrigue's Kay lies opposite to the *Great Inlet* of the Florida Reef, and near the Coast of Kayo Largo.
1813 MELISH 4 *Spiritu Santo,* or *Hillsborough Bay* . . . is a capacious inlet.
1823 ASPNA IV. 965 The salt ponds . . . extend to a bay or inlet which makes into the eastern end of the island [*sc.,* Key West].
1823 V 84 Jupiter inlet after a heavy freshet in the spring of 1769 was opened and so remained for three or four years.
1837 W 27 Just below Cape Canaveral is the main inlet to this river.
Ibid., 53 Jupiter Inlet has opened and closed three times, within seventy years.
1871 S 31 "Jupiter Inlet" is probably the most inaccessible and barren nook on the Floridian coast.

Preceded by a designating term. DRY INLET: An inlet sometimes free of water; an inlet usually separated from the sea by a narrow sand-bar (1796); possibly the sand-bar itself (1823).
1773 MS. 300 The twelfth [inlet] . . . called Barracuta, alias Dry Inlet . . . [is] only fit for Boats.
1796 G 20 *Dry Inlet,* or *Rio Seco,* as the Spaniards name it, lies 6 miles from New Inlet, its mouth is seldom open, and has a narrow bar of dry sand before it.
1823 V 49 Rio Seco, unable to discharge itself over the dry inlet, has forced itself by a natural canal through a neck of high land into the Middle river.

INTERVAL. (1) A gap or opening— here, in a reef or series of rocks. OED. (2) Interval land. DAE 1683. (A.) Probably formed by vegetation thrown upon clay by adjoining water (1827); the same writer distinguishes this type of land from *second bottom* (*q.v.*). According to one example under *bottom* (OED Sup. [1837] p. 107), "The term 'bottom' is used throughout the west to denote the alluvial soil on the margin of rivers, usually called 'intervals' in New England." DA 1647.

(1) 1773 MS. 335 These Rocks [*sc.,* Martyrs] . . . fathom in their Intervals from eighteen to forty-eight feet water, so that Vessels have crossed these Reefs on those Intervals without touching.
(2) 1789 MAG 476 The intervals between the hilly part of this country [E. & W. Fla.] are extremely rich.
1818 Y 23 In the intervals of those hills, there are generally small branches of excellent water.
1827 W 7, 20 This clayey substratum . . . produces little . . . except where the tide or the streams have thrown upon it fossil or vegetable remains; these form hammocks and intervals, rich in vegetable productions . . . The lands, on the banks of this river are rich, but are

often overflowed, which renders planting, on the intervals a hazardous employment.

INTERVALE LAND. Interval land. DAE
1653. (A.)

1871 H 136 These intervale lands are
in long wavy belts sometimes parallel
with the bay, bordered on each side by
the pine woods, and their margins clearly defined by the saw palmetto, which
makes a dense border of evergreen
along the edge of the upland . . . They
are natural grass lands.

ISLAND. (1) Land completely surrounded by water. OED. Spec., a
sand bank (1837). Note both the (c.
1590; c. 1596) reference to the Martyrs as "broken (i.e., disconnected)
islands," and the detailed description
of the same group as high, or low or
drowned, islands, by Vignoles (1823).
(2) A piece of ground rising from a
level tract. DAE 1638. (A.) (3) A
grove or clump of trees in a prairie.
DAE 1656. (A.) Extended to apply
to a cypress pond (1871). (4) A floating island; also, a floating island
which has sunk (1874).

(1) 1563 RIBAULD 32 This arme
doth deuide, & maketh . . . also many
other great Ilandes.
c. 1565 Hawkins in HAKLUYT (1589)
537 The fift of July we had sight of
certane Islandes of sand, called the
Tortugas (which is lowe land).
c. 1590 White voyage in HAKLUYT
(1600) 290 The 23 [of July] we had
sight of the Cape of Florida, and the
broken Ilands therof called the Martires.
c. 1596 Drake & Hawkins voyage, in
HAKLUYT (1600) 589 The 10 [of
March] we saw the Cape of Florida being but a reasonable low land and
broken Ilands to the Southward of the
Cape.
1625 PURCHAS 869 Los Martyres . . .
are many little Ilands inhabited, which
are neare the point of Florida.

1652 HEYLIN 117 The Tortugas are
seven or eight little Ilands lying on an
heap at the South-West point of the
Peninsula.
1741 GHDPOPW 190 They landed
on the Island of Eustatia (or Matanzas
as some call it).
1762 J 69 In latitude 26° 56' and a
good way upwards, the coast of the
main land of Florida cannot be approached, by reason of the shoals and
small islands, most of which are very
low and barren, and so close together
that canoes of bark can hardly pass between them.
1797 MAG under Espiritu Sancto Several low, sandy islands and marshes,
covered with mangrove bushes, lie before the main land.
1823 V 123 The Martyr keys lying
back between bay Honda and key West
may be divided into two classes: the
high, and the low or drowned islands.
The high islands are based upon grey,
white or black hard rocks; the low or
mangrove islands are founded on coral
rocks, covered with a rich but wet soil.
The high islands are heaped in places
with sand on which little or nothing
grows; in other parts they have a stratum of bluish marl, on which flourish
in great abundance . . . a large variety
of tropical trees, shrubs and plants.
1837 W 32 Egmont Island lies in the
entrance of Tampa Bay. It is merely a
sand bank about a mile in length.
1854 SMITH–F 13 There are yet
other islands, nearer to the main,
stretching between the west and east,
called the Martires.
1871 H 127 Half Dollar Island is a
patch of marsh grass growing on an
oyster bank about ten feet long.
(2) 1823 V 82-83 The vast bodies
of low lands that lie south of this trail
and fill up the interior of the southern
extremity of the Florida peninsula, appears to have scattered over it many
tracts of firm land in the form of islands
and promontories.
(3) 1822 SIMMONS 50 In some of

[the savannas] ... there were picturesque oak groves or islands.

1871 H 115 Round Island is a mile
further ... Instead of an island, it is a
cypress pond; the tall trees of which
lift their heads above the surrounding
forests, and suggested to some one's
fertile fancy the name of an island.

1874 SAR 197 The country ... extends into a savanna or prairie, interspersed with groves and clumps of timber from one to ten acres in area. These
islands of timber are the resort of deer
and other wild animals during the day.

(4) 1765 B 9-10 At the entrance of
the river into the great lake there floats
prodigious quantities of the pistia,
which grows in great plenty most of the
way from hence to the head of the river,
and is continually driving down with
the current, and great quantities lodged
all along the extensive shores of this
river and its islands, where it is entan-
gled with a large species of water-nu-
mularia, persicaria, water-grass, and
saxifrage, all which send down very long
fibrous roots deep into the water by
which they are nourished, growing all
matted together in such a manner as to
stop up the mouth of a large creek, so
that a boat can hardly be pushed
through them, though in 4 foot water;
these by storms are broke from their
natural beds and float down the river
in great patches, the roots striking deep,
often touch the muddy bottom, and
there anchor and fasten, and are ready
to catch and entangle those that drive
down upon them, and all together
gather mud, by the daily accumulation
of which they are formed into islands
which are very numerous in this river,
and are much enlarged by these plants
fixing on their shores.

1869 FICSP 114 Many of these islands
had to be cut in pieces with a cross-cut
saw before they could be removed from
the channel.

1874 S 17 The Captain asserted that
he had cut many a bay tree over a foot

thick from the sunken island [*i.e.*, which
had been a floating island].

See also BLUFF ISLAND (attrib.); CAB-
BAGE-TREE ISLAND; CEDAR ISLAND; CREEK
ISLAND (attrib.); CYPRESS ISLAND; DES-
ERT ISLAND; FLOATING ISLAND; HAMMOCK
ISLAND; ISLAND SWAMP; MANGROVE
ISLAND; MARSH ISLAND; SEA ISLAND;
SEDGE ISLAND; SWAMP ISLAND (attrib.).

ISLAND SWAMP. An island consisting
  of swamp land.

1823 ASPPL III. 800 Two hundred
acres of land, lying on an island swamp,
about two miles west from the Stock-
ades fort.

ISLE. Also, ILE. An island; usually
  applied to an island of smaller size.
  OED.

1563 RIBAULD 32 This arme ...
maketh many other Iles of May.

1587 L 6 Wee found there an Ile.

1770 WYNNE 347 It is not easy to
find this place by reason of the isles
and lakes before and about it.

1797 MAG under *Vaccas, Cayo* A
thick range of isles go by this name.

1822 ASPPL III. 519 This Presque
Isle lies on the southeast of the peninsula of East Florida.

1837 W 8 The sea ... makes a rough
coast, as far south as Isle Roman.

ISLET. (1) A little island. OED. Spec.,
  a rock (1854). (2) A grove or clump
  of trees in a plain or prairie—here,
  in or around a pond surrounded by
  pineland (1818 quotation, p. 32).
  DAE 1791. Prob. Southern.

(1) 1587 L 22 Neere the river
Belle, a man may beholde the medowes,
devided asunder into Iles and Islets in-
terlacing one another.

1796 G 24 Three narrow Kays, or Islands ... with several islots [*sic*] stretching off the South point ... [form] three
entrances.

1821 F 104 [Romans] does not recommend it as so advantageous as some of
the other islets.

1837 W 41 The Samboes . . . are sandy islets.
1854 SMITH-N 29 These islets [*sc.*, the rocks called Martyrs], the appearance of which suggested a name for the whole chain of islands, have received from the Spaniards the distinctive appellation of *Las Mucaras,*—a Lucayan, or provincial word, for rocks a little above the surface of the land or water. (2) 1818 Y 28, 32 In the wetter parts there are small islets of evergreen thickets . . . There are interspersed, through the pine land, a vast number of small isolated ponds, with a low growth of myrtle, laurel and a species of hawthorn. They have a clay and sand soil—a little miry and many of them contain water during the driest months. In the spring, these islets speckling the barrens . . . have a singularly handsome appearance.

See also MANGROVE ISLET.

ISTHMUS. Also, ISTMUS, ISTHMUSA. A narrow portion of land, enclosed on each side by water, and connecting two larger bodies of land. OED. (*Istmus* is *obs.*)

1635 Hondy's *Mercator's Atlas* 900 This Province [Florida] hath large bounds . . . on the South it looketh towards *Cuba,* running out in manner of an Isthmusa [*sic*] 100. miles.
1660 LE BLANC 352 Towards this point or tongue of land, in form of an *Isthmus,* 'tis dangerous sayling.
1773 MS. 243 A Peninsula from the Main, joining the Continent by a very narrow Istmus, which bears S.S.W. from Dartmouth Inlet.
1775 R 289 In latitude 25°: 20', is a . . . remarkable *isthmus,* joining what was formerly called *Cayo largo* . . . our researches for a passage, west of the keys, have convinced us of its being fast to the main land.
1825 GADSDEN 120 The southern extremity of the latter are separated from those of Indian river by a narrow

isthmus of less than one mile in width.
1837 W 25 Across this narrow isthmus there is a haulover, of about 100 yards.

See also HAULOVER ISTHMUS (attrib.).

J

JUNCTION. The place at which two or more streams join. DAE 1792. The meaning is extended to apply to the union of both a river with a bay (1837) and a bay with the Gulf of Mexico (1827).

1796 ASPPL V. 713 To the middle of the river Apalachicola, or Catahouche; thence along the middle thereof to its junction with the Flint.
1823 V 36-37 The St. Sebastian river . . . is of some width at its junction with Matanzas river.
1827 W 10 The bar [of Perdido bay], at its junction with the gulf, is shoal and constantly shifting.
1837 W 45-46 The Aliqua River . . . is navigable to Vaughns, fifteen miles from its junction with the bay.
1871 H 70 Amelia . . . river forms a spacious bay . . . near its junction with the sound or outlet of St. Mary's river.

JUNGLE. Land overgrown with underwood, long grass, or tangled vegetation. OED. Spec., a dried-up pond overgrown with grass, etc. (1836 SSW).

1836 SSW 240 As we were passing a jungle, or large dried up pond, grown up in tall grass, rush and palmetto, we were suddenly alarmed by the firing of the advance platoons.
1836 ASPMA VII. 258 [Your job is to prevent] . . . *the escape of the enemy,* or of *its retreat towards the Everglades,* or supposed hiding-places of the savages in the thickets or jungles of the south.
1874 S 30 It was a genuine jungle. The trailing vines were larger and more numerous than ropes in a gymnasium.

See also PALMETTO JUNGLE.

K

KEY. A low island or reef. Chiefly off the Florida coast. DAE 1772. Used interchangeably with *cayo* (*q.v.*) (1823 p. 119; 1869 p. 97). *Cf. kay(o)* under *cay(o)*. Described as a bank (1775 xli; 1797), bar (1823 p. 121), or group of rocks (1775 p. 290; 1797)—one cluster is called the "Rocky Keys" (1837). Spec., a peninsula (1823 p. 119); collectively, the archipelago known as the Florida Keys (1837). Also applied to a marsh island (1827) and an islet in the Everglades (1869 p. 41). In the 1818 reference to West Florida, keys are said to be shell banks detached from the coast.

1742 RCBH Apx. 43 Captain *Tyrrel* went in a Boat, and sounded between the *Point* and the *Keys,* opposite to the *Castle.*
1773 MS. 311 The wild cinnamon Tree grows very plenty [*sic*] upon the Martyr Keys, (Islands).
1775 R Apx. xli I found 18 foot water on sand, and saw a dry bank or key close too to westward.
Ibid., 290 The keys, or Martyrs . . . are a heap of rocks.
1797 MAG under *Florida Keys.* Florida Keys, or *Martyr's Islands,* a number of rocks and sand banks bounded W. by the gulf of Mexico, E. by that of Florida.
1818 Y 48 The keys [of W. Fla.] are only different from the shell banks in being detached from the coast.
1823 V 119, 121, 124 *Cayo Largo, Long key or Sound point key,* is actually a peninsula . . . Beyond these . . . is *key Looe,* a little sandy bar or island . . . It would seem that *key West* or *Thompson's island* is the best as a naval depot.
1827 W 87 On these marshes however, there are frequent keys, which rise like small islands, covered with live oak, cedar and tall cabbage palms. These are most frequent, where streams of water enter the [Appalache] bay.
1831 AUDUBON 58 Several of these kind men accompanied me to a small key called Booby Island.
1837 W 34 The Florida Keys, are altogether an extraordinary archipelago of islands and reefs . . . Rocky Keys are a considerable cluster of islands, above the mouth of Hujelos river. These islands are, for the most part, formed of curious coralines.
1856 USCHED vol. 893 Part I. 553 There is a coral bank extending one mile in length up to the main key [*sc.,* Sawyer's key].
1869 BRINTON 41 Between the coast-ridge and Lake Okee-chobee the "Keys" . . . are scattered through the Everglades.
Ibid., 97 The name Key West is a corruption of the Spanish *Cayo Hueso,* Bone Key, the latter word being of Indian origin (Arawack, *Kairi,* island).

See also CEDAR KEY; FRESH-WATER KEY; MANGROVE KEY; SAND KEY.

KNAP. A small hill, hillock, or knoll. Chiefly dial. OED. EDD.

1587 L 5L The day following [Ribauld] caused a piller of hard stone to be planted within the saide river, and not farre from the mouth of the same uppon a little sandie knappe.

KNOB(S). A prominent, rounded hill or knob. In the plural, the name of a particular region—here, in West Florida. DAE 1823. DA 1817.

1837 W 45 The Aliqua River rises in the Knobs of Walton county.

KNOLL. Also KNOWL. A small hill. DAE 1656.

1775 R Apx. li The first [entrance] has got a dry knowl of rocks above water.
1791 B 165 I seated myself upon a swelling green knoll, at the head of the crystal bason.

1836 BARR 10   In about three quarters of an hour the Indians moved from the knoll.

1837 W 127   [Walton County] is diversified with knolls and ridges of very poor land. The knolls . . . terminated the great ridge.

See also CABBAGE KNOLL; GRASS KNOLL; PINE KNOLL.

L

LAGOON. (1a) An area of shallow salt or brackish water separated from the sea by sand dunes. DAE 1750 [?] (b) A bay, inlet, or sound, as between the mainland and adjacent islands. DAE 1750 [?] (A.) Spec., a saltwater river (1823), or the branch of such a river (1766; 1825). With special reference to a bay within Pensacola Bay (1829; 1837). As the editors of the DAE comment, "It is not always possible to assign quotations definitely to 1 or 2"—the same is true with regard to (1a) and (b). (2) A shallow, fresh-water pond or lake . . . usually located near or connecting with a lake, river, etc. DAE 1766. (A.) The DAE editors point out that (especially where Spanish formerly was the current language) the word *lagoon* is often given a broad interpretation derived from the Spanish *laguna* (which is applied to ordinary lakes, etc.).

(1a)   1837 W 13   The waters thus barred out from the ocean, unite laterally, and form extensive lagoons.
Ibid., 151   You then pass on the winding lagoons from six to twelve miles westwardly.
(b)   1766 B 17   Here several more large branches or lagoons branched eastward.
1775 R 267   This pretended river is one of those arms of the sea commonly called a Lagoon.
1797 MAG under *Charlotte Haven*   Charlotte R. is fed by Spiritu Santo Lagoon.
1823 ASPPL III. 771, 804   300 acres, situated on the north side of Marrott's island, and lies between the lagoon of Indian river, bordering on the said island and the Musquito lagoon . . . On the west side of the Mosquito, South Lagoon or Hillsborough river.
1825 FHQ XIV. 153   A small marshy Island . . . is separated from the main land or rather marsh, by a lagoon or branch of the river [St. Sebastian], shoal at low water and about sixty yards wide.
1829 USCHED vol. 187 #147.18   The narrow bay [within Pensacola bay], called Great Lagoon . . . has, at its mouth, no more than 3 or 4 feet at high tide.
1837 W 20   The Grand Lagoon extends from the entrance of Pensacola Bay, below Barrancas, eight miles westward, and within three fourths of a mile of Perdido Bay . . . It has an inlet from the Gulf near the west end.
(2)   1784 HUTCHINS 78   There is a fine mineral spring . . . near the mouth of the lagoon.
1791 B 81   I made a convenient and safe harbour, in a little lagoon, under an elevated bank, on the West shore of the river.
1824 ASPPL IV. 693 tr.   15,000 acres to the southwest of the large lagoon known by the name of Lake George.
1874 S 28   All day long were we in this arm of the Everglades. The lagoon became a ditch barely the width of the boat.

Attrib. with *bank.*

1823 V 43-44   Fresh water . . . may be also thus procured along every part of the Florida coast, both on the sea beach and the Lagoon banks.

See also HEAD LAGOON (attrib.); LAGOON BANK (attrib.); SALT LAGOON.

LAGUNA. A shallow, fresh-water pond or lake; a lagoon (2). DAE 1838. Poss. Southern.

1763 ROBERTS 22 *Rio Jego o'Goga,* which leads into a laguna full of small islands . . . has several communications with the great *Laguna del Espiritu Santo.*

LAKE. (1) An inland body of water. DAE 1658. Note the (1837 p. 148) quotation on a disappearing [*i.e.,* sinking] lake. Spec., a bay (now called Bay of Florida) (1822); a spring (1874). (2) An expanded part of a river. NID. Called variously a bay or dilation (1793); an inundation or expansion (1837); "Dead Lakes" (1831; 1839; 1871). *Cf.* BAY, INLAND SEA. Extended to apply to a creek (1824), or river (1763). (3) A pond. *Obs.* ? OED 1609.

(1) 1563 RIBAULD 33 [We found] at the verye entrye a long, fayre, and greate Lake.

1587 L 40 There they discouered the entrance of a lake, upon the oneside whereof no land can bee seene, according to the reporte of the Indians, which had oftentimes climed on the hiest trees in the country to see land, and notwithstanding could not discerne any.

1609 VRV 29 They saw Indians a little from thence in a lake.

1708 OLDMIXON I 375 There's a pleasant Lake and Valley in it.

1741 GHDPOPW 188 Gen. *Oglethorpe* . . . took two Castles, both situate on a large Lake.

1762 AG II 23 Extending from . . . the Savannah to the lakes of Florida.

1797 MAG under *Cuscowilla* Within 300 or 400 yards of a large and beautiful lake.

1822 ASPPL III. 519 [Presque Isle is bounded] on the northwest by Grant's lake.

1823 V 41 The head of this N.W. branch of Indian river and the head

lake of St. John's river, approach each other.

1837 W 59-60 Randolph, or as the inhabitants call it, Ocean Lake . . . is one of the heads of the St. Mary's River. *Ibid.*, 136, 148 The Olocklikane, or Spotted Lake, is a tract of grass meadow, covered from one to six feet deep with water, sprinkled all over with islets of rich land and cypress swamps. Many of these spots were, before the war, and perhaps are at this time, thickly settled with Seminoles . . . Several considerable lakes also, sink through the summer season in dry weather, the bottoms become rich meadows of grass, and feed vast herds of cattle, but during the heavy rains of winter, the sinks cannot receive the water, which soon fills the vallies and swarms with myriads of fish. The river Styx drains the waters from Pithlachucco Lake, into the Allachua savanna, where it is joined by several other streams . . . At the beginning of summer, when the waters are withdrawing, it is crowded with alligators and fish. The grass quickly sprouts up from the savanna to such a height, as almost to conceal the heads of cattle that graze over its surface. During the winter the same valley presents a lake fifteen miles long, and six wide.

1852 IJ 23 I came to a beautiful Lake in the Pine Woods called the Horse-Shoe Lake—it is curved like a horse's shoe.

1873 S 5 The [steamer] Volusia runs from Sand Lake to Jacksonville.

1874 S 17 Cane Lake presented another obstruction. It is a small piece of water surrounded by high canes and a line of cabbage lilies.

1874 SAR 141 [Santa Fee] lake itself is nothing but a huge spring with outlets to both the Gulf and the Atlantic. Not a creek or river empties into it.

(2) 1763 ASPPL I. 56 Some [persons], it is said, have already gone far up St. Juan's lake or river.

1773 MS. 259 St. Juan's is more a Lake, than a Stream, widens itself in

many Places into large Lakes, & con-
tracts again in narrow Channels between said Lakes.
1793 AUG I. 625 St. John's river . . .
in several places spreads into broad bays
or lakes . . . Lake George . . . is only a
dilatation of the river.
c. 1824 ASPPL IV. 660 [The tract is]
situated on the west side of St. John's
river, and on the south by Doctor's lake
or creek.
1831 USCSD vol. 214 #136.16 Its
opening into the Chipola, is at the lower
termination of the dead lakes.
1837 W 57, 59 Little Lake . . . is an
expansion of the river [St. John's] five
or six miles in circumference . . . Hort's
Lake is an inundation of the Appalachicola River.
1839 FHQ XVII. 149 Having to
preach a funeral, as I thought, today
near what is termed the dead Lakes.
1871 H 49 The Chipola river . . . flows
south . . . and empties into the Apalachicola river, or what is known as the
"Dead Lakes."
(3) 1823 ASPPL III. 790 About
four miles from the lake or pond of St.
Mark's.
1837 W 59 Alligator Lake . . . has no
outlet, except a sink hole, which in summer drains the pond nearly dry.
1874 S 17 We entered Crow Lake, a
good-sized mill pond.
    Attrib. with *branch, creek, shore,
water(s)*.
1827 W 15 A navigable creek enters
the west side of Wapaluxy, from which,
to the lake branch of Choctawhatchee
river, is only four miles and a half.
1823 V 148 But the creek which flows
from the eastern end of Orange lake
into Ocklawaha river, called Orange
lake creek, has a narrow skirt of thick
swamp on each side.
1837 W 57 North of the lake is Mount
Tucker, formerly a very extensive plantation, with a high lookout mound, close
to the lake shore.
1870 BILL 136 Occasionally they

have been discovered boiling up in the
lake-waters.
    See also CLEAR-WATER LAKE; CREEK
LAKE (attrib.); FRESH LAKE; FRESH-
WATER LAKE; GRASS LAKE; HEAD LAKE
(attrib.); LAKE COUNTRY; SALT LAKE.

LAKE COUNTRY. A district abounding in lakes. DAE 1826.
1869 BRINTON 93 The traveller is
now approaching the Lake country of
Central Florida.

LAND. Ground or soil. OED. Here,
with defining word. (a) arable land;
(b) barren land; (c) broken or waving
land; (d) first-rate land; (e) floating
land; (f) light land; (g) middling land
(hammock land); (h) natural land;
(i) open land; (j) overflowed land;
(k) plantable land; (l) rich vs. poor
land; (m) rolling land; (n) second-
rate land; (o) strong land; (p) thin
land; (q) third-rate land; (r) uncleared or wooded land.

(a) 1763 *Acts and Records,* in
WALKER Apx. No. IX There were
several pieces of *arable land* in that district.
1824 ASPPL III. 726 A peasant's portion is a lot of fifty feet in breadth, and
one hundred in depth, arable land, capable of producing one hundred fanegas
of wheat and ten of Indian corn.
1871 H 49 The arable lands have a
substratum of lime, at various depths
from the surface, and are classed as
swamp, hammock and pine.
1874 SAR 95-96 Unimproved land (I
mean arable land) could be purchased
at from 50 cents to $2 per acre.
(b) 1609 VRV 47 From thence to
the Port *de Spirito Santo,* where we
first ariued in the land of Florida . . . is
a barren land.
(c) 1774 Barton in G 27 The North
end of Kay Largo . . . is rugged broken
land.
(d) 1823 STCW 22 The land continued first rate for several miles.

1837 W 132   There is also considerable
first rate land in the forks of the Ocilla
river.
1851 BYRNE 14 [A] great part of
which is first rate land of the different
denominations of high hammock, oak
and hickory, rich prairie, and pine.
(e) 1842 PREBLE 37 Camped [in
the Everglades] in our canoes around
some small lumps of floating land, just
enough to swear by and make a fire on.
(f) 1815 NWR 106 The ridge dividing their waters has high flats of light
land, well set with willow-leafed hickory.
1874 SAR 159-60 *A range of most excellent hammock lands* . . . lies just back
of the high light lands above referred
to.
(g) 1766 B 28 We then rowed to a
low bluff of middling land, well timbered with live and water-oak, great
magnolia and sweet-gum.
(h) 1869 FISCP 69 From 1,500 to
2,000 lbs. sugar per acre, and not un-
frequently 3,000 lbs. is produced from
an acre of *natural* land.
1871 H 99 Major M. Brasswell produced . . . from 100 measured acres of
natural land (not a bit of manure was
used) one hundred bales of short staple
cotton.
(i) 1743 CADOGAN 20 The Road
by Fort *Diego* is a very good one . . .
[a] great part of which is broad hard
Beach, and the rest open Land, except
two small Thickets.
(j) 1776 NAWIG under *Florida, East*
All the shores and overflowed lands are
covered with [Barilla].
1874 SAR 120 There is but little
swamp and overflowed land here.
(k) 1765 ASPPL V. 757 In order to
ascertain the quantity of plantable and
barren land contained in each grant.
1769 STORK 11-12 The strip of land
between the sea and the river consisting of much implantable and few plantable lands.
1823 ASPPL III. 845 tr. About one
hundred and fifty acres of hammock or
plantable land, known formerly by the
name of Stewart's swamp.
(l) 1852 IJ 34 You can stand with
one foot on rich land and the other on
poor, and there are no marks by which
these changes are indicated. On the
margin of the streams and lakes sometimes you see rich land, and then it
suddenly breaks off to very poor; so
being on a water course is no indication
that the land is fertile or rather rich.
1869 FICSP 32 The lands which in
Florida are, par excellence, denominated "rich land," are first the "swamp
lands"; second, the "low hammock
lands"; third, the "high hammocks," and
fourth, the "first-rate pine, oak and
hickory lands."
(m) 1871 H 54 Tallahassee, the
capital, is situated . . . upon high, rolling
lands.
(n) 1818 Y 34, 40 The Ochese Bluff
. . . extends several miles down the river,
affording a body of second rate land . . .
The land about this curious basin is sec-
ond-rate: the growth hickory and oak
with some cane.
(o) 1837 W 12 Peace and Macaco
rivers . . . rise in good strong land.
1871 H 61 Sugar requires natural
strong land, or well manured light land.
(p) 1837 W 160 They found the
country fertile for 20 miles generally.
Towards the sea it became cold and
wet, and northward and westward piney
and thin land.
(q) 1869 FICSP 30 The "third rate"
. . . class of lands may be divided into
two orders . . . The former of those, it is
now ascertained, owing to their calcareous soil, is well adapted to the growth
of Sisal Hemp.
(r) 1786 in SIEBERT II. 45 Upon
well wooded land as the swamp and oak
land of this plantation were, there
would be from 15 to 20 Chord upon an
acre.
1824 ASPPL IV. 681 tr. Mr. John
Russell . . . humbly begs your excellency
. . . to grant to him 1,200 acres of uncleared lands.

See also BACK LAND; BAY LAND; BIT-
TER LAND; BLUFF LAND; BOTTOM LAND;
BRANCH LAND; CABBAGE LAND; CABBAGE-
TREE LAND; CANE LAND; CAPE LAND
(attrib.); CLEAR LAND; COASTLAND;
COQUINA LAND; CORNLAND; COTTON
LAND; CYPRESS-SWAMP LAND (attrib.);
DROWNED LAND; FARMING LAND; FAST
LAND; FIRM LAND; FLAT-LAND; FOREST
LAND; FRESH MARSHLAND; FRESH-WATER
MARSHLAND; GRASSLAND; GRAZING LAND;
HAMMOCK LAND; HARDWOOD LAND;
HEADLAND; HICKORY LAND; HIGH-HAM-
MOCK LAND; HIGHLAND; HUMMOCK LAND;
INDIGO LAND; INTERVALE LAND; LIME-
STONE LAND; LIVE-OAK LAND; LOWLAND;
MAINLAND; MANGROVE LAND; MANGROVE-
SWAMP LAND; MARL LAND; MARSHLAND;
MEADOWLAND; MIXED LAND; MULATTO
LAND; OAK-LAND; ORANGE LAND; PAL-
METTO LAND; PASTURE LAND; PEACH
LAND; PINE-BARREN LAND; PINELAND;
PLANTING LAND; PRAIRIE LAND; RED-
CLAY LAND; RED LAND; RICE LAND;
RIVER-BOTTOM LAND (attrib.); RIVER-
LAND; RIVER-SWAMP LAND; ROLLING
LAND; RUSH LAND; SAVANNA LAND; SAW-
PALMETTO LAND; SCRUBLAND; SOBBED
LAND; SOUR LAND; SUGAR-CANE LAND;
SUGAR LAND; SWAMP LAND; TIDELAND;
TIMBERED LAND; TIMBERLAND; TURPEN-
TINE LAND; UPLAND; UPLAND HILL
(attrib.); WASTE LAND; WET LAND; WILD
LAND; WOODLAND.

LAND CARRIAGE. A haulover; a portage.

1821 F 90 From Matanza, by means
of rollers, a boat may be hawled over a
small space of land into *Halifax River,*
which runs, like it, parallel to the sea;
but its source, though certainly not far
from St. Johns, is not well ascertained,
although the land carriage to it is only
four miles.

LANDING. A landing-place. DAE 1658.
  Spec., a bluff (1870).

1742 RCBH Apx. 28 There was a
Party of Men coming from the Landing.
1791 B 96 But I should have ran by

the landing, if the centinels had not, by
chance seen me.
1815 ASPPL III. 837 Between the
place called Dunn's lake and that
known as Horse Landing.
1823 ASPPL III. 791 Three hundred
and fifty acres of land, lying on the
south side of St. Mary's river, on Live-
oak landing.
1837 W 57 Pain's Landing used formerly to be considered the head of navigation.
1870 BILL 79 Passing Yellow Bluff, a
small landing of trifling importance . . .
we heave in sight of Jacksonville.
1874 S 16 "Whar's Prevatt's wood
landing?" repeated the Captain.

LANDING-PLACE. A place where pas-
  sengers and goods are or can be
  landed or disembarked. DAE 1636.

1563 RIBAULD 13-14 One of appear-
aunce . . . commaunded one of the Indians to . . . approche our boates to
shewe vs the coastes landing place.
1741 GHDPOPW 190 They took a
Look-out about two Miles to the North
of the Landing-place.
1791 B 74 Finding a convenient landing place and harbour, I concluded to
remain here till morning.
1812 FHQ IX. 70 The distance to the
landing place is about a mile and a half.
1827 W 85 This has been long known
as a common landing place.

LANE. A narrow passage. OED. Here,
  a channel. (?Poss. "*Sc.* a sluggish
  stream of water." OED.)

1874 S 28 The watery lanes were
more perplexing than the streets of
Boston.

LAWN. A grassy opening or glade in
  a forest. DAE 1801.

1791 B 203 We next passed over a
level green lawn, a cove of the savanna.
1836 SSW 241 [We emerged into a
pine barren] stretching out into open
verdurous lawns.

LEDGE. A ridge of rocks, esp. such as are found near the shore beneath the surface of the sea. OED. Spec., breakers (1827); a rocky ridge below the surface of a spring (1852).

1763 ROBERTS 16   From the *Farellon de Pogoi* extends a ledge of rocks.

1775 R Apx. xx   Five leagues to the south of the ... point or ledge of rocks ... there is another ledge of rocks.

1796 G 20   Grenville Inlet ... [is known] by the Rocky Spring, a high ledge of rocks, out of which a large stream of fresh water rushes into the sea.

1827 W 13   He ran along a good musket-shot from the ledges, (breakers,) till he brought the Fort of Pensacola, (Barrancas,) N. and S. one-fourth E.

1837 W 48   About thirty miles from its mouth it falls over a rocky ledge, and twelve miles from the Gulf it sinks under ground.

1852 IJ 29   [At Silver Springs] there are projecting ledges of lime stone from the depth of forty feet to the bottom under which the water comes in.

LEVEE. The very low ridge sometimes built up by streams on their flood plains, on either side of their channels. NID. (DAE gives the artificial sense as "S. and W.") DA 1870.

1842 PREBLE 41   The river rapid and deep, with banks or "levees" thrown up by floods on each side, and crowned with willow and mangrove bushes.

LEVEL. An area of land having a level surface. DAE 1700.

1766 B 18   The west side [of the lake] ... was low and rich for 100 yards back, rising gradually from the water to 4 or 5 foot perpendicular, then comes to a level.

1821 F 77   From the sea this splendid river takes a course westward, alternately presenting along its whole length a variety of bluffs and levels.

See also PINE LEVEL.

LILY SWAMP. A swamp in which lilies grow. The reference here is to an area located in the Everglades.

1842 PREBLE 40   After dining hauled the canoes through a narrow streamlet into a lily swamp.

LIME GROVE. A grove of lime trees.

1837 W 112   South of that, the wild orange and lime groves were injured, but not destroyed [by frosts of 1835].

LIME PIT. A lime sink.

1827 USCHED vol. 217 #43.50   On approaching the Wythlacoochie, the face of the country is much altered. Here it becomes more undulating, and lime pits and lakes of pellucid water are skirted by slips of fertile land.

LIME SINK. A depression or sink hole in a limestone region. DAE 1837.

1852 IJ 25   The Lime sinks ... are large holes in the ground, thirty or forty feet in diameter, and fifteen or twenty feet deep. They were all dry and I was told that they did not often contain water.

1855 USCSED vol. 756 #76.5   From the Santa Fe the country ... is somewhat broken, a portion of the distance being sandy, with occasional lime sinks.

1856 LANMAN 136   The lime-sinks ... consist of perfectly circular basins, gathering to a point as they sink below the surface, and some of them are so deep as to bring the tops of large trees on a level with the eye of the spectator. They usually contain a small quantity of lime-stone water.

1874 SAR 59   [The creek] empties itself into the earth by means of a lime sink.

LIMESTONE COUNTRY. A region on or near the surface of which limestone abounds. DAE 1781-1782.

1837 W 9   The Uche creek drains the only limestone country, west of the Choctawhatche River.

LIMESTONE LAND. Land which abounds in limestone. DAE 1805.

1837 W 129   The limestone lands on this stream [Econfina River] are very fertile, producing in a natural state, the finest groves of white oak in Florida.

LIMESTONE SINK. One of the hollows in limestone regions, often communicating with a cavern or subterranean passage, so that waters running into it are lost; a sink hole. NID under *sink.* DA 1817.

1836 ASPMA VII. 147   Our dependence for water was on the wet savannahs and limestone sinks, "sinkholes," as they are termed in that country.

LINE BRANCH. A branch which is tributary to a river.

1836 ASPMA VII. 142-43   I had also great difficulty in crossing the two branches of the Withlacooche and the Hillsborough ... The banks of the line branches of the Withlacoochee and the Hillsborough were so precipitate that horses could not be used in crossing the wagons.

LIVE-OAK GROVE. A grove of live oaks.

1766 B 14-15   We encamped on a pleasant dry bank, but middling soil, in a grove of live-oaks.

1773 MS. 274   In sml. [small] live oak grove.

1821 F 82   A highway leads from it three fourths of a mile, through an orange and live-oak groves.

LIVE-OAK HAMMOCK. A hammock consisting of live oak trees.

1765 B 7   The hammocks of live-oaks and palmettos are generally surrounded either with swamp or marsh.

1831 ASPNA IV. 100   I sent my assistant to take the bearings of the live oak hammock.

1832 ASPNA IV. 223   The live oak is abundant in the hammocks bordering on

the rivers, the sea coasts, and the everglades, and particularly on the large islands on the everglades. Between Cape Sable and Cape Roman, after getting clear of the coast, are a great number of hammocks containing from one to five hundred acres, which are covered with live oak of a most superior kind.

1837 W 136   Southwest of Manatee River, on the borders of Tampa, and progressing towards the Sarrazota Bay, there is considerable live oak hammock.

1851 BYRNE vi   "Ten Mile Creek" Hammock ... is somewhat different in character of soil from the preceding. It is more grey, and might be termed a live oak hammock.

LIVE-OAK HUMMOCK. A hummock overgrown with live oak.

1842 PREBLE 41   The banks of the river lined with marshy weeds and tall canebrakes, with here and there a live-oak hummock draped with moss.

LIVE-OAK LAND. Land upon which live oak trees grow.

1773 MS. 266   In live Oak Land-surrounded with indifft. [indifferent] pe. [pine] land.

1831 ASPNA IV. 121   But the greater part of the live oak lands there are private property.

LIVE-OAK SWAMP. A swamp in which the dominating growth is live oak.

1818 Y 31-32   The *live oak* swamps are found nearer the coast than any of the others and with partial interruptions from the Bay-galls form almost a belt between the glades of the interior and the sedge marshes of the shore.

LIVE-OAK THICKET. A thicket of live oak trees.

1831 ASPNA IV. 120   Every five or six years, the fires break into the live oak thickets.

LOBLOLLY-BAY SWAMP. A swamp consisting of loblolly bay (a small evergreen tree of the Southern states; the black laurel).

1773 MS. 309   The fourth kind is also of a black Soil, but mixed with a great deal of white Sand, and goes by the Name of Loblolly Bay Swamp, bordered on both sides with high Pine Land, therefore has not that Nursery; for this kind of Tree require an ever moist ground; this Land is always overflowed by Running Water, and Freshes caused by Rains. In this Swamp the trees are also young.

LOW COUNTRY. A region or area of comparatively slight elevation. DAE 1797.

1766 B 14   I believe, that [the sea-shells] ... reach all under this whole low country at uncertain depths.
1775 A 456   Noxious vapours ... float over the surface of this low country.
1791 B 416   These rivers [divide] ... their numerous branches, over the expansive flat low country (between the two great rivers Apalachula and Mobile).
1825 FHQ XIV. 152-53   [The country] is literally under water for miles through the low country between St. Fe and St. John's rivers.
1836 SSW 69   The rains flood this low country [sc., the Florida peninsula], which seems formerly to have been one lake, or but lately reclaimed from the ocean.

LOW GROUND. Bottom land. DAE 1659. Spec., a savanna (1824).

1775 A 457   It is surprising that Britain does not improve the opportunity ... by adding to these unhealthy low grounds a sufficient quantity of waste high land.
1792 POPE 97   Lobelia ... usually grows in Meadows, and on the flat low-Grounds of Rivers, Creeks.
1803 E 288   Many of the trees in the low grounds are loaded with a variety of vines.

1824 FHQ XIV. 145   The only possible obstruction will be savannahs or low-grounds.
1827 W 7   Dark iron sandstone ... is often thrown up in small hills, especially in the low grounds near the water-courses.
1829 USCHED vol. 187 #147.4   In Florida, the fern grass is exclusively peculiar to low grounds and heads of water courses.
1831 ASPPL VI. 550-51   The low grounds are entirely inundated by rains.

LOW HAMMOCK. A swampy hammock; a swammock (q.v.) (1869). This type of "heavy" hammock is said to have a more tenacious soil than the high and "light" hammock (1869).

1818 Y 31   The high hammock is almost always fertile. The low has often too much sand.
1821 F 83   A large tract of low hammock, known as the *Twelve-mile Swamp.*
1823 V 87-88   The *low hammocks* are the richest kind of lands in Florida, and capable of producing for many successive years rich crops of sugar, corn, hemp, or other equally exhausting productions: they are however clothed with so heavy a growth of timber and underwood, that the task of clearing them is appalling, and they require ditching and banking to guard them from extraordinary floods and rains ... A thick vegetable mould of from one to two feet in depth, covers the surface of the ground in these low hammocks.
1832 ASPNA IV. 223   The lands on the South Atlantic coast of Florida consist of high hammock, low hammock [etc.].
1851 BYRNE 13   Low hammocks ... are not inferior to swamp lands in fertility.
1869 FICSP 29, 33   Then there is the high and light hammock, and the low or heavy hammock ... *Low Hammocks,* which from the fact of their participating in the nature of hammocks and

swamps, are sometimes termed *Swammock*, are not inferior to swamp lands in fertility, but perhaps are not quite as durable. They are nearly always level, or nearly so, and have a soil of greater tenacity than that of the high hammocks. Some ditching is necessary in many of them. The soil in them is always deep.

1874 SAR 147 In many places high rolling lands run down to the water's edge, and in connection with the river swamps constitute some of the most desirable sugar lands in the State, and are denominated *low hammocks* in contradistinction to *high hammocks*.

LOWLAND. Low-lying land, as that along a stream. Usually pl. DAE 1654. The 1823 example refers to the Everglades region.

1743 C II. iv Particularly Pine-Lands are often intermixed with narrow Tracts of low Lands.

1762 AG I. 13 All the low lands on the coast, as far as they can be approached, are bordered with mangler-trees.

1765 letter in STORK Apx. 34 On each side of this ridge, is as fine a body of rich low lands as any in the world.

1773 MS. 306 From the Mouth of [St. Mary's], the Soil consists of much fine low Land, for the culture of Rice.
1787 in SIEBERT II. 247 The low land upon the tract before spoken of was high marsh land.

1818 Y 40 The low lands of the river are generally good but somewhat swampy.

1823 V 51 The determination of the circumstances of this immense body of low land occupying the whole southern interior of East Florida, easily affords an explanation of those delineations upon antient [*sic*] maps, representing it as cut up by rivers and lagoons, communicating with each other and the sea.

M

MAGNOLIA SWAMP. A swamp consisting chiefly of magnolia trees.

1874 KEASBEY 63 A three hours' journey of fifteen miles, through pine forests, magnolia swamps and groves of wild oranges.

MAIN. Elliptical from *mainland*. Arch. OED.

1742 RCBH Apx. 31 The *General* went over to the *Main*.
1766 B 30 A large point of land projects out from the main.
1773 MS. 304 At Cape Florida ... the Main is ... situated open to the Gulf of Sandwich within and the Florida Stream without the Sound of Dartmouth.
1796 G 18 The watering places on the main ... may always be depended upon.
1829 USCHED vol. 187 #147.7 Inland Passage ... runs parallel to the coast between the main and the Islands of Amelia, Talbot, and Fort George.
Attrib. with *stream*.
1773 MS. 300 The same Water, which is upon the Bar can be carried up three miles upon the main Stream.

MAINLAND. That continuous body of land which includes the greater part of a territory, in contradistinction to islands or peninsulas. OED. Pl. once (1874).

1609 VRV 26 [The Gouernour] said that he desired no more then to find victuals, that hee might goe into the maineland.
1652 HEYLIN, *Cosmographie*, 117 Having thus taken a survey of the main land of *Florida*.
1741 GHDPOPW 181 This Island ... extends about ten Miles Southward along the Coast, leaving a Channel between it and the main Land.
1762 J 69 [In lat.] 26° 56' and a good way upwards, the coast of the mainland

of *Florida* cannot be approached, by reason of the shoals and small islands. 1784 HUTCHINS 85   There is a bank near the middle, between St. Joseph's point and the main land. 1796 G 15   The mangrove Islands . . . continue to the main land. 1837 W 126   The main land, on the east side of Pensacola Bay . . . is traversed by many streams of good water. 1874 SAR 159   North of Port Orange the [Halifax] river is . . . bounded by shores . . . from which . . . the mainlands gradually rise for a quarter of a mile.

MALPASS.   Possibly a malpais (bad lands).

1825 ASPPL IV. 610   Thence south 45° west, 13 chains, to a pine with a cross, in the line of *Ricard's malpass, known by Flenos.*

MANGROVE FOREST.   A forest of mangrove trees.

1856 USCHED vol. 893 Part I. 551-52 A belt of mangrove forests almost entirely surrounds Cudjoe. 1869 FICSP 109   Large forests of the mangrove abound in the islands and in the shallow places near the shores of the inlets.

MANGROVE ISLAND.   An island formed by or overgrown with mangrove shrubbery. The "drowned" (1775) type of mangrove island either has no firm ground (1796 p. 16) or is covered with water at high tide (1837 p. 39). However, some mangrove islands are high enough to support other vegetation (1837 p. 53).

1775 R Apx. xxxiii   Off the S W end of this key lies a small drowned mangrove island. 1796 G 12, 16   The Mangrove Islands, which are very numerous, and often form large clusters, are in general washed over at high water, wherein if a Mangrove bush takes root, it forms a

little island in the course of a few years; and one of these islands breeds in time a cluster of others round its own shores . . . *Fox Island,* is a pretty large mangrove Island, without any firm ground, the roots of the trees being constantly overflowed. 1823 V 39-40   The river loses its open character, and winds among an innumerable cluster of mangrove islands. 1837 W 39, 53   The Mangrove Islands, or Mule Keys, are small islets, scattered over a coral reef . . . Most if not all these islets are covered with water at high tides . . . The north end [of Hillsborough Lagoon] . . . is full of mangrove Islands; and some, that have high ground, [are] covered with palms and other timber. 1874 S 28   By 10 o'clock we were sailing through a labyrinth of mangrove islands.

MANGROVE ISLET.   A small mangrove island.

1869 BRINTON 107   Sarasota Bay is . . . dotted with numerous mangrove islets.

MANGROVE KEY.   A key consisting chiefly of mangrove shrubs.

1775 R Apx. xxxiv   *Key Matanca* lies SSW 2 miles from the small man-grove key. 1823 V 43-44   The channel is lost in the archipelago of mangrove keys at the north end of Meritt's island. 1837 W 291   Col. Murray . . . passed through a bay, studded with mangrove keys. 1856 USCHED vol. 893 Part I. 553 Large banks . . . spread from two and a half to three miles to the westward and one to the northward, covered with these small mangrove keys.

MANGROVE LAND.   Land covered with mangrove trees.

1773 MS. 227   High mangrove Land. 1775 R 283   It is a narrow slip of beach, and mangrove land.

MANGROVE SWAMP. A salt-water swamp in which mangrove trees grow; found only near the seacoast or on an island.

1769 STORK 11 As the mangrove swamp is always salt, or very brakish [*sic*], but exceedingly rich, it will do for the cultivation of the Barilla.

1773 MS. 309 Mangrove Swamp ... is only met with near the Sea Coast, and upon the Islands on the South Side of this Province.

1775 R 289 In the bay of Juan Ponce De Leon, in the west side of the land ... the land in general is drowned mangrove swamp.

1796 G 12 [These islands] are generally bordered with a Mangrove swamp just within the beach.

1823 V 82 Pavilion keys and Lostman's keys ... consist of drowned mangrove swamps.

1837 W 43 The eastern shore is mostly a low mangrove swamp.

MANGROVE-SWAMP LAND. The land within a mangrove swamp; a mangrove swamp.

1769 STORK 11 The mangrove swamp lands between the sea bank and branch of the river, consist of 4,693 acres.

MAPLE GROVE. A grove of maple trees (not the sugar-maple).

1842 PREBLE 42 Camped in a maple grove.

MAPLE SWAMP. A swamp in which the predominant growth is maple. DAE 1667. The soil of this type of swamp is not as rich as that of a cypress swamp (*q.v.* 1773). (A.)

1773 MS. 309 The next kind of low Land is called Maple Swamp, its Soil is rich, appears black, mixed with white Sand, on which the rain waters remain a long time before they sink through this Soil, or is dryed up by the Sun; this Swamp is generally overrun with canes; its highest and thickest, tho' all young Trees, and Canes stand in the middle of these Sands, and are surrounded with a Nursery of younger Trees and Canes from all Ages down to one year.

MARL-BED. A bed of marl.

1871 H 44 All he will have to do, is to apply to any of the numerous marl beds, rich in lime, to be found all over the county, to fertilize his land.

1874 SAR 118-19 The balance of the lands of Nassau county are pine barrens, mostly sandy, and interspersed with numerous "bay-galls," cypress ponds, savannas, some of them marl-beds, all of them mines of muck.

MARL HAMMOCK. A hammock the soil of which is marl.

1874 SAR 162 Thence again sloping back into excellent hammocks, bordered by pine lands, back of which, and a mile from the river, commences the range of rich marl hammock [near Daytona Beach].

MARL LAND. Land consisting of marl.

1874 SAR 118 The stiff clay soils ... of the little St. Mary's river, as well as the marl lands near Callahan ... are suitable for the production of the sugar cane.

MARSH. Also, MARCH (dial.), MARISH (dial.; obs.). (1) A tract of low-lying, watery land; marshland (1773 p. 253). DAE 1612. A pond (1823 STCW p. 21) or swamp (1803; 1823 ASPPL). Marshes have no trees, but shrubs sometimes skirt the edges of them (1827). Sometimes a marsh is inundated (1773 p. 279). The 1766 and 1823 (STCW p. 25) quotations probably refer to salt marsh. (2) A meadow; a stretch of grassland whether wet or dry. Local. OED Sup. Here, a prairie (1869) or savanna. (3) A kind of drain: *i.e.*, low ground which is sometimes inundated so that the waters collect and drain off in a stream.

(1) 1563 RIBAULD 25 They declared vnto vs thei toke [pearls] out of oysters, whereof there is takē euer along the riuer side, & among the reeds, & in the marches.

1587 L 6L Wee discouered a fayre and great medowe, devided notwithstanding with diuers marishes.

1731 C 99 [Blue-wing Teal] feed on a kind of Wild Oate growing in the Marshes.

1741 GHDPOPW 191 From a Marsh hard by they played with twenty Cohorns.

1744 KIMBER 23 We march'd thro' several scrubby Marshes, and Savannahs.

1766 B 35 [At Espiritu Santo Bay] several low sandy islands and marshes, covered with mangrove bushes, lie before the main land.

1773 MS. 253 Near half of its Borders from the Inlet is Marsh, the other half up to the Stream's Head is Swamp Land.

Ibid., 279 A sml. [small] Pond-here the marshes are under water, which joins [*sic*] the pond ... crossed the marshes under water.

1775 R 30 Marshes ... are of four kinds, two in the salt, and two in the fresh water; they are either soft or hard.

1797 MAG under *Alachua Savannah* The Indians removed ... on account of ... the noxious exhalations from the marshes of the savannah.

1803 E Apx. 139 The river St. Mary's is formed by the water draining out of the Okefonoke swamp along several marshes, or small swamps, which join into one.

1818 Y 48 The marsh at the delta of Apalachicola is lower than that at Sahwanne. The former is inundated every tide and is too soft to bear the weight of a man.

1823 ASPPL III. 758 The river St. Sebastian ... forms, by its diurnal floods, an extensive march or swamp.

1823 STCW 21 The old Tallahassee village ... extends over a high and uneven bank ... descending westwardly to a very large marsh or pond.

1823 STCW 25 The marshes along shore extend from three to five miles into the gulf.

1827 W 61 Marshes, are of two kinds, fresh and salt. The former are usually situated on the borders of some large body of water, in the interior of the country. The latter on the seacoast, or near the estuaries of rivers. There is a great diversity of marshes; much depends on the substratum, on which they are based. For instance, the most extensive marshes of West Florida are based on limestone, which renders them extremely fertile in aquatic vegetables; some of the fresh marshes, on the contrary are merely quicksands, covered with a very thin soil, and are of course quite barren. Others have a clay foundation, and may be cultivated to advantage. Marshes produce no trees; a few shrubs sometimes skirt the edges of them.

Preceded by a designating term.

1765 B 8-9 Behind [the bluff] ... is a high rich clear marsh producing grass as high as one's head, reaching to the pine-lands.

1827 W 16 It is wholly surrounded by green marshes, interspersed with keys.

1832 ASPNA IV. 223 The lands on the South Atlantic coast of Florida consist of ... high marsh, low marsh [etc.].

(2) 1787 in SIEBERT II. 239 1500 Acres one half at least good high land— high swamp rich feeding marches with large natural reserves of water.

1823 V 69 As far as the eye can reach the marsh or savanna appears to be interminable.

1869 FICSP 113 This marsh or prairie is from less than half a mile to more than two miles in width.

(3) 1803 E 279 The water issues along several small marshes or drains which soon unite in one ... These drains are sometimes quite dry.

Attrib. with *bend, country, flat, point, water.*

1773 MS. 226 Marsh bend of above pond.
1587 L 23 The parte which was towarde the Cape of Florida, was altogether a marish Countrey.
1823 V 49 Boca Ratone sound receives also from the south another creek, heading in large marsh flats.
1766 B 20 Some small marsh points project a little way into it.
1744 KIMBER 4 Our Drink [is] ... the first muddy Marsh-Water we can find.

See also FRESH MARSH; FRESH MARSH-LAND; FRESH-WATER MARSH; GRASS MARSH; HARD MARSH; REED-MARSH; RIVER MARSH (attrib.); SALT MARSH; SALT-WATER MARSH; SAW-GRASS MARSH; SEDGE-MARSH; SOFT MARSH.

MARSH GROUND, MARISH GROUND. Marshland. DAE 1634.

c. 1565 Hawkins voyage, in HΛKLUYT (1589) 539 The countrey was maruellously sweet, with both marish and medow ground.
1609 VRV 19 No Indians could bee taken, because the Countrie was full of marish grounds.

MARSH ISLAND. An island consisting of marsh.

1766 B 33 A little above this [creek], there is another little creek ... below which is an island of marsh.
1824 ASPPL IV. 385 Francis J. Fatio [et al.] ... claims ... two small marsh islands in front, on the river St. John's.
1871 H 126 Oyster Point ... is the north end of a marsh island.

MARSHLAND, MARCH LAND. Low-lying land, more or less watery, usually subject to periodic or seasonal overflow. DAE 1634. It is possible that the 1874 example is not a dialectal form, but merely an error.

1743 C II. iii These upper Tracts of Marsh Land ... might with small Expense be drained.

1769 STORK 13 The marsh land may do either for rice, indigo, or sugar canes.
1775 R 288 On the banks of such ... [rivers and lagoons] as are fresh we meet with great bodies of marsh land.
1786 in SIEBERT II. 57 There were ... two hundred acres more or less of marsh land.
1827 W 87 Low marsh lands border the Ocklockney bay.
1874 SAR 159 Along the banks of these streams are some extensive and exceedingly rich mash lands.

See also FRESH MARSHLAND; FRESH-WATER MARSHLAND.

MEADOW. A level, grassy lowland, esp. one which is moist or subject to inundation. "Chiefly New Eng." DAE 1636. Spec., a savanna (1769; 1775).

1563 RIBAULD 30 The channell & depth of this riuer of Seyne, is on the side of the medow that is in the Ile of May.
c. 1565 Hawkins voyage, in HAKLUYT (1589) 541 This land ... floresheth with medow.
1587 L 30 The medowes were at that season all greene, and halfe couered ouer with water.
1609 VRV 52-53 This Countrie ... hath goodly meadows by the Riuers.
1682 The Present State of Carolina 16 But their imbellished Meadows, fertil, and flourishing Savana's, are guarded with pleasant and solitary Woods.
1769 STORK 19 The buffalo is found in the savannahs, or natural meadows, in the interior parts of East-Florida.
1775 R 22 On account of their producing some species of grass ... [the savannas] are very often stiled meadows.
1796 G 20 There are Two wells of excellent water in a little meadow back of the sand hills.
1821 F 78 The entensive view of meadow, afforded by the open plains, exhibits a vast expanse of perpetual verdure.

1837 W 56 The banks [of the St. John's River north of Lake Monroe are] variegated with meadows of grass, twenty feet high, [etc.].
Attrib. with *valley*.
1836 SSW 308 Behold through the vista of hills, and over yon little meadow valley, the small smiling town.

See also GRASS MEADOW; MEADOW GROUND; MEADOWLAND; SAW-GRASS MEADOW.

MEADOW GROUND. Also, MEDOWE GROUNDE. Meadow. DAE 1633.

1563 RIBAULD 33 We espyed out of the South syde one of the fayrest, pleasauntst, and greatest medowe grounde that might be seene.
c. 1565 Hawkins voyage, in HAKLUYT (1589) 539 The countrey was maruellously sweet, with both marish and medow ground.
1589 DRAKE map of St. Augustine A lowe plaine or medow ground through the which our troopes passed.

MEADOWLAND. Land consisting of meadow. DAE 1640.

1821 F 147 *Prairie* or *meadow lands* are margined towards the sea by immense quantities of oyster shells.
1870 BILL 117 Again the river seems lost in a bewildering perspective of silver streamlets, separated only by some narrow knife-blade of meadow-land and flowers.

MEANDER(S). Pl. The sinuous windings of a bay (1829), creek or river. OED.

1744 KIMBER 13 [The Creek] in several Meanders gently roll'd its Waves from its Source.
1773 MS. 253 Nassau Stream is by its Meanders for a Distance of 18 miles navigable for Vessels which can sail over the Bar.
1824 ASPPL IV. 313 Thence along the meanders of said creek and river.
1829 ASPPL VI. 531 By platting the meanders of St. Rosa bay between the

section lines, the quantity may be estimated.

MIDDLE GROUND. A shallow place, as a bank or bar. OED 1801 under *middle*.

1773 MS. 288 The Bar of the Inlet has two Channels separated by a small middle Ground in the Bar.
1823 ASPNA IV. 965 The channel called Boca Grande . . . was represented to me as . . . having a dangerous middle-ground.
1829 USCHED vol. 187 #147.16 A middle ground, over which nine feet can be carried in every direction, extends from the end of the peninsula to St. Andrew's bay.
1837 W 40 [At Bocca Grande] there is a middle ground with patches of coral rock, but they have on them from two and a half to three feet water.

MINERAL SPRING. A spring impregnated with minerals. DAE 1783.

1784 HUTCHINS 78 There is a fine mineral spring of the Chalybeate kind, near the mouth of the lagoon.
1823 STCW 24 Near the fall of the rapids, on the right side, is a large mineral spring.
1837 W 56 A large mineral spring rises behind the north point of Berrisford.
1852 IJ 22 I regretted that I did not know sooner that I was at a Mineral Spring.

MIXED LAND. Land on which red oak, hickory, gum, and pine trees all grow together (1874).

1775 A Apx. 456 Here and there is some light mixt land.
1874 SAR 147 There are large districts of what are termed *mixed* lands, from the fact that red oak, hickory, gum and pine all grow together.

MORASS. A marsh or bog. DAE 1675. Spec., a boggy pond (1791); a swamp (1818); a wet savanna (1836). As distinguished from a marsh, a morass is spongy like a bog.

1741 GHDPOPW 180 Behind the Castle on the West Side is a Morass.

1791 B 172 Creeks or rivulets ... are the conduits or drains of the shallow boggy ponds or morasses just under the hills.

1818 Y 47 The soil of this morass [*sc.*, Eokafanoke swamp] is similar to that in the larger Bay-Galls—consisting of a deep mass of loose mould and vegetable fibre matter and strengthened by the intertwisted roots of large timber and resting on a base of sand and clay.

1821 DARBY 9 Next the Gulf of Mexico, interminable morasses extend, whose surface is in general as level and as low as are those of the gulf tides.

1823 V 78 Nothing can be more desolate than the situation of a traveller who ... roams without end over mossy rocks and shaking morasses.

1836 ASPMA VII. 146 The impracticability against military operations arises from ... the impossibility of passing to the islands, except on foot, through morasses of such depth that our troops, at the three points at which it was passed, were nowhere less than up to the middle ... These morasses are wet savannahs, grown up with tall sawgrass, ten or twelve feet high in most places.

See also EVERGLADE MORASS (attrib.); RIVER MORASS (attrib.).

MORNING-GLORY PRAIRIE. Prairie land overgrown with morning-glories.

1874 S 27 Strips of morning-glory prairie are dotted with red deer.

MOUND. A natural elevation of inconsiderable size, resembling a heap or pile of earth; a hillock, "mount." OED. Spec., a bluff (1871).

1791 B 155 We immediately find ourselves ... on parallel chains of low swelling mounds.

1837 W 57 North of the lake is Mount

Tucker, formerly a very extensive plantation, with a high lookout mound, close to the lake shore.

1871 H 128 *Massacre Bluff* ... is a mound.

MOUNT. A more or less conical hill. Obs. except in place names. DAE *c.* 1649. Spec., a bluff (1821 p. 82); a promontory (1823).

1744 KIMBER 34 We named the Mount at the Entrance of this Bar, Oglethorpe's Mount.

1765 B 6 Mount Hope is 50 yards long and 30 wide, near 20 foot high.

1773 MS. 259 The General's Mount (a high Sand Hill) makes the south Point of this Inlet.

1784 HUTCHINS 77 [The brooks] take their rise under Gage hill, a small mount behind the town [of Pensacola].

1787 in SIEBERT II. 251 [This tract had] ... in it's Front (on a branch of the river) a Beautiful Mount of several acres, 60 or 70 feet high which overlooked the whole Country for 20 or 30 miles round.

1821 F 76, 82 It ... is known by the high sand hill on the south cape, called General's Mount ... *Mount Hope* ... is a high shelly bluff on the little lake.

1823 V 39 The junction of the two latter [streams] forms an acute promontory called Mount Oswald.

MOUNTAIN. Mountains in the usual sense do not exist in Florida. However, according to NID, "In generally flat countries, any small hill, a few hundred feet in height, may be locally termed a mountain." The 1763, 1773, and 1776 quotations probably refer to a sand dune, or a mount. The designation of clumps of cypress trees (1874) as mountains constitutes a special usage. *Cf.* HILL.

1763 ROBERTS 98 The scene entirely changed from the most delightful prospect and fertile soil, to the most barren mountains.

1773 MS. 277, 278 On Sand Hills with young pe. [pine] & shy. [shrubby] Oak ... the Beginning of mountains Ridge. Each pond has a live oak Grove running up the mountain ... On the Ridge of sandy mounts. [sic] covered with pine Timber ... On ridge of sandy mountains.
1776 NAWIG under *Eustace, Island* of Eustace, or Eustatia, Island of, called also Metanzas, or Slaughter ... is long and narrow, consisting principally of sand and bushes, and but one mountain, of about 20 miles in circuit.
1837 ASPMA VII. 828 The Thlawhatkee (White mountains,), an elevated range of hills not mentioned by any geographer, nor described in any account of Florida which I have seen, was passed on the 24th. The ascent in many places was so difficult as to render dragropes and heavy details of men necessary to take the baggage-wagons over the heights.
1874 S 22 What are known [in the Ft. Pierce area] as the Blue Mountains attracted much attention. These mountains are clumps of cypress trees that stud the marshes, and stand out in the sky line like the Black Hills of the plains. The clearness of the atmosphere gives them the bluish tinge from which they derive their name.

MOUTH. The outfall of a river; the entrance to a haven, etc.—here, with reference to a bay, the Gulfs of Florida (1741 GHDPOPW) and Mexico (1773), and a narrows (1823). OED. Spec., a channel (1803); the entrance of a river into a lake (1765). The sense of *outlet* (1821) rather than *entrance* is illustrated by the 1827 quotation, and also the 1874 reference to the outfall of a river into a lake.

1587 L 60 He landed fifteen leagues from the fort, at the mouth of the Ryuer Tacata coureu.
1652 HEYLIN 116 S. Augustines [sic]

... [is] situate at the mouth of a small River so named.
1741 GHDPOPW 179 About seventy Leagues from the Mouth of the Gulf of [Florida].
1741 Tailfer, P., *et al, A True and Historical Narrative of the Colony of Georgia* 62 Mr. Og[lethor]pe ... caused a Garrison ... to be placed upon a sandy Island ... in the Mouth of St. *John's* River.
1765 B 8 Landed opposite to the mouth of the lake.
1769 STORK 6 Lake George ... is 170 miles from the mouth of the river.
1773 MS. 337 If then Vessels happen to be in the Mouth of the Gulf of Mexico, that is between the Island of Cuba and the Promontory of East Florida; they best endeavour to make the Bahama Islands.
1797 MAG under *Spiritu Santo* Spiritu Santo, or *Tampay Bay* ... has a number of shoals and keys at its mouth.
1803 E 234 The Chattahocha, communicates with St. George's Sound by three mouths, or channels.
1821 F 93 [The Indian River] runs parallel with St. Lucia ... to latitude 27 20, where there is a mouth, or outlet into the ocean.
1823 V 47 A beautiful piece of land reaches from the mouth of the narrows.
1827 W 14 Chactawhatchee bay ... receives the Chactawhatchee river through many mouths.
1829 USCHED vol. 187 #147.17 Its western extremity shelters from the southerly winds the mouth of Pensacola bay.
1874 KEASBEY 43 This is Volusia bar, a belt of sand drifted across the mouth of the river as it broadens into the lake.

MUD BANK. A bank of mud in a river or harbor that obstructs navigation or the flow of water. DAE 1774.

1822 ASPNA IV. 963 I have ... planted stakes on a mud bank that partly obstructs the channel into the harbor.

1823 V 124 [*Richmond bay*] is very shallow and full of grass and mud banks.

MUD FLAT. A low, flat area frequently covered with water. DAE 1813.

1823 FHQ XIV. 94 St. Sebastian's river . . . when the tide is full extends for a considerable distance over the mudflats on each side of the main channel.

1831 AUDUBON 53 Over these mud-flats a foot or two of water is quite sufficient to drive all the birds ashore.

1856 USCHED vol. 893 Part I. 551 The shore then again becomes rocky, till it changes into extensive mud-flats around Point Dora signal.

1869 BRINTON 106 In parts, the slope of the shore is so gradual that low water exposes a mud flat one to two miles wide.

MUD SHOAL. A shoal composed of mud. DAE 1842 under *mud*.

1835 ASPMA V. 658 *St. Mark's river and harbor, Florida.*—The obstructions in the harbor, consisting of oyster beds and mud shoals.

MULATTO LAND. Brownish-colored, fertile land. DAE 1741. (A.)

1871 H 44 South of this body of land . . . lies a remarkable country. It is high, rolling and reminds one of the red hills in Georgia. The land is what the residents term "mulatto land," which name is indicative of its color. It is quite productive, and yields the best quality of sea-island cotton raised in the county.

MULBERRY HAMMOCK. A hammock in which mulberry trees grow.

1787 in SIEBERT II. 251 This tract had about 160 acres of it rich low Cabbage Cedar and Mulberry Hammock.

MYRTLE SWAMP. A swamp consisting of myrtle.

1773 MS. 283 In low Pe. [pine] Ld. [land] myrtle Swamp far off eastwardly.

MYRTLE THICKET. A thicket of myrtle trees.

1836 SSW 139 The bland evening air, charged with the fresh odours of the piny forests and oak and myrtle thickets, conspired, together with the exercise of marching, to set the blood into motion.

N

NARROW(S). (Here, always pl.) A narrow part of a sound, strait, or river. OED. Extended to apply to a labyrinth of narrow channels (1837).

1742 RCBH Apx. 46 At Night I took the Company of Grenadiers and marched to the *Narrows,* between this *Island* and the *Main.*

1775 R 258 This passage continues through *Amelia* narrows.

1821 F 75 The navigation through the Narrows, for vessels drawing more than four feet, is intricate towards *Nassau River.*

1823 ASPPL III. 845 tr. [Cabbage swamp lies] opposite the Narrows, so called on account of said river being more narrow there than at any other part.

1837 W 52 These Narrows are a labyrinth of narrow, deep and crooked channels, that connect the south end of Indian Lagoon, with Hobe Sound. The tide passes swiftly through them; they are separated by a vast number of mangrove islands. These narrows extend about eight miles.

1871 H 131 This is The Narrows, and is occasioned by oyster reefs on the east side of the river which have obstructed that part of the channel.

NATURAL BRIDGE. A natural arch formation suggestive of a bridge. DAE 1817. (A.) Spec., in Florida, a limestone *causeway* (*q.v.*) formed by by the disappearance of a stream into a cavity and its reappearance above the surface of the earth shortly thereafter (1818). At times such a bridge is overflowed. Sometimes a natural bridge is timbered (1818; 1827) and has a width of several miles (1823 p. 64; 1837): in these cases this phenomenon is hardly distinguishable from the river-bottom land (1827).

c. 1767 FHQ XII. 119   This river is crossed by a sort of Natural Bridge.

1775 R 277   Twenty miles east from *Apalachia,* we cross a place over a creek, called by the savages, the natural bridge.

1818 Y 43-44   A quarter of a mile below the lower path there is a natural bridge over this creek covered with timber ... It is not easy to account for those singular causeways which are found on all the Florida creeks ... From the nature of the soil also there is never such a quantity of sediment as would cover a large raft with deep alluvion in a manner similar to those singular obstructions in Red river, Atchafalaya and some other streams of *Louisiana.* The only probable explanation of the fact is that the stream is engulphed in one of the many cavities peculiar to countries of secondary floetz formation, and that immediately after it finds vent through other openings and continues its course in a channel made by its own current.—One of those bridges on the creek east of Assilla seems from its conformation to strengthen this conjecture. The creek which is called *natural bridge* is thirty feet wide and five feet deep. A short distance above the lower path there is a stratum of limestone rock twenty-five feet wide, entirely across the channel and excepting at times of very high water affording a dry and secure bridge.

1823 V 61, 64   Over the Ekanfinna river is a natural bridge of rocks, a singularity which distinguishes several

parts of Florida ... We pause ... to mention the singular circumstances of the Santaffy river, some considerable distance from its junction with the Suwanee, sinking into the earth and rising again at a distance of three miles: this space is called the Natural bridge, and here an Indian path crosses: it is stated that in times of high freshets, the space above the subterraneous channel is inundated, and that on those occasions a parallel current runs over it.

1827 W 37   Two miles south-east from the Ladies' cave, is the natural bridge, over the Chapola river. The water at this place sinks through a stratum of limestone rock, until meeting some impediment in its course, it rises again, and flows on the surface of the earth. A great road formerly crossed this bridge: it is now travelled by some persons, during the summer; in winter, the whole is overflowed: a stranger, crossing here, would not be led to discover any difference in the appearance of the ground, from the river bottom, in any other place; the heavy forest timber appears the same, and there is no variation of ground.

1829 USCHED vol. 187 #147.9   The place under which the Santa Fe river runs, through a substratum of stratified limestone, is called Natural Bridge; it is subject to inundation from freshets, the waters not finding there a sufficient opening to their discharge.

1837 W 48   The natural bridge [near the Santaffe river and Alligator creek] covers the stream for about three miles.

1874 SAR 59   The St. Marks ... river rises from the earth, runs sluggishly for some miles, sinks, forming a natural bridge, and rising again flows uninterruptedly to the Gulf.

Attrib. with *creek.*

1818 Y 146   Eight miles and a quarter to natural bridge creek.

NECK. (1) A narrow strip of land, usually an area lying between two bodies of water, rivers, etc. DAE

1608. Spec., the East Florida peninsula (1778; 1822); the land in a bend of a river (1828); a point (1779); double land (*q.v.*) (1775). (2) The narrow part of a pond. OED.

(1) 1742 RCBH 25 The Neck of Land, leading to St. *Augustine,* was so narrow, that the Enemy's Motions could not be observed.

1765 B 8 We landed at the neck, which is about 8 foot above the water.

1775 R 288 From Hobé to the latitude 25:44, the coast is all double land, or narrow necks between the sea.

1778 *The Present State of the West-Indies, etc.* 3 But this Bay ... ought to be called the *West-Indian Sea,* which a simple neck of land separates from the great sea, to the East of it.

1779 HEWATT II. 79 Then [Gen. Oglethorpe] ... sent Colonel Vanderdussen, with the Carolina regiment, over a small creek, to take possession of a neck of land called Point Quartel.

1822 ASPPL III. 524 We see a neck of land four hundred miles long, and about one hundred and thirty miles broad ... In East Florida the land is neither too dry too wet, nor is the climate too hot or too cold. This narrow neck of land being washed by the sea on the south, east, and west, possesses all the advantages which an island enjoys.

1823 ASPPL III. 775 One hundred and eighty-six acres of land lying in St. John's county, on Cartel point neck.

1828 ASPPL VI. 107 The affidavit of Benjamin Wood states positively that claimant lived on the land situated in Little St. Mary's neck.

(2) 1773 MS. 270 Crossed the neck of Do. [ditto] pond.

NOOK. (a) A secluded or sheltered place among natural scenery. OED. Spec., a beach. (b) A small or sheltered inlet (1871). OED. Extended to apply to a small bay (1837).

(a) 1775 R Apx. lxxvi This nook

in the land ... is the beach of an island called *Sanybel.*

(b) 1837 W 26 Gallivans or Delaware Bay is the nook formed east of ... Cape Roman.

1871 S 31 "Jupiter Inlet" ... is probably the most inaccessible and barren nook on the Floridian coast.

NOTCH. A narrow passage between two elevations. NID. Here, a gap in a hill. (DAE [1718]: passageway between mountains. [A.])

1775 R Apx. lvii The entrance of *Porto Puercos* is readily known by two bluff islands at its mouth, and the notch of the *Saddle-Hill.*

O

OAKFIELD. A field overgrown with oak trees.

1836 SSW 174 The situation had not much to recommend it, looking out ... upon the dreary dead oak field.

1871 H 119 *Oakfield* ... residence.

OAK GROVE. A grove of oak trees.

1822 SIMMONS 50 In some of [the savannas] ... there were very picturesque oak groves or islands.

1827 W 84 As the valley extends, groves of oak, hickory, magnolia, gum and poplar, cover the surface.

OAK HAMMOCK. A hammock consisting chiefly of oak. DA 1766 (no def.).

1773 MS. 266 St. Sebastians Rivulet, near Oak Hammok.

1787 in SIEBERT II. 248 The land in general was oak hammock and palmetto.

1825 GADSDEN 119 On the west of these inlets and lakes is a parallel chain of sand hills ... intersected by inconsiderable pine flats and oak hammocks.

1837 W 55 The country here, is diversified with ... oak hammocks and clumps of palms.

1837 ASPMA VII. 874-75 After passing this open place we reached an oak hammock.

OAK HILL. A hill overgrown with oak trees.

1773 MS. 272 On a poor Oak Hill—a gall appears far off . . . at a shrubby Oak hill.
1818 Y 23 A gently rolling country intervenes between them and the oak hills.
1827 W 85 Oak hill is nearly round, and may contain one and a half sections of good land.
1871 H 104 East of this is Oak Hill.

OAK-LAND. Land covered by a growth of oak. DAE 1666. Spec., shrubby oak-land (1743). (A.)

1743 C II. iv Another kind of Land may be observed more sterril than that of Pine barren Land; this Land is rejected, and not capable of Cultivation, and produces nothing but shrubby Oaks, bearing Acorns at the height of two Feet, I think it is called *Shrubby Oak-Land*.
1773 MS. 277 Thick Oak Land near— . . . a point of Oak Land running to a large Lake ½ mile.
Ibid., 305 From the Mouth of St. Mary's up as far as Sander's Store . . . the Soil consists of . . . few high Oak Land [suitable] for Indigo.
1778 in SIEBERT II. 42 There were 905 Acres of Swamp, Marsh & Oak Land.
1823 FHQ XIV. 81 The road . . . will be chiefly through pine-barrens or oak lands in which there is scarcely any undergrowth.
1837 W 108 High oak land is the only kind which produces this crop [Mexican & Green Seed Cotton] to advantage.
Ibid., 133 This part of the country is rolling oak land.
1851 BYRNE 13 The "first rate pine, oak, and hickory" lands are found in pretty extensive bodies in many parts of the State.

OAK RIDGE. A ridge of land covered with oak growth. DAE 1789. (A.)

1766 B 16 Then came to a ridge of oaks about 20 roods wide.
1837 W 304 The oak ridges of the interior [produce] the best green seed cotton.
1869 FICSP 80 The oak ridges furnish the finest supply of red and black oak, post oak, hickory and dogwood.

OAK SCRUB. A region overgrown by stunted oak trees or brushwood.

1837 FHQ VII. 92 There were two camps, separated by an extensive and almost impenetrable oak scrub communicating with a large swamp.

OAK SWAMP. Swamp land bearing a growth of oaks. Prob. Southern. DA 1702 (no def.).

1786 in SIEBERT II. 44 This Tract . . . was all Pine barren Land except 20 or 30 Acres which were Cypress & Oak Swamps.

OAK THICKET. A thicket of oak trees.

1773 MS. 277 Crossed a bay gall-runs in . . . Oak thicket.
1836 SSW 139 The bland evening air, [was] charged with the fresh odours of the piny forests and oak and myrtle thickets.

OAK UPLAND. Upland covered with oak growth.

1823 FHQ XIV. 85 Both of these routes lie chiefly across pine barren or oak uplands.

OAK WILDERNESS. A wilderness consisting chiefly of oak.

1836 SSW 211 The yells appeared to be in the direction of the Dead Oak wilderness, about the sugar mill.

OAT POINT. A point overgrown with oat grass.

1834 ASPMA VI. 479 The said chiefs, with a majority of their band, have assembled on the northwestern margin of Apalachicola bay, on or near what is called "Oat Point."

OCEAN. One of the regions into which the vast body of water surrounding the land is divided. OED. Here, with reference to the Gulf of Mexico.

1821 F i The produce ... must descend these Rivers [Apalachicola and Chattahouchie] by Colinton to the Ocean.

1822 SIMMONS 38 It may, from analogy, be concluded, that all the unknown region between [the St. Johns] ... and the ocean on the west, is also ... a land of lakes.

1823 V 53-54 [Between Charlotte harbor and Tampa bay] an inland navigation is afforded between the ocean and the main land by a chain of islands. Attrib. with *beach, stream, water.* In every case, the reference is to the Atlantic.

1874 SAR 159 Above the [Halifax] river ... valleys ... alternate with ridges to the ocean beach, half a mile distant.

1836 SSW 203 The Halifax ... is here a wide and beautiful ocean stream.

1775 R Apx. xliv As you come round [*Isaac Rock*] ... you immediately get into ocean water.

OCEAN-RIVER. A large navigable river. OED. Sup. 1908. Spec., the Gulf Stream.

1869 BRINTON 41 This ocean-river rushes eastward through the Straits of Florida at the rate of five or six miles an hour.

OLD RIVER. ? The former bed of a river which has cut itself a new channel. DAE 1634 (last date: 1825). Possibly a river which has remained within its original bounds as contrasted with a stream which has recently found a new course through the bursting of old confines.

1837 ASPMA VII. 376 I then came to a run or branch of an old river.

OPEN. An opening (*q.v.*); a natural clearing. DAE 1846 (no def.). (A.)

1771 VIAUD 162-63 The trees stood so close together, that there were but few opens left for us to pass through.

OPEN COUNTRY. A region unimpeded by forests, or remote from towns and cities. DAE 1807.

1741 GHDPOPW 187 [Col. Moor] did some Harm in the open Country.

1744 KIMBER 30 The Siege of *Augustine*, ... quite render'd the open Country, from *St. Mathia's* to *Augustine*, useless to the *Spaniards*.

1762 J 71 Col. *Moor* ... ruined the villages and farms in the open country.

1784 GME 97 The open country or high lands bordering on those low rich lands, are generally pine.

OPEN GROVE. A grove which is clear of underwood, and in which the trees stand at some distance from each other. Apparently, a local peculiarity.

1769 STORK 4 Florida differs materially from the rest of America in this, that almost all the continent besides is covered with a thick forest; whereas the trees in Florida are at a distance from one another, and being clear of under wood, have more the appearance of an open grove than a forest.

1827 W 105 The natural open groves of oak, hickory, beech, and magnolia grandiflora, surpass in magnificence the proudest parks of the English nobility.

OPENING. (1) An area in a forested region which is by nature treeless or only slightly timbered. DAE 1798. Spec., a glade (1743); a pine opening (1874). (2) A bay, gulf, or other more or less wide indentation of the land. OED. Spec., the mouth of a river (1587; 1763); the place of exit for an underground stream (1818).

(1) 1743 C II. ii In woods of Pine-Trees are frequently seen Glades or Openings, occasioned by the Fall of Trees.

1791 B 142 I ... passed by several

openings of extensive plains and meadows.
1837 ASPMA VII. 874 We came to a stream waist-deep, across which was the opening on a lake where the whites had a camp when they turned back last winter.
1874 SAR 210 An opening of tall pines on the northwest does much to raise the temperature of a frosty night.
(2) 1587 L 9 [Captaine Ribault] commaunded the ankers to be weighed and to set things in order to returne vnto the opening of the river.
1763 ROBERTS 13 There is some difficulty in finding this opening, by reason of the many islands and lakes before and about it.
1796 G 12 At the East end of Cayo Hueso, there is a small opening called Boca Chica.
1803 E 266 We sailed into a large opening which we supposed led into the Sound.
1818 Y 44 Immediately after [the underground stream] . . . finds vent through other openings.

See also PINE OPENING.

OPEN POND. A pond whose surface is unobstructed by trees or other vegetation (possibly in contradistinction to the cypress ponds).
1773 MS. (317) The Ducks . . . leave the cold Northern Provinces to enjoy the agreeable Climate, on the Open Ponds, Lakes and Rivers of East Florida.
1818 Y 142 In the fifth mile, passed an open pond on the right with high banks.
1831 ASPNA IV. 121 [The tree] was found . . . on the open ponds inland.

OPEN PRAIRIE. A stretch of open, level country usually covered with grass. DAE 1819. (A.) DA 1804.
1822 SIMMONS 26 The Coolisihatchie . . . heads within twenty miles of the St. John's, and the intervening

country, is said to be an open prairie.
1836 ASPMA VII. 289 Nearly all the intermediate space was an open prairie extending far on the right to a large pond.

OPEN WOOD(S). A forested area in which there is no undergrowth. Cf. OPEN GROVE.
1823 V 77-78 Instead of the clear open woods generally seen, masses of young pine saplings are thickly spread over the rocky ground, which is strewn with half burnt light wood logs.
1824 FHQ XIV. 105 No road could be opened wide enough to prevent trees from falling across it, and in the open woods, especially in the pine barrens, these can always be avoided by turning out.
1837 ASPMA VII. 162 The Indians were driven off to the distance of a quarter of a mile in the open woods.

ORANGE GROVE. A grove of orange trees. DAE 1766. The reference here appears to be to an area in which wild-orange trees grow (note the last three examples).
1765 letter in STORK Apx. 34 A ridge of high lands runs across, on which is a continued grove of orange-trees.
1773 MS. 208 [Term from the Ephemerical Tables:] orange grove.
1791 B 76 We retired to the fragrant shades of an Orange grove.
1797 MAG under Alachua Savannah Alachua Savannah . . . is encircled with high sloping hills, covered with waving forests, and fragrant orange groves.
1821 F 80 Endless orange groves are found here; and, indeed, in all parts of the country.
1837 W 56 [The St. John's] then passes through the west end of Long Lake, at the entrance of which on the west bank, is a wild orange grove.
1869 FICSP 116 Nearly every hammock has one or more wild orange groves.

1869 BRINTON 94 The famous
*Orange Grove commences about twelve
miles south of Gainesville, and extends
nearly around Orange Lake. It is probably the largest natural orange grove in
the world.

ORANGE LAND. Land suitable for
growing oranges.

1874 SAR 153 The first-rate orange
land on the east side of the St. Johns,
well situated in every respect, is held as
one hundred dollars per acre in many
cases.

ORCHARD. A grove. DAE 1639. In this
case, the meaning has been extended
to apply to a grove which is not regularly planted and cultivated—*i.e.*, a
wild-orange grove. Poss. Southern
(and Western).

1870 BILL 196 It is a rare sight,
worth a journey, to be able to stand
within a wild orchard of these beautiful
trees, and feel the drowsing influence
of fruit and flowers.

OUTLET. A stream flowing out of (or
into [1822]) a lake, a larger stream,
or the like. NID. (?A.) The point at
which a lake or pond, bay (1827),
harbor (1821), or creek (1791) discharges into the stream which drains
it. Actually, the resemblance of an
outlet to a *drain* is very close—note
especially the 1803, 1837, and 1874
(p. 27) quotations.

1791 B 166 Directly opposite to the
mouth or outlet of the creek, is a continual and amazing ebullition.
1803 E 278 [We] went to the Swamp,
and the day following had a mound of
earth thrown up on the west side of the
main outlet, and as near to the edge of
the Swamp as we could advance on account of the water.
1821 F 109-10 Charlotte Harbour, or
Boca Grande . . . is the outlet of Charlotte River.
1822 SIMMONS 29 A snow-white

bluff and beach of periwinkle shells . . .
mark the southern side of the outlet into
the lake.
1827 W 14 Chacowhatchee bay . . .
has two outlets.
1837 W 48 Cedar River, . . . is the
outlet of a rich grazing country . . .
[The Santaffe river] receives the outlet
of Sampson's Pond, or Alligator Creek.
1874 S 17, 27 Puzzle Lake . . . derives
its name from its intricate outlet . . .
After sailing down this estuary to its
confluence with the ocean at Jupiter, he
[*i.e.*, the traveler] must ascend one of
the sluggish outlets from the Everglades.

OUT SHORE. A seaward shore; an outside shore in contrast to one which
lies inside—*i.e.*, towards the mainland.

1829 USCHED vol. 187 #147.16 Except at the Capes of St. George and St.
Blas, where a shoal projects to the south,
for four or five miles, the out shore of
the islands covering St. George's Sound,
as well as that of the peninsula forming the bay of St. Joseph, may be considered as bold within a short distance
from the land.

OUTWATERING. The place of exit of
a stream into the sea; a mouth.

1775 R 268, 282 The entrance, or bar
of *New Smyrna* . . . is the outwatering
of the . . . *lagoon* . . . There is a mouth,
or outwatering into the ocean, with several small inlets within it.

OYSTER BANK. A shallow area in a
river, bay, etc., where oysters breed.
DAE 1612.

1742 *An Impartial Account of the Late
Expedition against St. Augustine* 34
During this Campagne they had no
Leisure to regale at their Victualling
Office, as the Oyster Banks (very common in those Countries, and very un-
wholesome in Summer) were familiarly
called by the Soldiers of *Frederica*.
c. 1767 FHQ XII. 114 The Naviga-

tion of this channel for upwards of 4 miles is so intricate owing to a vast number of oyster banks, which form a labarynth [sic] that it would require at least a month's examination before one could attempt to give any just account of it.

1775 R 287   The branch which disembogues itself at *Hobé* is shallow, and full of oyster banks.

1787 in SIEBERT II. 251   [This tract] was only about the same distance from plenty of the Finest oyster banks.

1818 Y 49   The oyster banks . . . chock up the mouth of all the rivers and by their irregular courses and annual changes, perplex the oldest pilots.—They consist of a yearly increasing mass of oysters on an irregular stratum of calcerous rock forming the southern slope of the same rock seen at the surface in the flat land of the interior.

1871 H 127   *Half Dollar Island* is a patch of marsh grass growing on an oyster bank about ten feet long.

OYSTER BAR.   An oyster bank. "Southern U.S." CD.

1823 STCW 44   At 3 p.m. we entered the [Apalachicola] river at ebb tide and beat among the oyster bars until evening.

1837 W 47   Below St. Marks the navigation is very crooked and much impeded by Oyster bars.

OYSTER BED.   An oyster bank. DAE 1798. "In the northern U.S., oyster-beds are also called *oyster-banks*; in the southern U.S., *oyster-bars* and *oyster rocks*; in the Gulf States, *oyster-reefs*." CD.

1835 ASPMA V. 658   Oyster beds . . . extending over a space of about two miles, have been removed.

1869 FICSP 107   Immense beds of oysters are found almost everywhere beneath the waters of the [Indian] river, and may often be seen at low tide.

OYSTER CLIFT.   A cliff formed by oysters, or one on which oysters grow: such a formation must be under water some of the time.

1837 W 33   That [plantation] occupied by John Durant . . . lies about a mile from the western coast, the white oyster clifts of which, are seen half way through the Caximba.

OYSTER HILL.   Possibly a rock which is sometimes inundated so that oysters may grow on it.

1773 MS. 263   By Oyster hills per Run bearing S.W.

OYSTER REEF.   An oyster bed. "Gulf States." CD.

1823 STCW 40   The St. George channel or sound affords a passage for small vessels . . . but the shoals and oyster reefs render the navigation difficult and dangerous.

1871 H 131   The Narrows . . . is occasioned by oyster reefs on the east side of the river which have obstructed that part of the channel.

OYSTER ROCK.   A natural oyster bed. NID. "Southern U.S." CD.

1773 MS. (319)   Mukoso Creek . . . has its Bed between two almost continuing Banks of Oyster Rocks.

OYSTER-SHELL BANK.   A raised shelf of ground composed of oyster shells; a shell hammock. Poss. Southern. DA 1642.

1862 FHQ XV. 88   We disembarked on an oyster shell bank.

1871 H 92   In many places on the Indian river, is a range of oyster-shell banks, from three to ten feet high: these constitute the "shell hammocks."

OYSTER SHOAL.   A shoal where oysters abound.

1803 E 235   The sound is so full of oyster banks, and shoals, that it is difficult to navigate it, without a pilot.

1837 W 23 [Wakasasse Bay] is sheltered from the Gulf by Oyster Shoals.

P

PALMETTO FLAT. A level tract of land covered with palmettos.

1818 Y 28 In some places [the glades] ... are of greater extent than the palmetto flats.
1827 USCHED vol. 217 #43.77 In consequence of the manifest encroachment of the sphagnose marshes upon the dry palmetto flats.
1829 USCHED vol. 187 #147.10 In the upper parts of Santa Fe, numerous bay-golls, ponds, and extensive palmetto flats, are met with in every direction.

PALMETTO GROUND. An area overgrown with palmettos. DAE 1744 under *palmetto*. (All quotations, including those in OED, refer to Southeastern U.S.) Prob. Southeastern.

1766 B 20 We now coasted the southwest or Indian side, which is surrounded with pine-barrens, interspersed with some cypress, but generally poor sandy palmetto-ground.

PALMETTO HAMMOCK. A hammock consisting of palmetto trees.

1765 B 7 The hammocks of live-oaks and palmettos are generally surrounded either with swamp or marsh.
1836 SSW 192 We first struck a coruse [*sic*] into the dark, and deep palmetto hammock.
1874 S 16 Occasionally rich palmetto hammocks stud the marshes.

PALMETTO JUNGLE. A jungle composed chiefly of palmettos.

1874 KEASBEY 40 [The Palmetto House] stands about 100 yards from the Clarendon, but just on the edge of a palmetto jungle.

PALMETTO LAND. Land on which palmetto is the prevailing growth.

1773 MS. 225 Palmetoe Land.
Ibid., 270 "Crossed Run in Valley ... pal." [palmetto] Land both sides.

PALMETTO SCRUB. A region overgrown by palmetto.

1842 PREBLE 37 Reached the dry land,—a wide plain dotted with ... hummocks and a palmetto scrub.

PALMETTO SWAMP. A swamp consisting chiefly of palmetto growth. DAE 1853 under *palmetto*. Prob. Southern.

1836 ASPMA VII. 143 The same difficulty also occurred in a palmetto swamp of considerable extent where horses could not be used on account of the bog.

PALM HAMMOCK. A hammock of palm trees.

1874 SAR 198 The banks [along Lake Worth and Indian river] are from six to twenty-five feet high, with open pine woods, live oak and palm hammock skirting the river banks.

PASS. (1) A navigable channel. OED. Spec., the communication between the St. Johns and the St. Marys rivers (1835); a passage in the course of a river (1830). The term is used once to denote a passage smaller than a channel (1829 p. 14). (2) A place at which a river can be crossed by fording. "Now *rare*." OED.

(1) 1791 B 140 Crocodiles were already assembling in the pass.
1818 Y 34 Five miles from the mouth of the river and on the west side of the main pass into the Sound.
1823 STCW 37-38 The Pass Celestie is constantly wearing off the peninsula to the eastward.
1829 USCHED vol. 187 #147.14, 15 The bay of Espiritu Santo has three main channels, which, however, are subdivided into several passes ... The

third pass, called Main Pass, has a width, on the bar, of 300 yards, for a depth of 14 or 15 feet, at low tide.

1830 ASPMA IV. 595 A part of [the sum] . . . has, however, been applied to the removal of snags from some of the most difficult passes of the [Apalachicola] river.

c. 1832 ASPPL VI. 553 The pass BB is now a channel ,through which the tide ebbs and flows.

1835 ASPMA V. 658 *Inland Pass, between St. John's and St. Mary's, Florida.*

1837 W 20 East Bay . . . is connected with St. Rosa Sound on the south east, and through that with the Chactawhatchee Bay and thence into the Gulf, through the Pass L'Este.

(2) 1823 V 67 The Cowford or pass St. Nicholas . . . is distinguished by its narrowness.

PASSAGE. A navigable channel. OED. Spec., a passageway through a reef (1839); also, with reference to subterranean streams (c. 1767; 1827; 1874).

1741 GHDPOPW 181 A Large Sand-Bank lies before this Mouth of the Channel, having two narrow Passages thro' it, one called the North, the other the South Channel.

c. 1767 FHQ XII. 120 From the river Scilly to a small river, which at the crossing place takes a subterraneous passage for about ten yards and then appears again forming a Natural Bridge.

1775 R 258 Between [the Tyger islands] . . . and *Amelia* [island] there is a tolerable broad passage forming a convenient harbour . . . this passage continues through *Amelia* narrows.

1823 V 123 The fifth passage called by the Spaniards *Boca Chica*, lies between *key West* and *Mule keys*.

1827 W 106 [The lakes] have their subterranean passages.

1837 W 34 Here commences the passage, called on the English charts, Hawks Channel.

1839 *Winter in West Indies* 119 There

are several passages through the reef for large vessels.

1852 WFH 8 There is an inner passage from St. Marys to the St. John's which is used by the boats in rough weather . . . The Florida . . . takes the outside passage from Savannah, running as high up the river as Pilatka.

1874 SAR 136 There is no exit for this volume of water except by subterranean passages and evaporation.

See also INLAND PASSAGE; (INLAND) WATER PASSAGE (attrib.).

PASTURE. A grass-covered piece of land suitable for grazing; grassland. DAE 1624.

1563 RIBAULD 34 Ye riuer . . . deuiding it self into many . . . small goodly medow grounds & pastures.

1682 *The Present State of Carolina* 16 Besides delicious Fields, and Pastures that direct to Admiration.

See also CANE PASTURE; PASTURE RANGE.

PASTURE-GROUND. A piece of land suitable for feeding animals; spec., a natural feeding-ground for birds. OED under pasture (no def.).

c. 1565 Hawkins voyage, in HAKLUYT (1589) 541 This land . . . floresheth with . . . pasture ground.

1831 AUDUBON 53 The birds in myriads were probing their pasture-ground.

PASTURE LAND. Grassland suitable for grazing. OED Sup.

1731 C I 33 This plant grows plentifully in most of the open Pasture lands.

1763 *Acts and Records* in WALKER Apx. No. IV. tr. To the pasture and arable lands belonging to other inhabitants of this town.

1823 V 151-52 tr. By the law of the Indies . . . a *peonia* is described to be "a lot of fifty feet wide and one hundred deep: cultivatable ground . . . pasture land."

PASTURE RANGE. An expanse of open country suitable for grazing stock. DAE 1860. (A.)

1823 V 76 Luxuriant pasture ranges are found every where.

PEACH LAND. Land suitable for growing peaches. DAE 1868. (A.) DA 1831.

1867 letter in FICSP 131 There is an abundance of good peach land on the St. Johns.

PEAK. A hill having a more or less pointed summit. OED.

1827 W 82-83 The great ridge here terminates in a succession of high peaks [near the sources of the Alaqua River, Uche and Shoal creeks].

PEAT BED. An accumulation of peat; a peat-bog. CD. (Peat-bog is the American equivalent of the British Peat-moss. CD.)

1823 STCW 37 Vegetable remains are scarce and there is no clay underneath to support the soil. In a few places on the [Santa Rosa island] peninsula pea [sic] beds have been discovered enveloping numerous small cypress roots and stumps; but the whole betrays marks of recent decomposition.

1827 W 69 Peat beds are also frequent [near the coast].

PENINSULA. (1a) A piece of land almost surrounded by water. DAE 1608. (b) The land lying in the bend of a stream. DAE 1732. (c) With specific reference to the East Florida peninsula. DAE 1837 (1694 elsewhere).

(1a) 1762 AG I. 13 In lat. 26° 56′ and a good way upwards, the coast of the mainland of Florida cannot be approached, by reason of its being bordered with islands and peninsulas.

1773 MS. 331 The former [river] from the Northward of the (formerly called Island, now) Peninsula Larga.

1784 HUTCHINS 86 The peninsula between St. Joseph's and Cape Blaise is a narrow slip of land.

1827 W 14 A narrow peninsula divides the Pensacola bay from the sound, for thirty miles.

(b) 1797 MAG under *Apalachicola* [Ancient Apalachicola] was situated on a peninsula formed by the doubling of the river.

(c) 1652 HEYLIN 116 But it is generally agreed that the *Peninsula,* which pointeth on the Isle of *Cuba,* hath the name of *Tegesta* or *Florida* specially so called.

1762 AG I. 2 Florida Proper is, at present, that peninsula lying between Georgia and Cape Florida, between lat. 25 and 30. N.

1797 MAG under *Florida Keys* The great sand bank extends from the peninsula of East-Florida inward.

1813 MELISH 3 [The St. John's] rises in an extensive swamp, or lake, near the middle of the Peninsula.

1836 SSW 69 The peninsula is regarded by some as a prodigious mound, or wing dam confining the waters of the Gulf of Mexico, which are elevated above those of the Atlantic, and preventing them from falling with irresistible weight into the latter.

1874 SAR 140 [Alachua Co.] is located at the base of the Florida peninsula.

PINE BARREN. A tract of sandy or peaty land upon which the prevailing native growth is pine. Chiefly Southern. DAE 1735. The trees in the Florida pine barrens—in contrast to those farther north—stand at some distance from each other, so that it is possible for grass to grow underneath (1769); thus, this type of land is sometimes referred to as "open" (1836 ASPMA). There are two types of pine barrens: the one elevated and dry (1823 FHQ; 1836 SSW p. 241), and the other—being interspersed with ponds and lakes (1822 p. 32)—low and sobby (1823 STCS), or wet (1836 SSW p. 296). DA 1731.

1744 KIMBER 23 We arriv'd at a Kind of a Pine-barren (falsely and absurdly so call'd, from producing nothing but those Trees.).

1765 B 6 At Johnson's Bluff ... the sandy pine-barren comes close or near the shore.

c. 1767 FHQ XII. 119 The road very good all the way and the country pine barren.

1769 STORK 5 St. Juan's, now called St. John's river, lies 40 miles southward of St. Mary's; the tract of land between them consists of plains covered with pines; these plains are called in America, pine-barrens, or highlands, in contradistinction to the swamps and lowlands. We find a striking difference betwixt ... the pine-barrens to the northwards, from the poverty of the soil, do not answer the necessary expence of clearing. The closeness of the trees hinders the grass from growing under them, so that large tracts of land are no further useful than to make pitch and tar: whereas in Florida, by a difference in the climate, the trees standing at a greater distance, the pine-barrens afford tolerable good grass.

1775 R 15-16 The pine land, commonly called pine barren ... consists of a grey, or white sand, and in many places of a red or yellow gravel; it produces a great variety of shrubs or plants ... the principal produce from whence it derives its name is the ... yellow pine and pitch pine tree.

1818 ASPMA I. 694 From Amelia Island to the Lochway, the country is, for the most part, what is here called pine barren.

1822 SIMMONS 8 The timber of the pine barrens that abound in the country, is not of a very good quality. The trees are often below the usual height, and grow so sparsely, that the sun, in their regions, has nearly as much power as on an open plain.

Ibid., 32 I entered upon a tract of flat pine barren, interspersed, as usual, with small ponds and lakes.

1823 FHQ XIV. 94 From the Choctawhatchie to a point 56 miles east of the Suwannee the land is chiefly high pine barren.

1823 STCS 31 The lands through which we passed (the trail keeping near the river thus far) was a low, sobby pine barren.

1827 W 39 The pine barrens are composed, principally, of silicious sand, more or less mixed with calcareous and vegetable matter, and often divested of every fertilizing principle, by the frequent fires which run over them.

1836 ASPMA VI. 562 Our men were much exposed in the open pine barren.

1836 SSW 241 We emerged into a high and dry pine barren.

Ibid., 296 Here I first saw, growing in the water, near the margin, a conspicuous plant which is common in the wet pine barrens.

1837 W 8 So large a portion of Florida is of that quality, usually termed "pine barrens."

1874 SAR 118-19 The balance of the lands of Nassau county are pine barrens, mostly sandy.

Attrib. with *country, creek, spring, swamp.*

1827 W 83 It is in a pine barren country, where a branch of Shoal river rises.

1818 Y 163 Seventeen miles to pine barren creek ... Pine Barren is a branch of the Escambia and at the crossing place is thirty feet wide.

1833 USCHD vol. 255 #61.29 Pine Barren creek, a tributary of the Choctawhatchie.

1817 ASPIA II. 157 A part of them were met by several persons near the Pine Barren spring a few days after the murder was committed.

1827 W 52 Pine barren swamps ... are natural basins, containing the waters of the surrounding country.

PINE-BARREN LAND. Land consisting of pine barren. DAE 1743 under *pine barren.* Prob. Southern or Southeastern.

1786 in SIEBERT II. 44 This Tract ... was all Pine barren Land Except 20 or 30 Acres.
1827 W 84 The western part of Jackson, with the exception of Holmes Valley, and Oak and Hickory Hills, is poor pine barren land.
1837 ASPMA VII. 850 We at last reached high pine barren land.
1860 letter in FICSP 29 The poorest pine barren lands of Florida, will produce without manure, a luxuriant crop of Sisal Hemp.

PINE BLUFF. A bluff overgrown with pines. DAE 1766. (A.)

1773 MS. 230 Low P. [pine] bluff, & Savannah behind.
1823 V 43 On Indian river some of the best hammocks in the Floridas are to be met with, healthy and elevated: the occasioned breaks of pine bluffs are rather advantageous than otherwise as presenting better scites for settlements.

PINE COUNTRY. A region in which pine trees abound.

1784 GME 97 Then commences a fine high, pine country.
1818 Y 145 North of this there is good land, relieving a little the savannas of the pine country.
1823 V 48 Three large rivers coming altogether through a pine country, discharge into Grenville sound.
1837 W 25 From the south part of Sarrazota Bay to Charlotte Harbor, the pine country approaches near to the coast, is high rolling land, covered with tall pines.

PINE FLAT. A level tract of land covered with pines. DAE 1807. Poss. Southern. Once with reference to an elevated area (1818).

1815 NWR 106 The pine flats have

the wire grass, and in some places the saw palmeto.
1818 Y 26 The high pine flats ... [are] sometimes a transition from the broken country without much change of elevation ... the white sand being scarcely covered with a scanty herbage, whilst the low stunted pines and a few scrubby oak contribute an almost painful appearance of desolation.
1828 ASPNA III. 925 A fire ... extended several hundred yards, destroying many thousand young trees which I had counted upon to set out in the pine flats.
1837 W 11 The lands are diversified with rich hammocks, dense swamps, good pine flats, etc.

PINE FOREST. A forest of pine trees. DAE 1799. Possibly the 1874 writer intended to refer to a "pitch-pine" rather than to a "pine-pitch" forest.

1791 B 100 It appeared like a desart, to a great extent, and terminated, on the land side, by frightful thickets, and open Pine forests.
1827 W 7 This clayey substratum is generally covered with a fine, white, silicious sand, which in its native state, produces little more than pine forests and grass.
1829 USCHED vol. 187 #147.4 The pine forests afford every facility to the raising of cattle.
1837 W 7 A large portion of the country, is covered with pine forests.
1870 BILL 189 The pine-forests ... cover a majority of the surface in the northern and eastern half of the peninsula.
1874 SAR 104 With the constantly increasing value of the pine-pitch forests of our county, as well as of regions adjacent, the foreign timber trade of Pensacola is rapidly growing.

PINE GLADE. A wet glade in which pine trees grow.

1823 FHQ XIV. 94 A good road ... can be effected by ... ditching and

throwing up the road through the low pine glades and cypress ponds. From the Choctawhatchie to a point 56 miles east of the Suwannee ... there is not more than twelve miles of the low wet glades.
[1837 W 140   The country west of Graham, Turnbull and McDougal swamps, is, for about twenty miles, a piny glade.]

See also EVERGLADES; GLADE; WET GLADE.

PINE GROVE.   A grove of pine trees.

1791 B 155   The pine groves passed, we immediately find ourselves on the entrance of the expansive airy pine forests.

PINE HAMMOCK.   A hammock consisting chiefly of pine trees.

1773 MS. 272, 282   Path in great Savanh.–pine Ham: [hammock] runs S.E ... In Savanh ... to a sml. [small] Pe. [pine] Hammok.
1775 R 258   These islands consist chiefly of marsh and pine hammocks.

PINE HILL.   A hill overgrown with pines. DAE 1654.

1773 MS. 271   Edge of a pine Hill.
1775 R 16   Some high pine hills are so covered with ... varieties of ... oak ... as to make an underwood to the lofty pines.
1818 Y 24   The pine hills are well timbered, and perfectly open, except in places where there are spots overgrown with low, scrubby oak bushes.
1836 ASPMA VII. 291   Passing ... through a thick swamp and hammock ... [we] came out upon the pine hills.

PINE HUMMOCK.   A hummock in which the predominating growth is pine.

1842 PREBLE 37   Reached ... a wide plain dotted with ... pine hummocks.

PINE ISLAND.   An island or key (1796 p. 28) on which the principal growth is pine.

1796 G 12, 28   At the distance of 7 leagues from the West end of Cayo Hueso you find several large islands covered with pine trees ... Some of these Pine Islands are pretty large ... To the westward of this Kay, for about 4 leagues, are several large Kays called Pinara, (*the Pine Islands*) producing many pines, and being the only Kays that have any.
1823 ASPPL III. 774   Two hundred and seventy acres of land, called Pine island, on the river Nassau.
1837 W 33   Pine Island is the largest inside of the bay. It consists principally of high pine land; it is five miles long and two wide.

PINE KNOLL, PINE KNOWL.   A knoll overgrown with pine trees.

1773 MS. 285   Per sml. [small] boggy Savh: [savannah] on Pine Knowls.

PINELAND.   Land upon which pine is the prevailing growth. DAE c. 1660. (A.) De Brahm (1773) classifies pineland according to elevation, soil and product; namely, the low and black, the "midling" high and white, and the very high and yellow, which produce the shrubby pine, white spruce pine, and yellow pine, respectively. Sometimes this type of land is elevated and dry (1822 p. 50; 1823 p. 87), rolling (1822 p. 35; 1837 p. 136), and even rocky (1837). The two distinguishing features of Florida pinelands are that (1) they resemble open groves (1821), and (2) they are studded with rich hammock and swamp lands (1851 p. 12).

1743 C II. iv   Particularly Pine-Lands are often intermixed with ... *Bay-Swamps.*
1765 B 3   The pine-lands approached near the river.
1773 MS. 308   Pine Land if low, is of a black soil; if midling [*sic*] high, it is of a white Sand, and if very high its

Soil is of a Sand as yellow as Oker. The black Soil produces a shrubby Pine ... is chiefly covered with Wire Grass, not fit for Pasturage and mixed with cabbage Trees ... The white Sand produces as tall Pine Tree ... and has on its higher Ridges the white Spruce Pine. Its grass is of the wire kind, but mixed with Bunch Grass. Near the Head of St. Juan's River I have met this kind of Pine Land all covered with young Canes: (the sweetest Pasture of any). But the Yellow Sand produced yellow Pine very tall and straight.

1787 in SIEBERT II. 246   The land on the road was chiefly pine barren, but there was near the edges of the creeks little good yellow ridge pine land—a good part of the Pine had been cut by the Spaniards.

1815 NWR 106   The pine land, stiff generally and pretty good for corn.

1821 F 102   This southern end [of the divide east of the St. Johns] is a mere point of marsh, with some broken pine land in it.

Ibid., 147   *Pine lands* [in Florida] ... are more favourable to cultivation and pasturage than those in the neighbouring states, not only on account of the pine trees being more resinous, but by their distance from each other, without any underwood giving an appearance of open groves, rather than of forests; and thereby affording room for vegetation, which is promoted by the influence of the sun and the circulation of air.

1822 SIMMONS 35, 50   Beyond the scrub, a region of high rolling pine land occurs ... Some of this land, I should suppose to be good, as it is often mingled with the black-jack ... In the rear of these, there generally extend, high and dry pine lands.

1823 V 75-76, 87   The pine lands however are not all of the same elevated character: many of them being flat and covered with gall berry and huckle berry bushes: and sometimes interspersed with cypress ponds and bay galls ... The *elevated and undulating pine lands* are healthy and beautiful; the timber is taller, straighter and of a better quality than on the low grounds ... the *Saw palmetto* bushes are very rarely found in these high pine lands.

1837 W 131, 136   Twenty miles, from the coast, on the rocky pine lands, the waters are strongly tinctured with lime ... From the Wakasasse to the Suwanne, the country is rolling pine land until you approach the coast.

1851 BYRNE 11   That which is denominated first rate pine land in East Florida, has nothing analogous to it in any of the other States. Its surface is covered, for several inches deep, with a dark vegetable mould, beneath which, to the depth of several feet, is a chocolate colored sandy loam, mixed, for the most part, with limestone pebbles, and resting on a substratum of clay and limestone rock ... The second rate pine lands ... afford the finest pastures; they are heavily timbered with the best species of yellow pine; they are, for the most part, high, healthy, and well watered ... Pine lands of the third rate, or worst class ... are of two orders: the one comprising high, rolling, sandy districts, which are covered with a stunted growth of "black jacks" and pine; the other embracing low, flat, swampy regions, which are frequently inundated, but which are covered with luxuriant vegetation.

Ibid., 12   There is one general feature in the topography of Florida which no other country in the United States possesses ... the pine lands which form the basis of the country, and which are almost universally healthy, are nearly every where studded, at intervals of a few miles, with hammock and swamp lands of the richest quality.

1869 FICSP 29   Pine lands (pitch and yellow pine) form the basis of Florida. These lands are usually divided into three classes, denoting first, second and third rate pine lands.

1874 SAR 113 You can get wild pine land for one to two dollars per acre.

Attrib. with *pond, savanna, swell.*

1766 B 21 In the afternoon our host went over the river to shoot geese in the pine-land ponds.

1823 V 89 The *pine land savannas* have a very black and rich appearance, but notwithstanding they contain only white sands, though the clay beneath is perhaps nearer the surface; they are merely sinks or drains to the higher grounds, their low situation preventing the growth of pines.

1825 GADSDEN 120 The last seven miles [are] ... diversified with ... pine land swells.

See also FLAT PINELAND.

PINE LEVEL. A level on which the characteristic growth is pine. Also, with reference to a particular area (1827; 1837).

1827 W 81 The Pine Level lies north of Yellow-Water bay; it is a tract of high level land, watered by springs, which form the Cold Water and Black Water creeks. The soil is a sandy clay, which yields very good crops of cotton, rice, peas, and potatoes. But this tract of country is peculiarly adapted to the production of fruits.

c. 1828 ASPPL VI. 546 Nathaniel Hawthorn ... [640 acres.] Pine Level, Edgeley's creek.

1837 W 45 These waters generally, rise from fine springs on the borders of a good farming country, called the Pine Level.

PINE OPENING. An area in a pine forest which is only slightly timbered; an open pine grove; open pineland.

1836 ASPMA VII. 144 If small parties were discovered in the pine openings, they could generally take cover before they could be attacked.

1874 SAR 197 The country immediately adjacent to the Caloosahatchie river and Charlotte harbor is pine openings.

PINE PLAIN, PINE PLANE. A plain covered with pine trees. DAE 1665. (A.)

1825 GADSDEN 119 To the west of these ponds commence the pine planes and saw-palmetto flats common to low latitudes.

PINE POND. A pond around which pine trees grow.

1822 SIMMONS 5 The rest of the country ... may be described as an immense and sterile forest of firs, interspersed with cypress and pine ponds.

PINE RANGE. A cattle range consisting of pineland.

1823 V 75-76 Nevertheless like all the pine ranges, they [*i.e.,* pine lands] afford excellent pasturage for cattle.

PINE RIDGE. A ridge overgrown with pines. DAE 1802. Poss. Southern. DA 1788 (no def.).

1766 B 12 A pine ridge appears at half a mile distance.

1775 R 275 We next met with very great holes ... in the highest part of the pine ridges.

1787 in SIEBERT II. 209 The pine land was in general low pine with a small part of yellow pine ridge.

1823 V 35 There is a high pine ridge between the source of the stream and the [Oke-fin-o-cau] swamp.

1837 W 126 Between the Black Water and Yellow Water Rivers, the pine ridges are usually poor land.

PINE SAVANNA. A savanna with a scattered growth of pines. DAE 1735. Prob. Southeastern.

1766 B 31 Then to a pine-savannah of a vast extent, moist, and producing a great burthen of pretty good grass, knee-deep.

PINE TRACT. A tract of pineland.

1821 DARBY 10 [Hammock land] forms in most instances an interval between the pine tracts and the marshes or savannahs.

1837 W 9　Near the head of the stream there are good hammock and pine tracts.

PINE WOOD. (1a) A forest of pine trees. Usually pl. DAE 1694. (b) With reference to the openness of this type of land. *Cf.* PINELAND.

(1a)　1763　*Acts and Records* in WALKER Apx. No. XX　A piece of land . . . bounded . . . by a pine wood.

1766 B 27-28　Here is very good grass growing in the pine-woods knee high.

1775 R Apx. lii　Spars may be had here at all times, either out of the pine woods . . . or among the drift of the beeches.

1821 DARBY 9　The soil of the pine woods of Florida is, perhaps, as sandy as in any other part of the United States.

1836 SSW 262　The positions occupied by the Indians, were: a peninsular piece of pine wood, on our north side, bordering upon the river.

1869 FICSP 31　A general interspersion of rich hammocks, surrounded by high, dry rolling, healthy pine woods, is an advantage which no other State in the Union enjoys.

(b)　1818 Y 25　The transitions, from [the hills are] . . . oftener, by a gradual diminution of inequality, into open pine woods, with a waving surface.

1831 ASPNA IV. 120　The fires originating in the grassy, open pine woods.

1836 ASPMA VII. 246　I learned there were open pine woods on both sides of the [Withlacoochee] river.

1874 SAR 198　The banks [along Lake Worth and Indian river] are from six to twenty-five feet high, with open pine woods . . . skirting the river banks.

Attrib. with *country, plain.*

1825 FHQ XIV. 153　The Suwanee has its course through a high pine woods country.

1832 USCSD vol. 214 #136.16　The tongue of land between the northern and earten arms of the bay . . . is a sandy pine woods country.

1827 W 106　The pine wood plain . . . stretches towards the highlands of Tallahassee.

PIT. A naturally formed hole or cavity in the ground. OED. Spec., a gopher hole (1836).

1823 STCS 29　Frequent pits or funnel shaped depressions in the soil occurred in this and succeeding days' ride.

1836 SSW 165　It derives its name from the word *Gouffre* (French) from the *Pit* it makes in the ground.

PITCH. The portion of a cape which extends farthest into the sea. DAE 1677. Also applied to the projecting extremity of a reef (1775) or shoal (1803).

1774 Barton in G 27 ftn.　From the pitch of the Cape [Canaveral] to this place, the course is S. by E. about 21 leagues.

1775 R Apx. viii　Here is the easternmost pitch of the reef, as *Sound-point,* is of the land, and therefore more proper to be called *Cape Florida,* than any other part of the shore, particularly as *Sound-point* is a part of the main land.

1803 E 256　A N.W. course would carry us clear of the northern pitch of Cape Carnaveral shoal.

PLAIN, PLANE. (1) A comparatively small tract of level land free or nearly free from trees. DAE 1608. Spec., a pine barren (1587; 1821; 1827); meadow ground (1589); a savanna (1766); a vast, flat ridge or plateau (1869). Note the 1837 reference to the "San Diego Plains" from which the contemporary dialectal form *dago* is derived. (2) Extended to apply to a drift of vegetation in a river; a floating island.

(1)　1587 L 24L　Afterward we found a large plaine covered with high pine-trees distant a little one from the other.

1589 DRAKE map of St. Augustine A lowe plaine or medow ground through the which our troopes passed.

1766 B 16 Beyond [the hammock] . . . is a large plain or savannah, half a mile wide more or less to the pines.

1775 R 34 [The St. Johns river] runs through wide extended plains and marshes.

1791 B 160-61 The open forests . . . stood at a considerable distance from each other, through which appeared at N.W. an almost unlimited plain of grassy savannas.

1821 F i Colinton is laid off . . . on . . . level plain of pine land, 15 feet above the river at low water.

1825 GADSDEN 120 Cypress ponds and grassy planes, [are] converted from their lowness, after heavy rains, into ponds.

1827 W 130 Oak and hickory hills . . . stand insulated in the pine barren, which extends a great distance around them; above this plain they are elevated some hundreds of feet.

1837 W 183 Oglethorpe selected four hundred men and a party of Indians, with which he invested Fort Diego, situate on the Plains of that name, twenty-five miles from St. Augustine.

1856 USCHED vol. 893 Part I. 551 The surface of Sugar-loaf [Key] . . . [extends] into flat plains, carpeted with a short wiry grass.

1869 BRINTON 37-38 About the thirtieth parallel of north latitude this plain [sc., Appalachian] sinks to the sea level, except in middle Florida, where it still remains 200 feet and more in height.

(2) 1791 B 89 [Floating islands] gradually spread themselves into the river, forming most delightful green plains, several miles in length, and in some places a quarter of a mile in breadth.

Attrib. with *field*.

1609 VRV 20-21 Two leagues from the towne, comming into the plaine field, he espied ten or eleven Indians.

See also DESERT PLAIN (attrib.);

FLOATING PLAIN; GRASS PLAIN; PINE PLAIN; PINE-WOOD PLAIN (attrib.); SAVANNA PLAIN (attrib.); WASTE PLAIN (attrib.).

PLANTING LAND. Land suitable for growing crops. DAE 1640.

1825 ASPPL IV. 658 tr. Two thousand acres of planting land in the territory of Indian river.

PLATEAU. A comparatively flat or level stretch of elevated land. DAE 1853. Here, with reference to the dividing ridge of the central or upper Floridian peninsula.

1823 V 73, 76 The dividing ridge of the waters of the Atlantic ocean and the gulf of Mexico . . . may perhaps more correctly be designated as a *plateau* of land . . . Cypress ponds and bay galls . . . are but rarely found on the *plateau*.

PLATFORM. A natural terrace, a flat, elevated piece of ground; a table-land, a plateau. OED 1813. Spec., a grassy hill (1837).

1827 W 8 Near the Chapola river, this formation often rises above the earth, in tabular platforms; they are usually covered with grass, but not with trees.

1837 W 10 [The limestone] often swells into hills, or high platforms, covered with grass.

POINT. (1a) The tapering end of a piece of land or rocks (1775) that runs into the sea, a river, etc.; a neck of land bordered on each side by a river or bay; a promontory. DAE 1622. A projecting piece of marsh (1742 p. 54), or end of a reef (1823 V), sand-bar (1742 Apx. 20) or sand bank (1837 p. 28). Spec., a cape (1652; 1745; 1803; 1874); a tongue of land (1660; 1832; 1873; 1874).

(b) With reference to the East Florida peninsula, esp. the lower part thereof. (2) The tapering end of a forest or woodland that reaches down into the prairie or surrounding treeless country. DAE 1637. (A.) (3) A peak; an elevated piece of land above a stream. DAE 1667. (A.) It may be that these quotations belong under sense (1). Perhaps the 1625 example refers to a projecting rock. Note the phrase *points and bays* given just below the regular body of quotations.

(1a) 1563 RIBAULD 11 As farre as a certayne poynte of Cape.

1652 HEYLIN 117 *The Tortugas* are seven or eight little Ilands lying on an heap at the South-west point of the *Peninsula*, called the Cape of Florida, in the height of 25 degrees.

1660 LE BLANC 352 Towards this point or tongue of land . . . 'tis dangerous sayling.

1742 RCBH 32, 54 On the 6th, at *Six* in the Morning, they reached Point Cartell . . . Some *Spaniards* were landing at the Point of Marsh opposite to the *Castle.*

Ibid., Apx. 20 The *General* . . . went . . . to reconnoitre the *Point* of the *Bar.*

1745 OSBORNE 744 From thence to the point *Canaverall*, is sixteen leagues.

1765 FHQ XXII. 80 From there coasting along to the point in the Bay of Panzacola called point Benado.

c. 1767 FHQ XII. 114 The Fort of Apalachy . . . is situated on a small point of land formed by the confluence of two small rivers.

1775 R Apx. xx 3½ miles further south is a point of high rocks near ¾ of a mile long.

1779 HEWATT II. 79 A neck of land called Point Quartel.

1797 MAG under *Charlotte* Charlotte Haven . . . [has] Carlos bay on the S. and Rock Point on the northward.

1803 E 257 It was then certain that we had passed over the southern part of the Cape shoal, and that the point of land to the north, was the Cape itself.

1823 STCW 25 In running eight miles we passed three long points which, in succession, shot into the bay, each one farther than the former. The first we named Reef Point; the second, Round Point, and the third Long Point.

1823 V 118, 120 The north point of that reef (*Carysfort*) extends as far as *Angel-fish creek* and its south point which is dry, marks a deep channel . . . Nearly east from this key [Tavernier] lies the southern point of *Carysfort reef* making a wide channel called *Palmeston in and outlet:* this south point is dry, but in the channel is [*sic*] four and five fathoms, and ships in distress may find shelter under the point.

1831 ASPMA IV. 731 An experiment was made . . . to improve the navigation of this river, by cutting off the points forming some of the most difficult bends.

1832 ASPNA IV. 208, 213 This hammock is at the head of the fifth large bayou [of St. Rosa Sound] half a mile below "Pine Point." . . . At the extreme southern point of the tongue of land between the sound and the east arm of the bay known as Loftin's Point.

1837 W 28, 50 The point [of Cape St. Blas] is a low sand bank . . . St. Maria and Hujelos, or Swallow River, are separated only by a point.

1871 H 127 *Live Oak Point* on the left hand marsh; from this point the channel makes a sweep of a mile.

1873 S 13 Black Point is a tongue of land thickly wooded jutting out into the St. John's.

1874 S 22 They passed a low cape embowered with cabbage palmettoes. This they called Palmetto Point . . . An osprey had built its nest in a cypress tree upon this cape . . . The tongue of land was called Osprey Point.

(b) 1589 HAKLUYT title p. The third and last [part], including the English valiant attempts in searching almost

all . . . *America,* from 73. degrees . . . to
. . . the point of *Florida.*
1613 PURCHAS 642 The length of
this Region extendeth to the fiue and
twentith degree. It runneth out into
the Sea with a long point of land.
1625 PURCHAS 869 *Los Martyres* . . .
are neare the point of Florida.
1741 GHDPOPW 7 The Winds and
Currents . . . pass out (between the
Southern Point of *Florida* and the Island
of *Cuba*).
1789 ASPIA I. 15 Some of the most
southern towns of the Lower Creeks, or
Seminoles, are within the territory of
Spain, stretching towards the point of
Florida.
1813 ASPIA I. 838 The warring Indians have . . . gone down to . . . the
lands beyond the creek towards Florida
point.
1821 ASPM II. 911 The Indians, at
present are scattered from Florida Point
to the Choctawhatchie.
1823 V 10 In the observations on the
keys and reefs of the Florida point, the
information of the resident pilots at the
cape, have been chiefly relied on.
(2) 1765 B 6 [The] east and south-
side of [the lake] . . . is pine-land . . . except a point of good swamp.
1773 MS. 220 To point of swamp.
1852 IJ 25-26 There were points of
woodland shooting into the prairie on
both sides.
(3) 1625 PURCHAS 869 Beginning
on the West side, is called the *Point of
the Martyres.*
1765 B 8 We encamped on a rocky
point near a fine swamp.
1791 B 228 It is in the eddy coves,
under the points and turnings of the
river, where the surface of the waters
for some acres is covered with . . . amphibious herbs and grass.
1821 F 67, 79 Point Peter, on the St.
Mary's . . . At *William's Point,* out of
which issue several little springs, the
water is pretty deep.
Points and Bays The phrase *points
and bays* in the quotation below may be

formed on the analogy of *points and
bends* (in a river).
1821 F 95 The island is indented on
the west side, almost regularly, into
points and bays.

See also BLUFF POINT (attrib.); GRASS
POINT; MARSH POINT (attrib.); OAT
POINT; SAND POINT.

POND. (1a) A naturally formed pool
or lake. DAE 1622. According to the
NID commentary on *lake,* "When a
body of standing water is so shallow
that aquatic plants grow in most of
it, it is usually called a *pond.*" Spec.,
a basin (1766). The 1839 example
refers to a salt-water pond. Some
ponds are explained as being expansions of subterranean waters (1827);
and one type of pond shrinks within
its bounds or dries up altogether
(1823—*cf. dry pond* under (b) below).
Used synonymously with *lake* (1775;
1821; 1829). (b) Preceded by a qualifying term.

(1a) 1731 C I. 78 [Brown bitten]
frequent fresh Rivers and Ponds in the
upper Parts of the Country.
1766 B 19 Every minute it boils up
above the surface of the common pond
or bason.
1775 R 267 The upper part of this
[lagoon] . . . is a kind of lake or pond.
1821 F 125 The ponds, many of them
more properly small lakes.
1823 ASPNA I. 1119 During the dry
season, which continues from about the
middle of September to the middle of
June, many of the ponds either dry up,
or shrink considerably.
1827 W 9 Many of these ponds, however, are merely expansions of the subterranean rivers.
1829 USCHED vol. 187 #147.11
Sampson Pond, or rather lake, is formed
of two sheets of water, one of which is
one foot higher than the other; they are
separated by a narrow cypress swamp;
at high water, the latter is overflown

and the whole lake is on a same level.
1839 *A Winter in the West Indies* 124
A little pond in the center of [Key West
covers] . . . several acres with salt water.
(b) 1851 BYRNE 26 That bad wa-
ter may be found in . . . the "rich green-
scum alligator ponds" of the peninsula,
will not be denied.
1837 W 263 They were strongly post-
ed behind a deep creek, flanked by two
boggy ponds.
1773 MS. 279 On a Hill, few but good
Tim. [timber] a sml. [small] dry pond
ahead . . . Pine and oak in vally. dry
pond near.
1837 W 66 The Bull Frog . . . is found
in great numbers in some of our grassy
ponds.
1773 MS. 281 A half moon Pond—in
Pine Land.
1874 S 27 [Afterwards he must]
thread many of the almost numberless
slews and lily-padded ponds of this extraordinary swamp.
1818 ASPMA I. 700 A point of land
projecting into an extensive marshy
pond.
1832 ASPNA IV. 209 This is . . . separated from the hammock on that point
by a marshy pond on the bluff of the
bay.
1773 MS. 283 In low Pe. [pine] Ld.
[land] . . . cyp. [cypress] cab. [cabbage]
& Oak pd. [pond] near.
1823 ASPPL III. 805 One hundred
acres of land, lying on Amelia island, to
the north-east of the town of Fernandina, by the name of Willow pond.
    Attrib. with *branch, country, creek,
water.*
1827 W 133 A canal of five miles
would connect the Wapaluxy creek, of
St. Andrew's, with the Pond branch of
the Chactawhatchee river.
1837 W 21, 45 A creek enters the
western border, which interlocks with
the pond branch of the Choctawhatchee
. . . Yellow Water River . . . receives in
its course, Shoal River, from the S.E.
the principal branches of which are Titi
and Pond branch.

1836 ASPMA VII. 145 It was thought
. . . that they were still secreted in this
pond or cove country.
1827 W 21 [The Choctawhatchee
River] receives in its course . . . Big
Barren, Holmes, and Pond Creeks, from
the south-east.
1825 ASPIA II. 638 There is no running water in the country; and, from
their knowledge of pond water, in hunting excursions, disease and sickness must
ensue.

    See also BAY POND; CABBAGE POND;
CLEAR-WATER POND; CYPRESS POND;
FLAG-GRASS POND; FRESH POND; FRESH-
WATER POND; GRASS POND; OPEN POND;
PINE POND; PINELAND POND (attrib.);
SALT POND; SAND-HILL POND (attrib.);
SWORD-GRASS POND; WASTE POND
(attrib.).

POOL. (1a) A small body of standing
or still water. OED. In the 1818
illustration, probably a pool connected with an underground source.
    (b) A small, shallow collection of
standing water; a puddle. OED.

(1a) 1818 Y 25 The sinks of the
higher parts . . . have then a conical,
funnel-like appearance, with small pools
at the bottom.
1836 ASPMA VII. 154 The water . . .
was generally excessively bad, taken
from stagnant pools and ponds.
1837 W 168 The thirsty Spaniards
drew off to drink at a pool, near the
palisades. It was nearly half blood, but
they were forced to drink it.
1870 BILL 102 A log or two half submerged, lay across the arm of a projecting pool.
(b) 1771 VIAUD 149 We . . . thought
ourselves happy . . . in meeting even
with a pool of muddy water.
1836 SSW 145 We had to halt at a
scanty dirty looking pool.

PORT. A harbor or haven. DAE 1632.
1563 RIBAULD 12-13 The next day
. . . wee assayed to enter this Port.

1609 VRV 21-22 Coming to the port in the sight of the towne.
1708 OLDMIXON in CARROLL II. 424 The two Men of War entered the Port of *Augustino,* and took the Governour's Ships.
1741 GHDPOPW 181 The Port is formed by an Island, and a long Point of Land.
1770 WYNNE 346 The chief harbour betwixt these two rivers, and indeed the best upon all this coast, is Pensacola; it being a large port.
1821 F 89 As the spring tides afford more water, the port [of St. Augustine] is approached with greater safety from March to November.
1871 H 31 Apalachicola—A port at the mouth of the river of the same name.

See also SEAPORT.

PORTAGE. A narrow place over which boats and goods are carried between navigable bodies of water; a carrying place. DAE 1698. (A.)
1837 W 140 Between Hillsborough Lagoon and Indian River, there is a narrow portage of nineteen hundred and eighty feet. The land which it crosses, is dry savanna or prairie, quite rocky, but has a tolerable soil. Boats appear to have been hauled across this portage time out of mind. The land cannot be more than four feet above the water.

POTHOLE. A hole in the ground or rock shaped somewhat like a pot, esp. one formed by the rotation of stones in running water. DAE 1827.
1869 BRINTON 94 The rains frequently thus undermine the soil, which suddenly gives way, forming so-called "sinks" and "pot holes," common throughout Alachua and the neighboring countries. One of the largest is the *Devil's Wash Pot,* 200 feet in depth, into which three small streams plunge by a series of leaps.
1871 H 131 At the mouth of the creek, the coquina ledge of rock is worn

into pot holes, some as large as a barrel, and ten feet deep.

PRAIRIE. (1) The DAE (1773) defines this term generally as "a level or rolling area of land, destitute of trees and usually covered with grass," and then subdivides this interpretation into several specific meanings. However, it is not always possible here to assign a quotation definitely to one of the two following senses: (a) a meadow, esp. one alongside a river; a relatively small area of low-lying grassland; (b) a grass-covered opening in a forest; a. savanna. Note that the 1869 author (under [b]) uses prairie synonymously with *marsh.* (A.) (2) Short for PRAIRIE LAND. DAE 1805. (A.)

(1a) 1823 V 52 The land at these capes and for some miles eastwardly is very good . . . presenting an even surface like a meadow, without a bush: this was called many years ago the Yamasee old field, but there appears every reason to suppose it a natural prairie.
1837 W 143 On the south side of Hillsborough [river], there is a large prairie . . . It appears like an old Indian field [*sic*], but the land is rather poor.
1852 IJ 25, 26 The road passes through a small prairie, and, from its appearance, I am inclined to think that it was once the bed of a river—the margin has the hammock growth . . . These prairies cannot be cultivated. They are so level that they cannot be drained. They were very dry when I saw them, but I am told that sometimes they are covered with water. They are also very sandy.
(b) 1818 Y 28 In some parts [the savannas] . . . make prairies and lakes of considerable size.
1827 W 69 Wild strawberries are confined to the prairies and savannas.
1837 W 220 On the 17th they arrived at the Allachua Prairie.

1869 FICSP 113, 117   This marsh or prairie is from less than half a mile to more than two miles in width . . . There are also scattered through the country what are called prairies, but are more properly savannas.
(2)   1851 BYRNE 14   [In the Alachua country a] great part . . . is *first rate land* of the different denominations of high hammock . . . rich prairie, and pine.

Attrib. with *ground.*

1821 DARBY 10   The prairie grounds of Florida . . . are generally productive.

See also GRASS PRAIRIE; MORNING-GLORY PRAIRIE; OPEN PRAIRIE; PRAIRIE COUNTRY; PRAIRIE LAND; WET PRAIRIE.

PRAIRIE COUNTRY. Country consisting of prairies or a prairie. DAE 1806. (A.)

1874 SAR 198   The [Kissimmee] river runs through a prairie country.

PRAIRIE LAND. Land made up of prairies or a prairie; meadowland. DAE 1807. Here, savanna land. (A.)

1821 DARBY 10   Savannah, or prairie land, in Florida, is in strictness mere varieties of swamp.

1874 SAR 187   The prairie lands are vast plains or beautiful savannas—dressed in luxuriant verdure and living green—dotted ever and anon with clusters of trees, oasis-like, from one to ten acres, with a growth of palmetto, etc.

PRECIPICE. A vertical or very steep face of rock; a cliff or crag—here, beneath the surface of a large spring. OED.

1827 W 37   Looking into [Wakully spring] . . . the colour is similar to a clear sky . . . the eastern side presents a rugged rocky precipice; all else, is an abyss of boundless depth.

PROMONTORY. (1a) A cape, headland, or point of land jutting out into a sea, bay, etc. DAE 1789. Spec., a mount (1823 p. 39); a peninsula

(1775). (b) With special reference to the East Florida peninsula.

(1a)   1587 L 5L   Hee arrived in Florida, landing neere a Cape or Promontorie.

1743 C II. 36   These Crabs . . . frequent mostly those Parts of the Promontories . . . near the Sea, where . . . they are always wet.

1775 R Apx. xxx   This promontory [Key Largo] is a *peninsula,* though it has till lately past for an island.

1803 E 244   We steered for Cape Sable, the most southern promontory of east Florida.

1823 V 39, 43-44   The junction of the two latter [streams] forms an acute promontory called Mount Oswald . . . [Near Merritt Island] a promontory divides the water into two prongs.

Ibid., 84   Cayo Largo though ranked among the Florida keys is no more than a promontory from the main land.

1854 SMITH-N 29   These islets . . . are situate over against the southeast promontory of the Peninsula.

(b)   1773 MS. follows 342   The west and east extremities of the dreadful promontory of East Florida.

1797 MAG under *Chatham*   Chatham, or *Punjo bay,* a large bay on the W. side of the S. end of the promontory of E. Florida.

1825 GADSDEN 119   The country south of St. Augustine, to the very extremity of the promontory of Florida, is alluvial.

PRONG. (1a) A branch or fork of a stream. Southern. DAE 1725. (b) Extended to apply to a bay which is an arm or branch of another bay. (c) An arm or branch of the Everglades, possibly denoting a stream.

(1a)   1818 Y 46   The course of the western branch of Sahwanne is southeast until its union with the east prong.

1823 V 69   A third prong joins the marshes from whence the Ocklawaha river takes its rise, while the main branch loses itself in the deep cypress swamps.

1829 USCHED vol. 187 #147.7 The south prong... or fork [of Black Creek], receiving but one tributary... is not subject to high freshets.

1832 ASPNA IV. 207 This hammock is at the head of the middle prong of the bayou.

1837 W 50 A prong of this stream is connected with a branch of New River.

(b) 1837 W 20 East Bay is the third prong [of Pensacola bay].

(c) 1823 V 82 This path... traverses the great chain of low lands and the prongs of the glades at the narrow parts.

Q

QUAGMIRE. A wet, boggy place. DAE 1608.

1828 ASPPL VI. 540-41 Many difficulties arise in these surveys... from marshes and quagmires impassable.

QUICKSAND. A bed of extremely loose wet sand, easily yielding to pressure and thus readily swallowing up any heavy object resting on it. Quicksands are frequent on some coasts, and are very dangerous to travellers, stranded ships, etc. OED. (DAE 1672.) All but the 1827 quotation refer to submerged areas.

1784 HUTCHINS 92 Towards... Marques, the westernmost of the Florida keys, there is a very dangerous and extensive bank of quicksand, on many parts of which there are no more than four or five feet of water.

1827 W 61 Some of the fresh marshes, on the contrary are merely quicksands, covered with a very thin soil, and are of course quite barren.

1848 USCSD vol. 531 #30.12 By [means of the floating light]... a large class of trading vessels, drawing over ten feet, and less than sixteen feet may

avoid the dangerous navigation of the quicksands and the Tortugas.

1870 BILL 74 Three hundred years ago and more, Jean Ribault threaded his way over the dangerous quicksands at the entrance of this noble river.

R

RACE. A strong current in the sea. OED. Here, an island. Possibly the reference here is to the current on one side of an island.

1763 ROBERTS 21 *Cayo de Biscayno*, otherwise called by some *Portland Race* ... is seven miles long.

RAFT. A mass of driftwood impeding navigation. DAE 1772. (A.) Spec., a natural bridge (1818 p. 42).

1818 Y 42 The raft or bridge is swampy and almost impervious.

Ibid., 153 The Natural Bridge is in the center of a large swamp and appears to be a deposit of earth on a raft or some similar obstruction.

1836 ASPMA VII. 292 The Withlacoochee... disembogues itself by four large, that is wide, and almost innumerable small mouths, amongst oyster banks, rafts, sand-bars, islands, and without calculation.

RANGE. An area of wild country over which domestic or wild animals range for food; esp., a cattle range. DAE 1640. (A.) (b) Without article: Grazing-ground; pasture. DAE 1626. (A.) It must be noted that on the basis of these records it is difficult to see the distinction made by the DAE editors.

1784 GME 97 But what, in a very particular manner recommends this part of West-Florida, is the fine and extensive ranges for cattle which are so frequently to be met with here.

1787 in SIEBERT II. 245 There was a good range of fresh marsh for pasture.

1822 SIMMONS 48 The fine range of the [Alachua] savanna, would pasture numerous herds.

1869 FICSP 30 These lands afford a most excellent range for cattle.

(b) 1766 B 33 There is good pine-woods, and fine range for cattle.

1813 MELISH 4 Throughout the whole there are extensive ranges for cattle.

See also CATTLE RANGE; PASTURE RANGE; PINE RANGE.

RAPID. A place in a river where the water descends rapidly but without waterfalls or cascades. Usually pl. DAE 1765. (A.) Also, reference is made to the occurrence of such a phenomenon in a bay (1837) or inlet (1871).

1823 STCW 24 Two miles above this is a short rapids over a loose rock where the water is not more than four feet deep.

1827 W 23 Below this rapid the [Appalache] river becomes broad and deep.

1837 W 10 Here a ledge of rocks surrounds the Appalache Bay ... forming falls and rapids.

1871 S 31 At low tide the water rushes over these rocks, forming rapids [in Jupiter inlet].

1874 SAR 197 The Caloosahatchie river is navigable for river steamers to within ten miles of Lake Okeechobee, where the navigation is interrupted by rapids.

RAVINE. A long hollow, depression, gorge, etc., worn by a stream or torrents. DAE 1781.

1804 ASPPL IV. 160 Thence crossing the hammock and a ravine.

1823 STCW 22 An old Spanish fort ... is situated on ... a high narrow neck of highlands nearly surrounded by a deep ravine and swamp.

1827 W 33 A covered way led to a spring, in a deep ravine.

1874 SAR 121 An abundance of de-cayed vegetable matter is found in the form of muck in the ponds, ravines, and branches.

REACH. A long, straight stretch in a river. DAE 1607. Extended to apply to that portion of the Gulf of Mexico lying along the western coast of Florida (1745, 1784 [?]).

1745 OSBORNE 745 Between which [sc., Tortugas] and Tacobago, which lies near to the top of that great reach, lie the bays of Carlos, Tampa.

1766 B 15 [We rowed] several long reaches, generally poorish land.

1784 HUTCHINS 84 There is a large shoal with only 3 or 4 feet, about half way up the first reach.

1822 SIMMONS 7 Beyond Bonavista, the river loses somewhat of its lake-like character, and winds in reaches.

RED-BAY HAMMOCK. A hammock in which the predominating growth is red bay.

1823 ASPPL III. 821 Two hundred and fifty acres of land, situated on St. John's river, near the Cow Ford, at a place known by the name of Red Bay Hammock.

RED-CLAY LAND. Land consisting of red clay.

1827 W 89 The Atlantic coast of East Florida, Georgia and Carolina, varies in many respects from the coast within the Gulf of Mexico ... In the gulf, the tide rarely ascends ten miles up the rivers, and the same high rolling, red clay lands approach within eighteen or twenty miles of the coast, which in the Atlantic states occupy the centre of the country between the tide waters and the mountains.

RED LAND. Soil of a reddish hue. DAE c. 1772. Here, red-clay land.

1874 SAR 65 The lands on the Miccosukie are stiff red lands with clay subsoil, and are considered the best for cotton culture.

REED-BRAKE. A brake consisting of reeds. Apparently not found east of the Suwannee. This type of swamp is distinguished by the fact that it surrounds the best kind of clear water (1818). Prob. Southern. DAE 1850 (def. in quotation).

1818 Y 32-33 The soil of the reed-brakes is very similar to that of the Baygalls—a loose spongy mass of vegetable mould on a foundation of sand and clay, they differ however essentially from the other kinds of swamp in having the best water of the country—which is found in the center of the reed-brakes, in narrow, deep little channels with clear currents and sandy bottoms.

1836 ASPMA VII. 137 The country west of the Suwanee abounded with reed-brakes, which constitute fine food for horses. I have never seen one east of the Suwanee.

REED-MARSH. A marsh overgrown with reeds. DAE 1819 under *reed*. Poss. an Americanism.

1766 B 13 After some miles rowing round several points of the compass, it being generally good reed-marsh and some cypress-swamps.

REEF. (1a) A narrow ridge or chain of rocks, shingle, or sand, lying at or near the surface of the water. OED. Spec., a bank (1773). (b) *Reef of rocks.* Obs. OED. (c) With special reference to an extensive formation —including keys, banks, shoals, and sunken rocks—which is composed principally of coral banks (1803) on a stratum of stone, namely, the Florida Reef, sometimes called the "General Florida Reef"; also, the Carysford Reef (1837; 1848).

(1a) 1773 MS. 324 Broken Islands ... known this day by the Name of Dry Tortugas, and ... a Reef (out of sight of any Land) West of these Islands known by the Name of the Tortuga Bank.

1821 F 108 Many of these reefs are composed of lime stone, or calcareous rocks a few feet above the surface of the water, covered with a thin stratum of earth, bearing many palm trees, and prickly pears or opuntia, producing cochineal.

1837 W 41 From Sombrero to the west end of Old Mattacumbe the reef is broken and irregular in breadth and depth. There are patches of coral rocks, some under and some above water.

(b) 1796 G 9 The harbour ... is entirely sheltered from the sea by a large Reef of rocks, and a flat shoal within them.

1837 W 23 A great reef of rocks project from the shore of the bay from ten to twenty miles.

(c) 1796 G 9 Due south from the western extremity of this bank, the West end of the General Florida Reef, is situated in Latitude 24° 22'; which is nearly the most southerly part of this extensive Reef, that runs parallel to the Kays, and forms a kind of general Bar to the coast.

1803 E 252 The Florida reef, (as it is called,) appears to consist of a number of coral banks on the outer edge of an extensive stratum of calcarious stone, which extends from the main land, to the edge of the Gulf Stream.

1823 V 52 The Florida reef and chain of keys commence at Key Biscayne or cape Florida.

Ibid., 84-85 The keys and banks, known under the designation of the general Florida reef.

1831 "The Wreckers' Song," anon., in AUDUBON 62 And when you are passing by this way, On Florida Reef should you chance to stray, Why, we will come to you on the shore, Amongst the rocks where the breakers roar.

1837 W 35 Carysford reef commences opposite the north end of Largo and ends just below N. Sound Point.

1848 USCSD vol. 531 #30.11 A great

extent of dangerous shoals and sunken rocks is commonly known among the wreckers as Carysfort reef, but distinct names are given to individual parts of it; as Great and little Coach reef, [etc.]. 1854 SMITH-N 30 The fishermen of the Bahamas and the Florida Reef.

See also CORAL REEF; OYSTER REEF.

RICE LAND. Low, wet land on which rice can be grown. DAE 1743.

1765 letter in STORK Apx. 35 Above Piccolata, for 40 miles along the river is as good swamp, or rice land, as any in Carolina. 1773 MS. 300 A fine and large Body of Rice Land lays between, and at the heads of said four Branches. 1791 B 95 Large swamps of excellent rice land are also situated on the West shore of the river, opposite to Charlotia. 1830 ASPPL VI. 77 His excellency had already granted him one thousand acres of rice land.

RICE SWAMP. A low, swampy area, covered usually or periodically with shallow water, on which rice can be grown. DAE 1775. Poss. Southern. DA 1731.

1819 NVSM 156 The rice swamps, or fields, are [located] . . . on the margin of rivers or creeks, to have the convenience of water necessary to its cultivation.

RICE TRACT. A tract of rice land.

1787 in SIEBERT II. 254-55 A fine Creek running thro the middle of it . . . made it one of the compleatest situations for Rice tracts any where to be found.

RIDGE. (1a) A long, narrow stretch of elevated ground. DAE 1624. (b) A divide, esp. the East Florida dividing ridge located in the central part of the peninsula (1823; 1829). Poss. Southern. (c) A line or reef (1821) of rocks. OED. Also applied to a sand-bar (1871) or shoal (1827; 1837).

(2) A range of hills. DAE 1835. Here, usually with reference to sand hills. The meaning is extended to apply to a range or chain of islands (1773).

(1a) 1742 RCBH 25 At one Mile's Distance the Way to *Fort Diego* striking up from the Sea over a high Ridge of Sand. 1765 B 4 Landed on Dunn's Island on a large snail shell ridge. 1791 B 132 For some time I passed by broken ridges of shelly high land. 1827 W 19 The southern shore of the island is thrown up into two or three parallel ridges of a yellowish brown sand; some of them forty, some fifty feet high. 1874 SAR 196 Calcareous rock crops out in the central part of the island, forming a ridge which rises about ten or twelve feet above the water level.

(b) 1815 NWR 106 Between Ko-en-e-cuh and Chatahouchee, the land is broken or waving—the ridge dividing their waters has high flats of light land. 1823 V 64 In the centre a ridge of more elevated country spreads along dividing the waters that flow into the opposite seas. 1827 W 82 A high ridge divides the Chactawhatchee bay from Shoal river. 1829 USCHED vol. 187 #147.3, 4 Major P. H. Perrault . . . was enjoined to divide his brigade into two parties, to be employed, one on the eastern side, the other on the western side of the Florida ridge . . . The ridge, which divides the waters emptying into the Atlantic from those running into the Gulf is sloping gradually from north to south. (c) 1821 F 94 [The] rocks . . . are placed at about high water mark; and a small ridge, or reef, runs off, sloping from the northernmost one. 1827 W 17 Cape St. Blas . . . stretches into the sea near twenty miles, in successive ridges. 1837 W 28 [Cape St. Blas] lies at the south end of St. Josephs bay. Its shoals extend more than twenty miles into the Gulf, in successive ridges.

1871 H 108   Inside of the ridge or bar the water is twenty feet deep or thereabout.

(2)   1742 RCBH 32   [They] encamped behind a Ridge of Sand Hills.

1773 MS. 323   Cape Florida ... almost joins (when discovered from the Southward) a Ridge of Islands on its south.

1775 R 35-36   In my journey by land from the Bay of Tampe across the Peninsula to St. Augustine, i crossed twenty three miles from east to west of miserable barren sand hills ... this Ridge ... extends ... for about an hundred and fifty miles.

1797 MAG under *Cuscowilla*   Cuscowilla, in East-Florida ... stands ... upon a high, swelling ridge of sand hills.

1812 FHQ IX. 71   Continued our route ... along the top of a ridge of hills.

1821 DARBY 9   A ridge of dry and in great part unwooded hills ... destitute of water, extends from the Eokefanoke swamp.

1837 W 43   The ridge of sand hills is high.

See also BACKBONE RIDGE; BLACK-JACK RIDGE; COAST-RIDGE; DIVIDING RIDGE; HAMMOCK RIDGE (attrib.); OAK RIDGE; PINE RIDGE; SAND RIDGE; SHORE RIDGE (attrib.); SPRUCE-PINE RIDGE; SPRUCE RIDGE.

RILL.   A small stream or rivulet. DAE 1738.

1744 KIMBER 24   This charming reviving Rill, is seated between two large Pine-barrens.

RIPPLE.   A shoal, reef, or rocky obstruction in a river or a piece of shallow, rapid, or broken water caused by this; a riffle. DAE 1755. (A.)

1827 W 87   A ridge of rocks ... causes falls or ripples in all the streams, betwixt the Wakully and Suwannee.

1837 W 48   Above the Santaffe there are several ripples, where the waters are no more than six feet deep.

1873 FHQ XIV. 270   Silver Run ... gives to that river a preceptible [*sic*] flow and frequent ripples.

RIPPLING.   A ripple. *Obs.* DAE 1745. (A.)

1796 G 23   On the edge of that stream [*sc.*, Gulf Stream], especially in fair weather, there are great ripplings.

RIP-RAP.   A rippling caused by the coming of the Gulf Stream into contact with a strong eddy. (Naut. OED —no def.)

1821 F 111-12   Generally a strong s.w. eddy prevails, and the transition from the [Gulf] stream to the eddy is sometimes very visible, by causing what those pilots call Rip Raps; at other times it is not to be discovered.

RISE (OF LAND).   A piece of rising ground. DAE 1741.

1837 W 54   The St. Johns [is] ... separated from the waters that run south, into the Everglades, by a very crooked rise of cabbage land, but little elevated above the adjoining meadows.

RISING.   A piece of rising ground; a small hill. DAE 1671.

1766 B 30   The floods had been so high up this branch, as to flow over its banks, and the first rising of the pine-lands.

1775 R 23   [The savannas] consist of a high ground often with small gentle risings in them.

RISING GROUND.   Ground which is elevated above the surrounding or adjacent level; a small hill. (OED under *rising*: no def.) Spec., a bluff (1784).

1784 GME 97   There are on each side of the river a number of rising grounds or bluffs.

1784 HUTCHINS 81   The rising

grounds are chiefly covered with pines, oak, and hickory.

RIVER. (1a) A large stream of water flowing through the land into another stream, a lake, or the sea. DAE 1607. Construed with *of* (the name of the river) (*c.* 1565; 1873 under [c] below—possibly literary); now somewhat *rare*—OED (last date: 1817). Note the preservation by American authors of the British custom of preceding the word *river* with the proper name in the 1811 (under [e] below), 1821, and 1869 (FICSP under [c]) quotations. The American practice of placing the name before *river* is illustrated by the 1854 writer and also the 1741 and 1762 (both under [c]) writers. (b) According to the NID, "in parts of the United States and Canada, esp. in New England, *river* is applied to streams the size of brooks, while streams of river size are sometimes called *creeks.*" With regard to this problem, see the *brook* (1771; 1791) and *creek* (1766; 1797; 1821) references below. Overlapping this meaning is the interpretation of the term *river* as a *branch* (1823; 1827; 1828) or *drain* (1837). (c) With specific reference to the St. Johns river. (d) With particular reference to Indian *river* as a *bay* (1871), *inland sea* (1825), or *lagoon*. (e) A subterranean river, esp. one that sinks, runs underground for a part of its course, and reappears. (f) Used in various specific senses: an arm of the sea; a channel or inlet of the sea; an inlet; a lagoon. (g) Preceded by a qualifying term. Note the river called both "White" and "Black."

(1a) 1563 RIBAULD 32 This riuer ... we haue called Sene.

c. 1565 Hawkins voyage, in HAKLUYT (1589) 539 [The captaine] neuer left sailing along the coast till he found [the Frenchmen] ... who inhabited in a riuer, by them called the riuer of May, and standeth in thirtie degrees and better.

1587 L 5 The captaine imbarked himselfe to passe over to the other side of the River [R. of May].

1609 VRV 41 Because of the great current, they made a cable with chaines, which they fastened on both sides of the Riuer.

1635 Hondy's *Mercator's Atlas* 900 All the country is watered with divers Rivers and Streames.

1663 Charles II Patent to Edward Earl of Clarendon, in OLDMIXON I. 330 The King *granted them all that Territory ... Southerly, as far as the River* San Mattaeo, *which borders on the Coast of Florida.*

1728 ASPPL I. 38 The first grant ... was by King Charles I. in the fifth year of his reign, to Sir Robert Heath his Attorney General; in that patent it is called Carolina Florida, and the boundaries fixed for it are from the river Matheo.

1758 ASPPL I. 51 We cannot approve your having given him a license to settle at the river St. Mary's.

1821 F 120 The river Little St. John, or Suannee ... is by some termed the pelucid [*sic*] river.

1823 V 49 The Potomac river ... is merely the head of Middle river.

(b) 1766 B 29 This river or creek is about 100 yards wide and 3 fathom deep.

1771 VIAUD 80 Without being forced to pass any river larger than what we should term a brook, in Europe.

1791 B 82 When we consider the number of large rivers in America, in comparison with which, this river is but a brook or rivulet.

1797 MAG under *Sebastian River, St.* Sebastian River, St. or *Spanish Admiral's Creek,* on the E. Coast of East-Florida, has communication with Indian river.

1821 F 77 The river Pablo, by some called Pablo Creek.

1823 V 73 The Ocklawaha river ... is the principal branch of the St. John's.

1827 W 19 James Island ... is made by a branch of the Ocklockney, called Crooked river.

1828 ASPPL VI. 546 The Conecuh river ... is the main branch of the Escambia.

1837 W 51 Middle River is a drain somewhat larger [than Jupiter Creek].

(c) 1741 Tailfer, P. *et al., A True and Historical Narrative of the Colony of Georgia* 62 Mr. Og[lethor]pe ... caused a Garrison of about *Fifty* men to be placed upon a Sandy Island ... in the Mouth of St. *John's* River.

1744 KIMBER 13 A creek ... roll'd its Waves from its Source, the River St. Wan's.

1762 AG II. 21 They acknowledge ... all the lands along the sea-coasts as far as St. John's river.

1822 SIMMONS 38 This river ... preserves this lake-like form through its whole extent, and ends in a lake.

1829 USCHED vol. 187 #147.5 The St. John river may be considered as an arm of the sea; it runs from south to north, which is contrary to the generality of the streams of the United States: perhaps it has been formerly a sound, which the washing of the Gulf stream has closed up at the southern end.

1854 SMITH-N 38 The San Mateo, now Saint John's River.

1869 FICSP 97 The river St. Johns.

1869 BRINTON 52 The St. John river is ... rather an arm of the sea than a river, and probably is the remains of an ancient lagoon.

1873 BRYANT in FHQ XIV. 258 East Florida ... is divided for nearly its whole length by the majestic river of St. John, which rises in the southern part of the peninsula, a broad, deep, placid stream, as black as a Claude Lorraine mirror, with no motion that makes a ripple, and here & there spreading into lakes.

(d) 1821 F 80 The lagoon, called Indian River.

1825 GADSDEN 121 The great width of Indian river at the Haul Over, and for many miles above, presenting more the appearance of an inland sea, is the only objection to the selection of this direction for a road to Cape Florida.

1837 W 51 Indian River is a vast lagoon. It was formerly called Ys. The distance from its head branches to Jupiter Narrows is about one hundred miles. It is in some places four miles wide; in others not fifty yards.

1871 H 91 The Indian river is, more strictly a bay. Its waters are salt, and it has no current independent of the winds. It varies in width from two to eight miles.

1874 S 21 The Indian river is a bay or salt water lagoon, stretching along the eastern coast of Florida.

(e) c. 1767 FHQ XII. 117 The N.E. River takes its rise from some small brooks near Mikisuki ... it runs under ground for some small distances and then shows itself here and there like ponds.

1811 ASPPL IV. 167 On the west margin of the river St. Mark's, a little distance above the spot where the same runs under ground; thence the line runs through the thicket in the neighborhood to where the said river appears again.

1821 F 84 It is common, when travelling near the sea, to hear a hollow sound, proceeding from the footsteps of the horse, which tends to confirm an opinion, in which some indulge, that there are in Florida subterraneous rivers.

1827 W 37 The course of subterranean rivers, can usually be traced by persons acquainted with the country, by the growth of timber, and by frequent sink holes, which usually occur at short distances from each other.

1837 W 148 Several considerable rivers sink under ground and rise again. The Santafee sinks about a mile above the Tallahasse road, in Allachua County, and it rises again about two miles below ... Such also, are the Ocilla, the Chipola, Econfina, and others.

(f) 1770 WYNNE 329 A narrow channel, called Matanza river, though in reality an arm of the sea.

1825 FHQ XIV. 153 The St. Sebastian's river is more properly speaking an arm of the sound or inlet, upon which St. Augustine is built.

1769 STORK 9 This island is ... divided from the main land by a narrow channel, called Matanza river, though in reality a channel of the sea.

1773 MS. 339 The river between the two [prehistoric] Peninsulas, now Hawke Channel, affords a very safe Communication between the Martyr Reefs, Shoals & Islands.

1823 V 40 The summit of [Mount Tucker] ... is about 80 feet above the level of Hillsborough river, as the channel is called.

1824 GADSDEN 118 The only land fit for cultivation is on the immediate margins of the rivers, which, strictly speaking, are inlets from the sea and run parallel with it.

1823 V 70 Rich fertile hammocks and swamps are found on the margin of Matanzas, Halifax, Mosquito, and Indian rivers or lagoons.

(g) 1589 DRAKE 46 Enforced to imbarke againe into our Pinnaces, we went thither vpō the great maine riuer, which is called ... S. Augustine.

1874 S 18 The boat ... retraced her steps through the water lillies to the open river.

1874 SAR 161 Port Orange ... is agreeably situated, with an open river in front and a shore free from marsh.

1766 B 29 About two miles below it, branches out White or Black River, it bears both names, the last by the English.

Attrib. with *marsh, water.*

1823 ASPPL III. 797 Fifty acres of land, lying on the St. John's river, about half a mile above Hester's Bluff, and is river marsh.

1836 ASPMA VII. 154 What was the general quality of the water, other than river water, drank by your men and horses, on your return march from Tampa towards the north of Florida?

See also FRESH RIVER; FRESH-WATER RIVER; OCEAN-RIVER; OLD RIVER; RIVER CHANNEL; SALT-WATER RIVER; SHOAL RIVER (attrib.).

RIVER-BANK. The raised or sloping edge of a river; the bank or ground adjacent to a river. OED.

1775 R 23 Some [savannas] come to the river banks.

1823 V 90 Sometimes the land on the river banks is rather higher than the grounds a little behind.

1863 FHQ IV. 137 A march of fourteen miles ... brought the party before daylight to the river-bank.

RIVER BOTTOM. Low, level land along the margin of a river. DAE 1752. (A.) Spec., a flat (1803); hammock (1869).

1803 E 235 The river bottoms, or flats are all fertile.

1827 W 81 The river bottoms on the Escambia are rich.

1869 BRINTON 42 The hammocks are rich river bottoms, densely timbered.

Attrib. with *land.*

1871 H 27 Most of the river bottom lands are ruined by being washed by powerful currents during the high water in the rivers.

RIVER CHANNEL. The bed or course of a river. DAE 1704.

1871 H 126 *Sharpe's Creek*, a crooked channel with strong tide, running from the southeast side of the bay, between the islands, into the main river channel.

RIVER-LAND. Land, esp. cultivable land, along a river. DAE 1781. (A.)

1775 R 172-73 A man who has a good piece of river land, bordering ... on ... barrens, ... will think his staple land of less value on that account.

1870 BILL 189 These pine-lands are

not so desirable for crops as the river-lands.

RIVER SWAMP. A low region adjacent to a river, usually subject to over-flow. DAE 1737. Poss. Southern.

1773 MS. 272 In low Pe. [pine] Ld. [land] ... River Swamp.
1818 Y 160 The glady flats interven-ing between the hills and the river swamp.
1823 V 90 The *river swamps* are an-nually overflown.
1874 SAR 147 River swamps consti-tute some of the most desirable sugar lands in the State.

RIVER-SWAMP LAND. Land consist-ing of river swamp.

1786 in SIEBERT II. 60 There were 100 Acres of River Swamp Land Com-pletely dammed in With a large reser-voir of back Water.
1871 H 27 There is a considerable quantity of valuable river swamp-land, which is high enough to prevent being over-flowed.
1874 SAR 21 There are hundreds of thousands of acres of river and inland swamp lands densely covered with a growth of water oak, etc.

RIVULET. A small stream or river. DAE 1636. Spec., a river (1821; 1827).

1682 *The Present State of Carolina* 16 I shall particularize ... of their Rivu-lets, whose christaline streams are clear, and transparent.
1731 C I. 63 On the banks of Rivulets and running Streams this Shrub is most commonly found.
1765 B 5 We crossed several small rivulets of clear sweet water.
1775 R 258 Many small rivulets, which all joining very soon, by their confluence form a considerable large stream navigable ... up to its forks.
1821 F 97 At the mouth of the river is a bay, into which runs a rivulet from

the south, called by Mr. De Brahm, Grenville River.
1827 USCHED vol. 217 #43.33 Im-mediately above the mound B, the river [St. Mary's] could not be navigated in a canoe, for it is a narrow rivulet, in the middle of wide bog.
See also FRESH-WATER RIVULET (RUN).

ROAD, RODE. A sheltered stretch of water near shore. DAE 1622. Spec., a cove (1796).

1587 L 55 Sixe great Spanish ships arriued in the rode, where foure of our greatest ships remained.
1763 ROBERTS 9 The *Road* of *Pensa-cola* is one of the best in all the *Gulf of Mexico,* in which vessels can lie in safety.
1773 MS. 298 This Fort commands the Road of the Bay [of St. Augustine].
1796 G 20 The shore here forms a little cove, which makes a good road for small craft.

ROADSTEAD. Also, ROADSTED. A place where ships may safely lie at anchor near the shore. OED. Spec., a bay (1766); a harbor (1775); a chan-nel between the Reef and the Keys (1796).

1766 FHQ XIX. 113 Pensacola Bay is a very good Roadsted.
1775 R Apx. xi There is a harbour, or rather a road stead inside of the wester-most point of [Key West].
1796 G 19 The channel between the Reef and Kays ... you will find not a bad Road-stead.
1826 ASPMA III. 295 Pensacola bay ... is perfectly landlocked, and has a very capacious roadstead.
1848 USCSD vol. 531 #30.8 At the settlements on Indian key there is a very good roadstead.

ROCK. (1a) A large, rugged mass of stone forming a natural prominence on land or in the sea. OED. Usually pl. Spec., with reference to (b) the

Keys, or (c) a reef—note the 1773 quotation referring to an oyster reef.

(1a) 1796 G 20 About 12 miles to the northward of Grenville Inlet are several high black rocks standing on the beach, which, with a hill in land [*sic*] to N.W. of the rocks, makes this part of the shore remarkable.

1821 F 99 There are four little inlets between this [large blue] rock and latitude 25 35.

1837 W 43 The Gap [is] . . . about four miles south of the black rocks.

1873 S 10 A dozen lines of breakers crash over these rocks.

(b) 1652 HEYLIN 117 The *Martyres,* called also the *Caios,* are three great Rocks rather then Ilands, covered with a white sand, and full of bushes.

1745 OSBORNE 744 Having to the west side those dangerous rocks called *Marteries,* to the east those called *Roques.*

1797 MAG under *Florida Keys* Florida Keys . . . a number of rocks and sand banks.

1803 E 246 This island [*sc.*, old Matacombe], like those already mentioned, may be considered as a large flat calcarious rock, elevated but a few feet above the water, and covered with a stratum of earth.

(c) 1773 MS. (319) Oysters are not only very plenty [*sic*], but whole Rocks of one hundred and more Fathoms in Length met with, which are nothing but Oysters cemented together.

1796 G 17 Kay Biscayno . . . lies about 2 leagues West of the *Fowey Rocks,* which are the first dry spots on the Reef, and where it ends.

1803 E 246 This island is . . . surrounded by a greater number of ragged rocks near the surface of the water.

1823 V 120 Abreast of this key [*sc.*, Young Matacombe] is a clump of sunken rocks called the *Hen and Chickens.*

1837 W 34 The Fowey rocks lie about two miles S.E. of this island, and form

the commencement of the reef, that shuts Hawk Channel from the sea.

See also OYSTER ROCK.

ROLLING COUNTRY. Undulating land. DAE 1837 under *rolling.* (A.)

1818 Y 25 In many parts, the rolling country is an isolated tract, entirely surrounded by the perfectly flat land.

1823 STCW 19 The land . . . rose into a delightful high rolling country.

1837 W 141 For several miles, from its mouth, it traverses a high and rolling country.

ROLLING LAND. Land resembling the swell of the ocean; undulating land. DAE under *rolling* 1872. (A.)

1837 W 25 From the south part of Sarrazota Bay to Charlotte Harbor, the pine country . . . is high rolling land.

1871 H 54 Tallahassee, the capital, is situated . . . upon high, rolling lands.

1874 SAR 147 In many places high rolling lands run down to the water's edge.

RUN. A small stream; a branch (1837). "Chiefly *U.S.* and *north. dial.*" (OED) —DAE 1605. Spec., a *spring* (1765). Both 1823 quotations indicate that a run is considered smaller than a creek.

1742 RCBH Apx. 24 Passed over some bad Runs and pieces of Marsh.

1765 B 5 [Landed at] Johnson's Spring, a run of clear and sweet water.

1775 R 36 The river St. Mary . . . has a current of . . . water supplied from the pine lands through which it flows, with many fine springs, runs, and rivulets of very clear water.

1823 ASPPL III. 777 One thousand acres of land, lying at a place called the Three Runs or Little creek.

1823 V 44 Crane creek for half a mile up is wide, but it is soon confined in a narrow run, through a strip of marsh.

1837 ASPMA VII. 376 I then came to a run or branch of an old river.

1873 FHQ XIV. 270 [Silver Spring] feeds a stream called the Silver Run.

Attrib. with *creek*.

1828 ASPPL VI. 105 This land is situated on St. Mary's river, on Deep Run creek.

See also FRESH-WATER RUN; SULPHUR-SPRING RUN (attrib.); SWAMP RUN (attrib.); WATER RUN.

RUSH LAND. A rich type of hard salt marsh on which rushes grow, and which is occasionally inundated by fresh water. OED under *rush* 1886 (no def.). Poss. a localism in Florida. *Cf.* SALT MARSH.

1823 V 91 That hard kind of salt marsh upon which fresh water occasionally flows and known commonly as *rush land*, is extremely eligible when properly prepared for agricultural purposes.

1874 SAR 117 On Amelia Island, the edge of the mainland, and scattered along her rivers are soils of calcarious sand ... the branch, fresh marsh and black rush lands attached to them are especially suitable for gardening.

S

SALT CREEK. A creek the waters of which are salty. DAE 1639. (A.)

c. 1824 ASPPL IV. 392 tr. Ending to the north with the first salt creek to the east of said river.

1837 W 31 The Cedar Keys ... are ... separated by innumerable salt creeks.

SALT FLAT. An area of low, flat land subject to overflow by salt water; a salt marsh. DAE under *salt* 1816 (no def.). Poss. a localism in Florida.

1874 SAR 97 Hundreds of salt-works were erected upon the "salt-flats" along the sea-shore within the limits of Wakulla.

SALT LAGOON. A lagoon consisting of salt water.

1827 W 27 Salt lagoons are ... favourite residences [of alligators].

1837 W 38 Among these islands there are numerous salt ponds and lagoons, to and from which the tide flows and ebbs with great rapidity.

SALT LAKE. A lake the water of which is salty. DAE 1799.

1775 R 289 In latitude 25: 20, is a salt lake.

SALT MARSH. A coastal marsh overflowed periodically by the sea. DAE 1624. There are two types of salt marsh; namely, *hard* (1787; 1823; *cf.* RUSH LAND) and *soft* (1823). The 1831 author appears to be referring to either the bottom of the sea close to shore, or an extensive marsh which is covered by the sea most of the time.

1769 STORK 7 There are many salt marshes on both sides of the [St. Johns] river.

1775 R 30 Marshes ... are of four kinds, two in the salt, and two in the fresh water.

1787 in SIEBERT II. 241 The land next the river was hard salt marsh.

1823 V 91 The *salt marshes* are likewise of two kinds, *hard* and *soft* ... The *hard salt marshes* however are often altogether clay, and like those in Indian river are covered with purslain: these when fully embanked and redeemed, and freshened by the cultivation of cotton or hemp for a year or two, would undoubtedly become the finest sugar fields ... The *soft salt marshes* are totally useless except as manure.

1831 ASPNA IV. 101 The coast ... [is] bounded by a salt marsh from one to two miles wide, through which roads could scarcely be made; and it is so shoal, that, for miles, boats drawing only a few inches would ground two miles from shore.

Attrib. with *land.*

1821 F 147 *Salt marsh lands,* generally bordering, with banks of oysters, on the sea coast, afford an abundance of grass, excellent food for horses and cattle.

SALT POND. A shallow depression connecting with the sea from which salt may be obtained by the natural evaporation of the sea-water. DAE 1643. (A.) Here, with reference to such an area located on an island.

1821 F 104 Cayo Huesos . . . has a salt-pond.

1823 ASPNA IV. 965 The salt ponds [of Key West] commence about two miles from the southwest point of the island, and extend to a bay or inlet which makes into the eastern end of the island from the passage between it and the next key; and are separated from this inlet only by a narrow and low strip of land, over which the sea flows in blowing weather and at high tides. There is also an inlet from the bay on the western side of the island to these ponds, which are about two feet deep in the middle, and from a quarter to half a mile wide.

1837 W 38 Samba Keys are six in number, or rather one great Key, the surface of which is cut by the currents into six parts . . . they are however merely the shells of islands of which the centres want filling up. The shores are high and look promising but they immediately fall back into salt ponds.

Ibid., 114 At Key West several hundred bushels are annually collected from the natural salt ponds.

SALT SPRING. A spring the water of which is salty. DAE 1651. Also, a mineral spring (1843).

1822 SIMMONS 29 There is a salt spring a little further north.

1823 ASPPL III. 818 The place known as the Salt spring, west side of lake George.

1843 FHQ XV. 58 I must not omit something of the mineral springs. There are two, known as the Salt and Basin Spring. The first is situated seventy or eighty yards from the margin of the lake, is one hundred and twenty yards in circumference, and sends off a cold stream, which flows into the lake.

1869 BRINTON 52 [The brackish quality of the St. Johns river] may be partly owing to several large salt springs which empty into it.

SALT WATER. Sea-water—with reference here to local areas. DAE 1608. Spec., an inlet of the sea (1823).

1823 V 112 Upon the salt waters, such as Matanzas, Halifax, and Indian rivers, no such disorders exist.

1837 W 13 This timber [mangrove trees] extends as far into the country as the salt water.

1871 S 31 The shallow salt water [of Jupiter Inlet] swarms with fish.

SALT-WATER MARSH. A salt marsh. DAE 1754. Prob. Southern.

1769 STORK 9 Near the mouth of this creek are extensive salt-water marshes, overflown at high tides.

1773 MS. 288 The Town [St. Augustine] . . . is surrounded with salt-water marshes.

SALT-WATER RIVER. An inlet of the sea.

1775 A Apx. 456 St. Augustine stands on a pleasant hill, at the conflux of two salt water rivers [*sc.,* Matanza and St. Sebastian].

SAND. (1a) The shore. *Obs.* OED. (b) Pl. A tract of sand along a shore. OED.

(1a) 1823 *Florida Pirate* 3 I found a small boat lying upon the sand.

(b) *c.* 1565 Hawkins voyage, in HAKLUYT (1589) 539 In ranging this coast along, the captaine found . . . Also

Deere great plenty, which came vpon the sands before them.

SAND BANK. (1a) A sand-bar. DAE 1673. (b) Collectively, the Florida Keys, Reef, and adjacent sand-bars. (2) A sand hill or dune.

(1a) 1741 GHDPOPW 181 A Large Sand-Bank lies before this Mouth of the Channel.
1762 AG I. 14 Their vessels . . . were often cast away upon the sand-banks, which are thick sown all along this coast.
1773 MS. 248 This Bar is formed by a Sand Bank, which resembles a Lobster's Claw.
1823 V 37 The water . . . has already traced a channel towards the narrow sand bank which rises from the beach.
1829 USCHED vol. 187 #147.15 But hence, westward to the main Pass, the Sound is much obstructed by oyster banks and sand banks.
(b) 1797 MAG under *Florida Keys* The great sand bank extends from the peninsula of East-Florida inward, to the gulf of Mexico, in the form of a hook; its W. point is divided from the bank called the Dry Tortugas, by Tortuga channel.
(2) 1589 DRAKE map of St. Augustine Some fourteene great and long peeces of artillerie . . . at our arriuall there to the sand banke plaied vpon us.
1743 CADOGAN 15 The General . . . ordered Major *Heron*, with a Party of Soldiers, to dislodge the *Spaniards* from a Battery on the Sand-banks at the Entry of the Harbour.
1837 W 146 [Florida is] not absolutely a sand bank, as alledged by Mr. Seagrove, but a calcareous fragment of the Appalachian mountain, clothed with some sterile sand banks, some rich variegated clay banks, and some beautiful coralines.

SAND-BAR. A deposit of sand in the form of a bar, ridge, shoal, etc., found in or along rivers or coasts. DAE

1781-1782 (OED: 1802). Spec., a shifting sand-bar (1829), a phenomenon very common along the Florida coast; an island (1827).

1766 B 27 Towards the opposite shore there is a sand-bar.
1818 Y 42 At the mouth [of the Apalache river] there is a sandbar.
1829 USCHED vol. 187 #147.8 The Suwannee . . . at its entrance into Vassasousa bay . . . is closed up by shifting sand bars.
1827 W 16 A small sand bar lies outside of the entrance, which is called Flag island.
1837 W 55 The river [St. John's] enters Lake Monroe over a sand bar on which there is little more than three feet water.

SAND BARREN. A tract of poor, light, sandy land having scanty vegetation. DAE 1766. (A.)

1829 USCHED vol. 187 #147.29 Respecting the ground through which the [canal] line runs, it is generally sand barren, interspersed with hammocks and savannas.

SAND BEACH. A beach consisting of, or covered with, sand. DAE 1709.

1773 MS. 225 The white sand Beach very rounding.
1825 GADSDEN 119 The route of the road . . . is . . . from thence on the sand beach of the ocean.
1837 W 143 At the east side of the river, a sand beach extends nearly six miles S.W.
1869 BRINTON 106 Cape Sable . . . shows from the sea a sand-beach three feet high.

SAND BLUFF. A bluff or headland composed of sand. DAE 1834. (A.)

1766 B 15 Came to a high bluff of sand on the east-side.
1773 MS. 259 To the West of this Mount appears a Sand Bluff.
1823 V 45 The mouth of St. Sebastian

river ... [is] distinguished by a high red sand bluff on the south point of entrance.

SAND FLAT. A level sand-bar. DAE 1794.

1773 MS. 288 From this Point runs a sand Flat 1 1/6 mile from the Shore of Anastasia Island.

SAND HILL. A hill, dune, or other natural elevation composed of or covered with sand. Usually pl. DAE 1622. Spec., a ridge (1744); a hillock thrown up by a salamander (1837). The sand hills of Florida—as contrasted with those to the north—are regular in form and generally covered with grass and other vegetation (1823; 1825). According to the 1874 writer, these formations were originally sand islands surrounded by marshes and lagoons. *Cf.* SAND RIDGE.

1589 DRAKE map of St. Augustine A Beacon or high scaffolde standing on the sand hills, wherein the Spaniards did use to discouer ships at sea.
1744 KIMBER 13 We took up our Quarters on the other Side of a Sand-Hill, or Ridge, overgrown with Palmettos, and divers Kinds of Weeds.
1766 B 31 Back there is pretty high sand-hills.
1769 STORK 12 The west side of this marsh and river is bounded chiefly with barren sand-hills, on which are scattered oak-shrubs and other bushes.
1791 B 155 We immediately find ourselves on the entrance of the expansive airy Pine forests, on parallel chains of low swelling mounds, called the Sand Hills, their ascent so easy, as to be almost imperceptible to the progressive traveller.
1818 Y 23 The sand-hills are uniformly barren presenting on the surface of the highest, the bare sandrock mineralized with iron.
Ibid., 138 Along this path it is about three miles to the Ochese Bluff ... over

broken sand hills near the river the hills are entire masses of sand rock cut by the rains into fantastic shapes of many colours.
Ibid., 160 For some distance above the line and to its entrance into the bay its upland is of poor pine sand hills with bottoms of second rate soil.
1821 F 148 *Sand hills* which run parallel with the sea, afford little more than small shrubbery, saw palmetto, wire grass, and prickly pears.
1823 V 47 The western shore of Jupiter sound presents a series of very high sand hills with undulating tops covered with forests of low spruce pines.
1825 GADSDEN 120-21 The sand hills do not present the naked appearance of more northern latitudes but are generally covered with grass, and occasionally crowned with a thick overshadowing growth of sea or mangrove grape. From being exposed generally to a wind, blowing uniformly from the same quarter, regularity has been given to their figure, and instead of the sea-sand undulations common to the north, and the dazzling reflection of light from the convex and concave inequalities of their surface, these ridges present the appearance of artificial parapets, with their scarps and berms all seemingly sodded with the skill of an engineer.
1827 W 17-18 St. Rosa ... island ... is conspicuous for its pure white sand hills, which at a distance appear like hills of snow.
1837 W 63 The Salamander ... is peculiar for throwing up rows of small sand hills over the woods.
1874 SAR 118 The clay bluffs along the St. Mary's river and the so-called sand hills in the northwestern corner of the county form a third distinct body of agricultural lands ... The latter, sand islands of an older formation among the marshes and lagoons that early surrounded them, and from which the present flat-woods arose, are the favorite choice for settlement of the herdsmen.

Attrib. with *peak, pond.*

1837 W Map Sand Hill Peaks.
1871 H 115 Passing some shallow sand hill ponds.

SAND HILLOCK. A small sand hill.
1836 SSW 307 The eye reposes next on the ever rolling sand hillocks.
1874 S 28 Spanish bayonets were squatted on hillocks of sand.

SAND KAY. A sand key.
1774 Barton in G 28 Off the West end of Kay Vacas lies a sand Kay on the Reef.

SAND KEY. A key composed principally of sand.
1775 R Apx. xli We found ourselves surrounded by three very small low sand keys (full of prickly pears).
1829 ASPNA IV. 968 An effort is now making to form a naval establishment on the insulated cluster of sand keys called the Dry Tortugas.
1837 W 23 Anclote Sound is sheltered on the west, by Anclote, Jacs and Sand Keys.

SAND POINT. A point composed of or covered with sand.
1773 MS. 299 The Channel through the Bar [of Jupiter Inlet] . . . was made by ranging the second Sand Point.

SAND RIDGE. (1) A ridge of sandy land. OED. Possibly a chain of sand hills. (2) A sand bank; a sand-bar. OED.
(1) 1791 B 179-80 Now the sand ridges become higher, and their bases proportionably more extensive . . . the summit of the ridges more gravelly.
1823 V 77 Another kind of land, are the ridges of white sand covered with the small black or post oak, commonly called black jacks. These are sometimes so thick as to exclude the pines, and when this is the case there is scarcely any grass found on the sand hills.
1826 ASPIA II. 689 The Indian trail winds over an extensive sand ridge for eight or nine miles.

1827 W 72-73 The land, to which they are *legally banished*, consists of dry sand ridges and interminable swamps.
1837 W 128 Holmes Valley . . . [extends] parallel with Holmes Creek, from which it is separated by a sand ridge from one to two miles wide.
(2) 1871 H 108 Across the mouth of the St. John's this sand ridge is piled up to within eight feet of the top of the water, at low tide, while inside . . . the ridge or bar the water is twenty feet deep.

SAVANNA. Also SAVANA, SAVANNAH. (1a) A treeless, grass-covered plain, esp. in the South; a lowland meadow. DAE 1671. In Florida, a savanna is commonly understood to be any grassland possessing some degree of saturation. The earliest writer to go into detail, De Brahm (1773), gives the fact that the soil of savannas is not sandy enough to allow the water to penetrate as the fundamental reason that they are (1) under water most of the time, and (2) very spongy even when dry. Romans (1775) explains savannas as a kind of drain to the higher adjacent lands; and Williams (1827) accounts for them as being reservoirs of water, like swamps, but distinguished from the latter by being covered with grass and herbs instead of trees and vines. On the other hand, though savannas are as a rule flooded, or "drowned" (1791 p. 209), sometimes they are so dry that fires sweep over them and destroy the grass upon them (1823 p 75). Because a *savanna* is characterized by this low, wet, and grassy condition, it bears a close resemblance to an *everglade* (*q.v.*), the former term being used synonymously with *glade* (1818 p. 28), and *wet glade* (1818 p. 144)—

moreover, a savanna is called a "sea of grass" once (1818 p. 28). Furthermore, savannas are said to correspond to what is called *intervale land* in New England (1871).

Since no mention at all is made of the saturation element, it is to be doubted that the second DAE definition of *savanna* as "flat grassland covered with scattered trees" (1863) is absolutely accurate. At any rate, the three authors quoted below (1766; 1773; 1818 p. 28) who refer to hardwood vegetation in Florida savannas make it clear that moisture is characteristic of this type of land. The corrected definition, then, would read, "a savanna covered with scattered trees." The usage of the term in this sense is probably Southern.

This type of land is also referred to specifically as follows: a basin (1825); a flat (1870 p. 74); a marsh (1823 p. 41; 1870 p. 75); a plain (1791 p. 165); a moist prairie (1869); and a waste (1822 p. 24).

(b) A savanna characterized by high ground and hillocks, occurring chiefly in West Florida, esp. in the immediate vicinity of a river. Possibly the same thing as *second bottom* (*q.v.*).

(1a) 1682 *The Present State of Carolina* 16 Their imbellished Meadows, fertil, and flourishing Savana's, are guarded with pleasant and solitary Woods.
1742 RCBH Apx. 16 The Land is mostly fine *Savannas* with fresh Water Ponds.
1744 KIMBER 13 We took up our Quarters . . . in a Savannah, defended on all Sides by a Wood; [*sic*] whose only Vacuities were some few Glades, made by the Entrance of a Creek.
1766 B 16 Beyond . . . is a large plain or savannah, half a mile wide . . . to the

pines, producing pretty good grass, low shrubs, oaks, and myrtles, the soil black on the surface and moist, though stiff enough to ride upon.
1769 STORK 19 The buffalo is found in the savannahs, or natural meadows, in the interior parts of East-Florida.
1773 MS. 310 The fifth are the great and open savannahs (:Meadows:), some twelve miles across, on which grow bunch grass, button snake Root and the blessed Thistle. They are covered for the greatest part of the year with Rain Water on account of their rich Soil having scarce any mixture of Sand, of course no Passage for the Water to sink through; and their Beds are so level, that hardly any Water can drain off, but entirely depends from the Sun's Exhalation. Altho' I have passed over them in a dry Season, when they had no Water, yet the Soil was so loose and moist, that my Horse only with a slow and easy Gate could traverse them, and yet every Step made three or four inches deep Impression. These Savannahs are spattered over, as it were, with little Groves of twelve or twenty-trees, some Pine, of the worst kind, some Cabbage and Maple Trees, and are chiefly surrounded by Maple or Cypress Swamps, which seem to extend themselves upon said Meadows.
1775 R 22 The savannah's are in this country of two very different kinds, the one is to be found in the pine lands; and notwithstanding the black appearance of the soil they are as much a white sand as the higher lands round them . . . they are a kind of sinks or drains to those of higher lands . . . on account of their producing some species of grass . . . they are very often stiled meadows . . . These savannahs often have spots in them more low than common, and filled with water.
1791 B 187 The extensive Alachua savanna is a level green plain, above fifteen miles over, fifty miles in circumference, and scarcely a tree or bush of any kind to be seen on it.

Ibid., 249   There was a little hommock or islet containing a few acres of high ground, at some distance from the shore, in the drowned savanna.

1818 Y 28   The glades or Savannas are tracts a little lower than the palmetto land, and in winter are covered with water from a few inches to several feet in depth. They extend, with great variation of length and breadth through the whole country, sometimes forming long and narrow vistas through the pineland covered with luxuriant and nutritious herbage and in places, spreading into ponds or lakes many miles in extent only dry in the warmest seasons. The soil in the Savannas is a thin black mould, on a bed of firm white sand with a large mixture of white clay. The only timber is a few stunted pines and dwarf cypresses. In the wetter parts there are small islets of evergreen thickets.

Ibid., 144   The path crosses Savannas or wet glades.

1822 SIMMONS 24   [Mr. Turnbull ascertained that the river] terminated in this savanna. This immense waste is mostly inundated.

Ibid., 48   [The Alachua Savanna] is surrounded by rich hammocks, some of which, point like promontories into the sea of grass; while others appeared like islands in the level waste of weeds . . . The savanna, in many parts, had the appearance of a beautiful lake, whose purple expanse, bordered by lofty groves or level fields of reeds, afforded a novel and pleasing prospect. Though two or three feet deep in water, in many places . . . it is often quite dry in summer.

1823 V 41   The head of this N.W. branch of Indian river and the head lake of St. John's river, approach each other very near heading in the same savanna or marsh.

Ibid., 75   The great savannas are also remarkable: after periods of heavy falls of rain, they are inundated to the depth of several feet; but when the warm seasons have evaporated this deluge, they often become so entirely dry that the fire runs over them, and sweeps down the tall grass which has sprung up over them to a great height.

1825 GADSDEN 119   Immediately west of these pine planes is an immense grassy savannah, inundated the greater part of the year, and forming the source of the river St. John's. This great basin, receiving the overflowings of all the interior swamps and ponds, branches to the east and west.

1827 W 53   Savannas are no more than natural reservoirs of water like the swamps; except that they are covered with grass and herbs instead of trees and vines; they are usually founded on clay or marle, but sometimes only on a hard sand. They are frequently extensive, and form excellent grazing lands.

1869 FICSP 52   In the southern portion of the peninsula are found large moist prairies, called savannahs, covered with tall grasses.

1870 BILL 75   Passing the headlands, an open flat, or savanna, appears . . . Having passed through this savanna, or low marsh, we steam close to the bank of the river.

1871 H 136   The savannas correspond to the New England intervale lands; they are perfectly level, and vary in their degrees of moisture according to their elevation; they are free from rock, of an alluvial clayey soil, containing so much lime as to effervesce when vinegar is poured on it; and they are subject to an annual overflow of fresh water from the Everglades.

1873 S 2   The ridges of palmetto scrub alternate with what are termed savannas—low, sandy spaces running for miles at the sides of the ridges, and covered with a coarse saw and wire grass.

(b) 1775 R 23   The other savannahs differ very widely from these, and are chiefly to be found in West Florida, they consist of a ground often with small gentle high risings in them, some are of a vast extent . . . there is generally a rivulet at one or other, or at each end of the savannahs, and some come to the river banks.

Attrib. with *branch, country, ground, plain, swamp.*

1823 ASPPL III. 776 Three hundred and fifty acres of land lying on Funk Savannah branch, a branch of Nassau.

1823 V 47 Two or three miles S. W. of the forks is a body of hammock, and pine lands beyond that again to the borders of a flat savanna country.

1773 MS. 265, 271 In Savannah ground full of palmetoe Bushes . . . A great bay Gall runs N.W. into a savanh. [savannah] Ground.

1791 B 181 A level expansive savanna plain presents [itself] to view.

1823 V 51 [The crossing place is made by] crossing the Haffia or Manatee river, and journeying in a S.E. course along the edge of the savanna swamp or morass to the narrowest spot.

See also CYPRESS SAVANNA; GRASS SAVANNA; HAMMOCK SAVANNA; PINELAND SAVANNA (attrib.); PINE SAVANNA; SAVANNA LAND; SAW-GRASS SAVANNA; WET SAVANNA.

SAVANNA LAND. Land consisting of savanna. DAE (1741), OED (1697), under *savanna* (no def.). Poss. Southern.

1742 RCBH 22 *Fort Diego* . . . [is] scituated in fine *Savanna* Lands, with fresh *Water* Ponds, about *Twenty* Miles distant from St. *Augustine.*

1773 MS. 273 In low Pine Land, mixed . . . with Savannah Land.

1821 F 125 General Harris and his party . . . selected for themselves about 350,000 acres of the best savanna lands.

1851 BYRNE 14 There are, besides the lands already noticed, extensive tracts of savanna lands, which approximate in character, texture of soil, and period and mode of formation, to the swamp lands, differing only in being destitute of timber.—Some of these lands, however, are extremely barren.

SAW-GRASS MARSH. A wet prairie overgrown with saw grass.

1869 FICSP 113 After leaving Cow Ford, the swamp disappears, and the course of the river is through a Saw Grass marsh or prairie, at present overflowed by the waters of the river . . . This entire strip appears once to have been part of an immense lake, of which Lakes Griffin and Eustis constituted portions.

SAW-GRASS MEADOW. A meadow (probably wet) in which saw grass flourishes.

1874 SAR 173 The distance between the lake and [the Withlacoochee] river is about four miles, and they are frequently connected by saw-grass meadows.

SAW-GRASS POND. A pond or small lake covered with saw grass.

1825 GADSDEN 119, 120 The western base of . . . [the chain of sand hills] is washed by another succession of smaller lakes or saw-grass ponds and swamps . . . For the next six miles cypress swamps and saw-grass ponds.

SAW-GRASS SAVANNA. A savanna on which the characteristic growth is saw grass.

1874 SAR 173 Marsh lands and saw-grass savannas make this section difficult of access.

SAW-PALMETTO FLAT. A flat abounding with saw palmettos (a species of palm common in southern Florida).

1825 GADSDEN 120 For the next six miles cypress swamps . . . diversified occasionally with saw-palmetto and baybush flats.

SAW-PALMETTO LAND. Land overgrown with saw palmettos.

1825 GADSDEN 120 Occasional swells of saw-palmetto lands . . . [are] interspersed with grassy flats.

SCRUB. A region overgrown with stunted trees or brushwood. DAE 1809. The sterility of the soil of this land is caused by the fine, white sand found therein (1823; 1871).

1822 SIMMONS 33, 34 The *Little Scrub* . . . is an untimbered region, covered with dwarf firs, oak, and myrtle, and the prickly pear . . . The *Big Scrub* . . . is seven miles wide . . . Nothing can be more sterile than the soil; and these tracts are, in fact, concealed deserts, as they are too poor to admit of cultivation, and afford nothing that is fit, even for the browsing of cattle.

1823 V 77 Large veins of scrubs extend to lake George and chiefly fill up the neck. These scrubs and undulating grounds, consist of a sand of a very small and ferruginous grain, producing an infinite variety of dwarf oaks and a number of parasitical plants; where the land swells to a considerable elevation, there is generally to be seen a growth of small spruce pines, most of which however seem to die, after springing up to the height of twenty or thirty feet.

1836 SSW 18 What is called *"scrub"* in Florida, and in the southern states, is a barren tract of land, covered with tough stunted thickets; of scrubby oak, dwarf pine, myrtle, prickly pear, etc.

1869 BRINTON 42 The northern portion of the Peninsula is composed of "scrubs" (dry sterile tracts covered with thickets of black-jack, oak, and spruce), pine lands and hammocks.

1871 H 115 *The Long Scrub* . . . consists of a half mile or more of deep white sand.

Attrib. with *ground.*

1775 R 264 Within many miles is really a miserable sand, a dreary scrub ground.

See also OAK SCRUB; PALMETTO SCRUB.

SCRUB HAMMOCK. A hammock overgrown with stunted or dwarfed trees.

1823 V 44 Further on the bluff is of shells with a scrub hammock.

1871 H 93 The interior of the county . . . [is] interspersed with bay galls, savannas, cypress ponds, and spruce pine, and dwarf oak scrub hammocks, which are worthless for cultivation.

1874 SAR 210 Some of our lighter or scrub hammock is good.

SCRUBLAND. Inferior land overgrown with scrubs or scrubby vegetation. DAE 1779 under *scrub.* (A.)

1823 V 89 The *scrub lands* . . . are of too forbidding an aspect to lead the farmer to expect from them any advantage.

SEA. (1a) The continuous body of salt water that covers the greater part of the earth's surface. OED. Here, that portion of the Atlantic Ocean which washes the East Florida coast. (b) The Gulf of Mexico. (c) With reference to both the Atlantic and the Gulf collectively.

(1a) 1773 MS. 306 This Sea [along the Atlantic coast] in a calm is so clear, that the Fish, Corals, Rocks . . . can be clearly discerned in four fathom water. *Ibid.,* 342 W. and N. Winds bend the Sea from the Coast, and leave the Bars at times near dry.

1775 R 37 On the beach between St. John's and St. Augustine . . . there are . . . springs running into the sea.

1839 *Winter in West Indies* 142 St. Augustine . . . is situate . . . within half a mile of the open sea.

(b) 1771 VIAUD 114 My negro . . . had gone to search the border of the sea for some kind of sustenance.

1784 HUTCHINS 73 The bar of Pensacola is of a semicircular form, with the convex side to the sea.

1817 ASPPL IV. 200 [The 1,181 arpents on St. Rosa I. extend] four English miles to the east . . . terminating at a line drawn from sea to sea.

1818 Y 27 The Palmetto [of the St. Marks region] . . . is more abundant as the flats approach the sea.

1823 STSW 28   The center of this tract
[between Apalachicola & Suwannee riv-
ers] is occupied by a mass of clay from
150 to 250 feet above the sea.
1837 W 122   Pensacola is situate on
the north side of the bay of the same
name about ten miles from the sea.
(c)   1776 NAWIG under *Florida, East.*
The situation of this colony between
two seas renders the air colder.
1821 F 101   The entry into this Lake
... [forms] the grand central source of
communication between the Atlantic
and the Mexican Sea.
1822 SIMMONS 9   This poverty of a
great proportion of the country, is further counterbalanced by the extraordinary abundance of the seas along the
coasts.
1822 ASPPL III. 524   [There are]
about forty small rivers, whose sources
are at from thirty to forty miles distant
from both shores, and whose waters are
emptying themselves into the opposite
seas.
1823 ASPIA II 438-39   He "objected to
the location of the Indians south ... The
sea, too, being on each side of them,
bad men from over the big water would
see his young men."
1823 V 64   In the centre a ridge of
more elevated country spreads along,
dividing the waters that flow into the
opposite seas.

SEA-BANK. (1a) The sea-shore. *Obs.*
OED. (b) A dune or sand hill. OED
1848.

(1a)   1769 STORK 11   The sea bank
contains but indifferent high plantable
land here and there in spots.
(b)   1563 RIBAULD 13-14   This
[river] being entered we perceyued a
great number of the Indians inhabitants
there, commyng alonge the sandes & sea
banckes.

SEA-BEACH. The shore of the sea; the
beach. OED 1775.

1742 RCBH 21   He encamped that
night at ... the first Palmeta Hut on the
Sea-Beach.
1773 MS. 208   On the Sea beach.
1823 V 47   Jupiter Narrows ... are
eight or ten miles in length, with several narrow channels through a body of
mangrove islands lying between the sea
beach and the main land.
1837 W 21   One mile from the sea
beach, an arm ... runs westward.
1874 SAR 157   A *sea-beach*, hard as a
plank road, clean-swept, and washed by
breezes ever fresh, and tides daily re-
newed ... is easily approached by a
short walk from any point along the
Halifax.

SEABOARD. (1a) The coastline; the
area or land adjacent to the coastline. DAE 1788. (A.) (b) With special
reference to the Atlantic coast. DAE
1851.

(1a)   1792 POPE 46   In about 20
Miles from *Pensacola* we reached the
Indian Boundary, no Part of their Territory ever approaching higher than that
Distance to the Sea-board.
1821 ASPIA II. 413   Waw-ka-saw-sa,
on the east side of the mouth of Suwanee, on the seaboard.
1832 ASPMA IV. 829   The forts on the
seaboard of Florida.
1856 LANMAN 140   On the seaboard
of Florida their [*i.e.,* alligators'] most
formidable enemy is the porpoise.
(b)   1823 V 53-54   Between Charlotte harbour and Tampa bay ... the
coast partakes more of the character of
the Atlantic seaboard than it has hitherto done.
1826 FHQ XIV. 190   A scattering population along the seaboard between the
St. Mary's and the St. John's Rivers.

SEACOAST. (1) The shore of the land
along the sea. DAE 1640. (2) Coastal
waters (an extension of meaning).
Cf. COAST (1).

(1)   1609 VRV 179   The Indians ...
of the Inland have greater store of Maiz

... then those that dwell upon the sea coast.

1731 C I 86 They frequent the Rivers and Sea Coast of *Florida.*

1763 ROBERTS 4 The sea-coast is very flat, sandy, and full of shoals.

1773 MS. 260 I also surveyed ... along the Seacoast across the Inlet of St. Augustin.

1791 B 150 They are never seen on the salt sea coast.

1823 ASPM II. 1025 Above all, its exposed situation, possessing, a seacoast of twelve hundred miles.

1837 W 7 The whole extent of the sea coast, is indented with bays and lagoons.

1874 SAR 170 There is no sea-coast anywhere more inviting to the immigrant than that from the mouth of the Withlacoochee to the Anclote.

(2) 1827 W 131 The seacoast is about twelve hundred miles in extent, and the southern part in particular, the most dangerous, perhaps, of the western continent.

Attrib. with *island.*

1791 B 68 There is a large space betwixt this chain of sea-coast-islands [incl. Amelia] and the main land.

SEA ISLAND. One of a chain of islands off the South Carolina, Georgia, and Florida coasts; also, pl., the whole chain of islands. DAE 1763 (Florida ref.: 1880). Prob. Southern.

1708 OLDMIXON I 375 In it is the great River *Cambage,* which joining with the River *May,* forms with the Sea Island *Edelano.*

1821 F vii On the coast are some of the finest sea islands for the cultivation of cotton.

1831 AUDUBON 64 The hawk-billed [turtle] ... keeps to the sea-islands.

1855 USCSED vol. 756 #76.5 With the exception of the two ends running from the main land to the Sea Islands, the line of road would be on two tangents joined by a curve at the Santa Fe river.

SEAPORT. A port on the seacoast; an inland river port (1791)—possibly an individualism. DAE 1691; 1816 (for the latter def.).

1609 VRV 23 *Ucita* fled to another towne that he had in another sea port.

1791 B 194 The Spaniards of Cuba likewise trade here or at St. Mark's, and other sea ports on the west coast of the isthmus.

1827 W 93-94 Very great exertions were made by the English ... to extend the commerce of the two sea-ports, St. Augustine and Pensacola.

See also PORT.

SEA-SAND HILL. A sand hill or dune by the sea. Poss. an individualism.

1825 GADSDEN 120 The last seven miles ... [are] occasionally diversified with sea-sand hills.

[1825 GADSDEN 120 Ridge of Indian river, 23 miles 40 chains. For one half of this distance high ridged, diversified with sea-sand undulations.]

SEA-SHORE. The coast of the sea (1587; 1775; 1837), or the land lying adjacent to the sea. OED.

1587 L 2 The Countrie ... is sandie towards the Sea shore.

1609 VRV 22 They demanded [the letter] ... of foure or five Indians, which walked along the sea shore.

1742 RCBH 24 The General ... marched with about *Two Hundred* and *Fifty* of his men ... along the Sea Shore.

1773 MS. (318) The Tortoise lay their Eggs on the Sea Shores in the Sand.

1775 A 308 The lands of West-Florida, for a considerable distance from the sea-shore, are very low.

1791 B 157 I at length by dusk made a safe harbour ... on the sea shore.

1837 W 12 Two or three miles from the sea shore, there is a strip ... covered with excellent land.

Attrib. with *country, tract.*

1828 ASPPL VI. 527 You will readily conceive the advantages, in many respects, of having this sea-shore country settled as speedily as possible.

Ibid., 527 As yet, (with the exception of a very few spots) this sea-shore tract of country [near Tallahassee] is unexplored.

SEA-WATER. The water of the sea. OED. Here, applied to the Florida coastal region.

1773 MS. 306 The Sea Water as far, as it covers these Soundings [along the Atlantic coast], assumes in a calm the colour of a Beryl.

1821 F 98 The true colour of our sea water here is a fine Saxon or celandon green.

1869 FICSP 63 In a country ... where salt from the Salt Springs or from sea-water can be more easily manufactured than elsewhere, in the whole world, the price of pork is exorbitant.

SECOND BOTTOM. The second or higher level of bottom land. DAE 1691.

1827 W 81 The river bottoms on the Escambia are rich, but are subject to overflow. A kind of second bottom, resembling hammock, rises between the interval and pine barren; these are mostly cultivated, and produce very good crops: they usually embrace springs of excellent water.

SEDGE ISLAND. An island overgrown with sedge. DAE 1711 under *sedge* (no def.). Poss. an Americanism (not in OED at all).

1818 Y 48 The peculiar features of the coast are the cockle-banks, or bluffs —the sedge islands—the keys and the oyster banks.

SEDGE-MARSH. A coastal marsh on which the predominating growth is sedge.

1818 Y 48 The sedge-marsh is found at the mouth of all the Florida rivers in all the indentations of the coast—and at almost all the points. It is formed

by a gradual deposit of sand and mud on a stratum of calcareous rock, and is the first stage in the physical formation of the country. Its only growth is high coarse grass and rushes with occasionally cabbage trees and some stunted cypress.

SEDGE SWAMP. A coastal swamp overgrown with sedge.

1818 Y 31 Cabbage palmetto ... grows ... on the higher parts of the sedge swamps along the coast.

SET. A strong swift current running along the coast between a reef or bar and the shore; here, with reference to that part of the Gulf of Mexico along the Florida Keys. OED.

1823 V 126 The great effect of gales of wind upon the Florida or gulf stream, the uncertainty of the line of the *eddy*, and the numerous baffling currents continually drive the mariner upon the reefs: the unexperienced navigator too is sometimes by light winds and unknown *sets* of the gulf accidentally carried within side the reef, through some of the inlets.

SHALLOW. A shallow place—here—in a stream. OED.

1823 V 76 The Amanina river ... but for the impediment of the shallows at its mouth, would afford a great outlet for produce.

1829 USCHED vol. 187 #147.7 At low tide, the channel is obstructed, at four places by shallows formed at the meeting points of tides. The first obstruction is found between St. Mary's and Nassau rivers: for two miles the channel is left dry at low tide, and affords but 3 feet at high tide.

SHELF. (1) A sand bank in the sea rendering the water shallow and dangerous. Also loosely applied to a submerged ledge of rock. OED. Poss. the shelves in Florida waters are oyster beds. It is not clear what is meant by "shelves with mouthes" of the 1625 quotation, unless possibly *mouth* refers to a channel providing a passageway for boats through a shoal forming a kind of shelf. (2) A ledge, platform, or terrace of rock. OED 1809.

(1) 1609 VRV 179 It is a gentle coast, but it hath many sholdes, and great shelues of sand.

1625 PURCHAS 869 [This Province] stands about fiftie leagues from *los Martyres*, which are many little Ilands inhabited, which are neare the point of *Florida*, whereby it ioyneth most with the Island of *Cuba* a league and a halfe, and lesse, the one from the other, with a ranke of shelves with mouthes, in twentie three or twentie foure leagues, which these *Martyres* haue in length.

(2) 1836 SSW 308 Here is a high bluff washed by the sea, with projecting shelves of this curious rock.

SHELL BANK. A shelly bank or bar, usually covered at high tide. DAE 1891 under *shell* (def. is quoted from the CD). (A.) However, as recorded here the Florida shell banks are high enough to be dry, probably all of the time. According to one writer (1818), in formation, appearance and characteristic vegetation, shell banks are identical with the keys.

1818 Y 48 The keys are only different from the shell banks in being detached from the coast their [*sic*] formation appearance and growth are precisely the same.

1823 ASPNA IV. 965 On the side next the sea is a sand or shell bank, from eight to ten feet high, having little soil, and that of the poorest description.

1827 W 12 The post of Barrancas ... is situate ... on a high shell bank.

1837 W 28 Each of these projections [terminating Cape Sable] are high and pleasant shell banks.

1870 BILL 136-37 [Lake Jessup's]

shores are low and marsh, as a rule; but here and there are dry shell-banks on which the wild orange grows.

SHELL BEACH. A beach wholly composed of sea-shell. OED Sup. under *shell.*

1874 S 23 Toward night a shell beach was seen west of a small grassy island ... The shore was strewn with fossil shells of a common order.

SHELL HAMMOCK. A hammock in the soil of which marine shells abound. DAE 1887 under *shell.* Spec., an oyster-shell bank (1817). DA 1886.

1837 W 21 The eastern shore is low ... with small shell hammocks.

Ibid., 117 The site [of St. Augustine] was originally a shell hammock, scarcely twelve feet higher than the surface of the sea.

1869 FICSP 47 There is no place where the tree does better than upon the shell hammocks, indicating that lime is a valuable fertilizer.

1871 H 92 In many places on the Indian river, is a range of oyster-shell banks, from three to ten feet high: these constitute the "shell hammocks."

SHIP CHANNEL. A channel used by ships. DAE 1775. (A.)

1837 W Map Ship Channel [in Appalachicola Bay].

1848 USCSD vol. 531 #30.5 Vessel and cargo valued at $80,000; ashore at Ship channel.

SHOAL. Also SHOALD. A place where the water is shallow; a sand-bar. DAE 1612. De Brahm (1773) appears to use the term to denote an island or key consisting of rocks and the sand covering the rocks; however, if he is referring to sand-bars, these are high enough to have sand hills. Note the dry shoals mentioned by Gauld (1796 p. 11).

c. 1565 Hawkins voyage, in HAKLUYT

(1589) 537-38 The 12 day in the morning we fell with the Islands vpon the cape of Florida, which we could scant double by the meanes that fearing the shoals to the Eastwards.

1609 VRV 17 Because of the shoalds, they came to an anchor a league from the shore.

1762 J 5 Salt Tortuga Island, so called, says Captain *Dampier*, to distinguish it from the Shoals of *Dry Tortugas* near *Cape Florida*.

1773 MS. 334-35 The Shoals, especially Sombreros . . . [distinguish] themselves by shewing their Sand hills— above Water visible at four and five miles Distance, evidently appear to be the Remnant of the southern Peninsula, torn first into Islands, which deprived of their natural Products and rich soil retain only at this time their barren Sand cover over their rocky Fundation [*sic*].

1796 G 6, 11 The next danger that offers will be the *Tortugas Kays and Shoals* . . . Near this Kay [*sc.*, Sandy] there are dry shoals and breakers for upwards of 3 miles to the westward.

1821 DARBY 12 The whole north side of the gulf may be designated a vast shoal.

1837 W 23, 28 Many round shoals rise in different parts of [the great reef of rocks] . . . From a S.W. point a succession of sandy shoals extend [from Cape Roman] fifteen miles farther, in a S.S.W. direction.

1854 ESB 53 The squadron having already begun to make sail, the Governor went off to conduct it in over the shoals.

Attrib. with *bank, cape, river*.

1823 ASPNA IV. 964 Thompson's Island, formerly called Key West, is situated on the southern edge of an extensive shoal bank, off the south shore of East Florida.

1837 W 21 Many shoal capes extend . . . into the bay.

1827 W 83 A large creek issues from this pond, and forms one considerable branch of Shoal river.

See also MUD SHOAL; OYSTER SHOAL.

SHOAL WATER. Shallow water; the water over a shoal, or bank; hence, water within soundings. NID.

1743 CADOGAN 46 Captain *Warren* . . . would have destroy'd some of them, had they not run into Shoal-Water and escaped him.

1825 ASPPL IV. 201 The space described in certificate C includes almost the whole of the shoal water.

SHORE. Also, SHOAR. (1a) The land bordering on the sea or a large lake or river. OED. Used in reference to an extensive area (1762; 1769; 1796). (b) Extended to apply to the waters along the shore.

(1a) 1563 RIBAULD 11 We being not past 7 or 8 leagues frõ the shore.

1589 DRAKE 42 We descried on the shore a place built like a Beacon.

1609 VRV 21-22 On the shore they saw a cane sticking in the ground.

1743 C II 33 I have seen . . . [Hermit Crabs] feed on the Fragments of Fish and other animal Substances, cast on Shoar.

1762 J 69 All its shore abounds in mangrove trees.

1769 STORK 5 To take a view of the eastern shore of Florida.

1796 G 8 The bank of soundings extends . . . all the way northward along the Florida shore.

1823 ASPNA I. 1119 The shores are somewhat elevated above the interior grounds by the surf continually throwing up pulverized shells, which give a concave form to its superficies.

1837 W 30 The north shore [of St. Vincent I.] is broken by large marshes and Lagoons.

1858 FAIRBANKS 185 During the month of February, 1835 . . . The St. Johns river was frozen several rods from the shore.

1869 BRINTON 106 In parts [of the west coast], the slope of the shore is so gradual that low water exposes a mud flat one to two miles wide.

1871 H 108 These obstructions [*i.e.*, bars] exist wherever a river empties into the sea, through a coast or shore of quicksand.

1874 SAR 159 On the east the shores are usually bold, the lands rising quite abruptly ten to fifteen feet above the [Halifax] river.

(b) 1765 B 2-3 The shores of the river are generally very shoal for above 100 miles, at 50 yards distance more or less from the banks.

1821 F 79 The shores are level and shoal, extending in some places, where it is three miles wide, one or two miles into the river.

1829 USCHED vol. 187 #147.18 A considerable extent of its shores is shallow [context: Pensacola bay].

Preceded by a designating term: *ironbound shore*, a rock-bound shore; *main shore*, the shore of the mainland as opposed to that of an island.

1822 ASPPL III. 518 Key Largo is represented as presenting what is generally called an iron bound shore, surrounded on all sides by limestone rocks, and by shoals.

1823 STCW 25 Deep bays and islets vary the prospect [of the marshes along the Gulf shore], beyond which the main shore rises.

1837 W 30 The eastern end [of St. George's Island] is about three miles from the main shore.

1874 S 22 About noon they struck a lone cypress tree on the main shore.

Attrib. with *ridge.*

1869 BRINTON 104 The abundance of game on the shore ridge from Cape Sable to the Miami, led it to be chosen as a favorite spot of resort by the Indians.

See also BAY SHORE; BLUFF SHORE (attrib.); GULF SHORE; LAKE SHORE (attrib.); OUT SHORE; SEA-SHORE; SEA-

SHORE COUNTRY (attrib.); SEA-SHORE TRACT (attrib.).

SINK. (1) A low-lying tract, area, or basin where water collects, forming ponds or marshes, or where it disappears by sinking or evaporation. "Now U.S." (OED) DAE 1690. (2) A sink hole. DAE 1791. Sometimes these sinks act as subterranean outlets or drains of other waters; *e.g.*, a lake (1837 p. 132), or pond (1874). According to one writer (1829), sinks are caused by cavities in the rotten sub-stratum.

(1) 1869 FICSP 63-64 In many of the sinks or depressions where the cypress is found are familiar deposits of vegetable mould or muck.

(2) 1818 Y 41 In the extensive hammock which [lies] northeastwardly from its head there are hundreds of sinks with the purest water at their bottoms.

1823 STCS 31 We reached a remarkable sink, which I called the Rockwell.

1823 V 77 Water is very scarce here, and only found in a few sinks or ponds similar to those in the pine lands, but without trees around them.

1829 USCHED vol. 187 #147.4-5 It is owing to the numerous cavities of this rotten sub-stratum, that the surface of the ground is seen interspersed with numberless inverted conic hollows, called *sinks*, the size of which varies from a few square yards, to many acres.

1837 W 132, 148 The Massasaugea Sinks are situated about two miles S.E. from the lake, on the line between Leon and Jefferson counties. Here the waters of the lake, with several other streams unite, and together plunge into the earth ... [Several streams] fall into a sink of a semicircular form, about one hundred and twenty yards across, which is almost surrounded by high rocky banks.

1874 SAR 59 A radius of one mile from this sink will reach a circle in which is included Long Pond sink coming from west southwest, Black creek sink from south southwest, and Bailey's Mill creek sink, from east southeast. Thus four running streams coming from different directions sink near the same spot.

See also CYPRESS SINK; LIME SINK; LIMESTONE SINK; SINK HOLE.

SINK HOLE. A hole in the surface of the earth, freq. shaped somewhat like an inverted cone, formed by the action of water on the soil or underlying rock. DAE 1749. According to Williams (1837), a sink hole is a hole (p. 148) caused by a caving-in (p. 149-50) above a subterranean reservoir. Spec., a pond (1823; 1836); a lime sink (1837 p. 148); a dell (1837 p. 135).

1823 STCW 18   From the head of the Wakully to the ferry on the Ocholockney, a distance of twenty miles, the country is a high, sandy, pine barren, intermixed with sink holes and ponds, reservoirs, undoubtedly of the waters which sink through the sands and forming these subterannean [sic] streams, emerge from the great spring of the Wakully.

1827 W 7-8   Ponds and sink holes are numerous between the Chactawhatchee and Chapola rivers.

1836 ASPMA VII. 143   The water was generally obtained from ponds, or, as they are generally termed there, "sink-holes."

1837 W 135   The sink hole that receives these waters is a deep rocky dell in the north bank of the prairie, shaded with lofty oaks.

Ibid., 148   The sink holes, or lime sinks ... are usually formed by holes in the earth, above these subterrene reservoirs, like the sand in an hour glass, the earth caves in and the hole is filled with water. They are often very deep ... Two instances have occurred within

our own knowledge, where persons have camped under the pines one night, and the next, earth, trees, and all have disappeared, and an unfathomable sink has supplied the place.

Ibid., 150   It is evident that the debris of the rock, is in rainy seasons carried off by the currents of water that pass through these caves, and thus they become more and more enlarged, and when the rock is fritted quite through, the earth losing its support, falls into the cave, and forms a sink hole.

SLEW. A slough. DAE 1805. (A.)

1874 S 27   After sailing down this estuary to its confluence with the ocean at Jupiter, he must ... thread many of the almost numberless slews and lily-padded ponds of this extraordinary swamp.

See also SLOUGH; SLUE.

SLIDE. A river-bank which is sufficiently steep so that an animal can slide down it into the water; here, an alligator slide.

1874 KEASBEY 53   The Yankee ... left the alligators to repose upon their "slides" with a gravity of demeanor suited to the day.

SLOPE. A stretch of rising or falling ground. OED.

1791 B 76   On the other side was a spacious garden, occupying a regular slope of ground, down to the water.

1818 Y 131   The slope of the ridge on both sides marshy.

1837 W 140   The sea shore below Cape Canaverel is cut up into islands which are not usually more than a mile in width, the eastern slope being washed by the sea.

1874 SAR 170   From the mouth of the Withlacoochee to the Anclote, [is] a slope of country containing not less than six harbors.

1874 KEASBEY 102   Seventy-five miles above Jacksonville, the river is of immense breadth, with beautiful green slopes.

SLOUGH. A comparatively narrow stretch of backwater; a sluggish channel or inlet; a pond (1874). DAE 1665. Spec., a watercourse (*c.* 1832). (A.)

1828 ASPPL VI. 543 There are many sloughs that run through the islands.

c. 1832 ASPPL VI. 553 As respects the slough, marked BB, being a permanent water-course, it is like the rest of those sloughs, changing their position.

1836 ASPMA VII. 291 These ponds feed a series of sloughs, overgrown with thick woods, and at this point [near Boca Grande] very wide; but as the waters gather together they form little streams.

1874 S 22 At dark they were near an old slough made up of rotten lily pads and floating cabbage.

See also SLEW; SLUE.

SLUE. A slough. DAE 1822. (A.)

1874 S 27 Near New Smyrna...an old loggerhead had been stranded at high tide in the slue of a sand bar.

See also SLEW; SLOUGH.

SLUICE. A channel, drain, or small stream carrying off surplus or overflow water. DAE 1644. Spec., a river (1874, p. 21).

1870 BILL 133 One [road] is by the beach, where little swails and sluices, emptying into the lake, have to be leaped in wet weather.

1874 S 18, 21 We saw more birds after leaving Lake Winder. Acres of teal, widgeon, and other ducks dotted the marshy sluices ... [The waters of Lake Okeechobee] pour over the encircling marshes into the Everglades, and are slowly funnelled into the Gulf of Mexico and Atlantic Ocean through sluggish sluices, like the St. Lucie, Jupiter, Shark, and Withlacoochee rivers.

SOBBED LAND. Land having a subsoil almost impenetrable to moisture so that the rainfall on it cannot be absorbed.

1874 SAR 32 There is another species of pine land called by the natives "flatwoods." About four feet from the surface of this land a stratum of what is called sand rock is found. This is composed of common fine sand and cemented by sulphate of iron and aluminum; and a subsoil thus formed is almost impenetrable to moisture. As a consequence, it holds up all the rainfall, so that the land becomes packed, and is known to the natives as "sobbed land." Such soil is of very inferior quality and is scarcely fit for profitable agriculture.

SOFT MARSH. A marsh whose spongy nature allows water easily to penetrate its particles. DAE 1737 (no def.).

1775 R 30 The soft marshes [consist] ... of a very wet clay or mud.

1823 V 91 The *soft marshes* lie lower and are more subject to overflow and require in the embankments, earth from the high land to make them substantial, and consequently are more expensive in their redemption; but this once accomplished they are undoubtedly the most fruitful; affording in the dry culture means of raising sugar, hemp, corn, cotton, and indigo.

SOUND. A narrow stretch of water not a stream, as a strait or inlet. DAE 1607. Spec., a bay (1823; 1837 p. 8); an arm of a bay (1837 p. 136-37); an outlet of a river (1871).

1739 Oglethorpe letter, in CADOGAN 52 I am very sorry Captain *Fanshaw* could not stay in *Jekel Sound* 'till my arrival.

1742 RCBH 68 I Desire therefore that you would think of protecting St. *John's*

River, or at least *Frederica,* where Ships may come into *Jekyll* Sound.

1773 MS. 300 Sandwich Gulf has more Inlets to the Southward, the greatest of which is Dartmouth Sound.

1817 ASPMA I. 683 The British agent at Oakelockines Sound is giving presents to the Indians.

1823 V 47 Some miles beyond St. Lucie river are found Jupiter narrows, connecting the sound or bay of Indian river with that of Jupiter or Hobe.

1837 W 8 The first [coral rock] that we discovered near shore, is at Sarrazota sound or bay.

Ibid., 136-37 Below [Palm Sound] . . . the pine lands extend to the Gulf for a distance of 12 or 15 miles, to Cleni Sound, an arm of Charlotte Bay.

1843 Letter in BRYANT 113 In crossing the Matanzas sound . . . we passed two Minorcans in a boat.

1871 H 70 Amelia . . . river forms a spacious bay, directly in front of the city, near its junction with the sound or outlet of St. Mary's river.

SOUNDING. A place at sea where it is possible to reach the bottom with the ordinary deep-sea lead. Chiefly pl. OED 1626 (pl.). Here, with reference to the Florida coastal region.

c. 1565 Hawkins voyage, in HAKLUYT (1589) 537 So the 29 wee found our selues in 27 degrees, and in the soundings of Florida.

1775 R Apx. xliii Many people talk about going southward thro' the *Gulph of Florida* by keeping upon soundings outside the reef.

1797 MAG under *George's, St.* The coast between it and Cape Blaize, forms a kind of hollow bay, with deep soundings and a soft bottom.

1823 V 117 The edge of soundings, which are chiefly one hundred fathoms, are nearly parallel to the outer edge of the [Florida] reef.

1822 ASPNA IV. 964 But if lighthouses were erected on the Florida keys, vessels, in passing and repassing through the gulf, might keep on soundings the whole distance.

SOURCE. The fountainhead or origin of a river or stream; the spring (1827) or place from which a flow of water has its beginning. OED.

1731 C I. 45 This Plant I found at the Sources of Great Rivers.

1763 ASPPL I. 35 [Defines the bounds of East Florida:] To the source of St. Mary's thence, by the course of that river, to the Atlantic.

1818 Y 37 *New River.* This stream rises opposite to and interlocks with the head branches of Big-log creek of Apalachicola. Its source is among very large and intricate bay-galls.

1827 W 21 The Alaqua [river] rises north of the Chactawhatchee bay, and increases rapidly from large springs, some of which are large enough to turn mills at their source.

1837 W 49 Macaco, or Charlotte River, is supposed to have its source in Myacco Lake, in the heart of the Peninsula.

SOUR GROUND. Sour land.

1775 A Apx. 456 The province is a large peninsula, consisting chiefly of sandy barrens; level sour ground, abounding with tussucks; . . . [etc.].

SOUR GROVE. A grove of sour citrus trees; probably a wild-orange grove.

1874 SAR 177 Five years ago this was a sour grove.

SOUR LAND. Land that is cold and wet through retaining stagnant moisture. OED under *sour.* Here, a gall.

1827 W 53 The third kind of swamps are those spongy tracts, where the waters continually ooze through the soil, and finally collect in streams and pass off. These are properly termed galls, sometimes sour, sometimes bitter lands. They are the coldest soils we have, and the waters arising through them are frequently impregnated with sulphur, vitriol, and iron.

SPINE. A ridge or elevated stretch of ground. OED 1796 (MORSE *American Gazetteer*). Spec., an elevated plain. Poss. an Americanism.
1869 BRINTON 38 This plain ... forms a ridge or spine about sixty miles in width.

SPIT. A tongue of land projecting into the water; a reef. DAE 1738.
1773 MS. 288 The South Channel is made by ranging a white Spit running Northwardly from Anastasia Island.
1784 HUTCHINS 85 St. Joseph's bay ... shoals regularly towards the point, from which a spit of sand runs out a little way ... The end of the peninsula forms two or three points, from each of which a small spit runs off for a little distance.
1796 G 11 Give the Southwest point [of Kay West Harbor] a birth of ¾ of a mile as a rocky spit runs out from it.
1829 USCHED vol. 187 #147.18 *Pensacola Bay* ... is sheltered ... from the southerly winds by a spit of sand projecting from the main.

SPRING. (1a) A natural fountain or supply of water flowing from the ground, sometimes forming the source of a stream. DAE 1612. Several of the writers refer to the unusually large springs found in Florida (esp. 1766 p. 14; 1775; 1827 p. 7-8). Spec., a basin (1827 p. 38); a creek (1766 p. 23-24); a creek or river (1823 III); a fountain (1837); a hole (1852); the mouth of a creek (1823 IV); a river coming out of the earth (1827 p. 37-38); a run (1765); a well (1873). (b) An oceanic spring—i.e., a freshwater spring rising in the ocean. (Surviving form.) Cf. FOUNTAIN.

(1a) 1744 KIMBER 27 Our *Indians* discovered a fine, cool Spring.

1765 B 5 Landed ... at Johnson's Spring, a run of clear and sweet water.
1766 B 14, 23 A few hundred yards from the last spring is another much like it in taste, but much larger, and near 30 yards broad, having three heads with 30 yards ... Then came to a large creek called Johnson's Spring.
1775 R 34 High up this river [*sc.*, St. John's] are found some extraordinary springs, which at a small distance from the river on both sides, rush or boil out of the earth, at once becoming navigable for boats, and from twenty five to forty yards wide, their course is seldom half a mile before they meet the river; their water is (contrary to that of the river) clear.
1793 AUG map facing I. 532 The Spring in the Rock [near Rio Seco].
1823 ASPPL III. 796 Two thousand acres of land, lying on a creek or river called Big Spring, on the west of the river St. John's, about twenty-five miles south of lake George.
1823 ASPPL IV. 705 A creek ... empties into the river St. John's, about two miles north of a lake known by the name of Long lake—the mouth of the above creek is called "Big spring."
1827 W 7-8 Large springs, forming navigable streams, often burst from this formation [between Chactawhatchee & Chapola rivers].
Ibid., 37-38 The Big spring of Chapola, offers a very different scene; here another river bursts from the gaping rocks, with giant force, and furious rapidity ... The orifice ... is near thirty feet one way, by eight the other.
Ibid., 38 The Big Spring of Chactawhatche ... is a round basin of a few rods in circuit, very deep, and very clear.
1837 W 57 The Silver Spring, a beautiful fountain, rises on the S.W. border of the lake.
1852 IJ 22 "What!" said I, "do you call this immense hole a Spring?"
1873 FHQ XIV. 258 The [Green Cove] spring itself is one of the most

beautiful objects of its kind that I ever saw—a natural well of twenty feet in diameter, throwing up the translucent water in huge gushes.

Preceded by a specifying term.

1871 H 134 A third well was dug, a little further from the lake, and afforded a liquid clear as water, but strongly brackish and sulphury. The Governor called it an aperient spring.

1874 SAR 138 A few grains of some salt of iron alone would have no effect on the system, but, imbibing the same at some chalybeate spring . . . gives strength to the blood.

1766 B 24 Then [we] came to the main springs, where a prodigious quantity of very clear warm brackish water boiled up between vast rocks of unknown depth.

1827 W 38 Several medicinal springs are scattered over the country; the largest and most numerous are in, and on the borders of the Wakully and St. Marks rivers.

1766 B 20 In our going up the river viewed the north side and stinking springs.

(b) 1822 SIMMONS 40-41 It is asserted, that a spring of fresh water rises in the ocean, opposite to the south end of Anastatia Island, five or six miles from the coast. I have met with persons who averred, that they had seen this fountain, and drank fresh water from it. They further said, that they had sounded round it, and had obtained seven fathoms water; while in the middle, they could find no bottom. This spring may be one of the outlets of the great interior mass of waters, for which, there seems to be no sufficient exit on the surface.

1852 IJ 35 Is there not a very large spring of fresh water in the Atlantic off the coast not very far from Saint Augustine? Ships have got a supply of water from it.

See also BASIN SPRING (attrib.); BLOW-ING SPRING; FREESTONE SPRING; FRESH SPRING; FRESH-WATER SPRING; HEAD SPRING; MINERAL SPRING; PINE-BARREN SPRING (attrib.); SALT SPRING; SULPHUR SPRING; WARM SPRING.

SPRING BRANCH. A branch or brook fed by a spring or by springs. DAE 1650. (A.)

1823 ASPPL III. 811 One hundred [acres] on Sweet spring branch, St. Mary's river.

1825 FHQ XIV. 155 [The route] half a mile further up the road to the Cowford on St. John's crosses where it is nothing more than a small spring branch.

SPRING CREEK. A creek fed by a spring or by springs. DAE 1800. (A.)

1823 ASPPL III. 797 Five hundred acres of land, lying on the head of Spring creek, about six miles east of St. John's river, and seventy miles southwardly from St. Augustine.

1827 W 85 Near the centre of the North line . . . Spring Creek rises, which, with several other large springs on both sides of the line, form[s] the Chipola River.

1837 W 57 Twenty miles below Spring Creek, Orange Creek enters from the west.

SPRINGHEAD. A fountainhead or source of a stream or pond. DAE 1666.

1766 B 12 The spring-head is about 30 yards broad, and boils up from the bottom like a pot.

1818 Y 27 They are the springheads of several creeks which enter the Apalachicola below the Ochese Bluff.

1827 W 21 Six or seven feet water may be carried up to the spring head [of the Big spring of Chactawhatchee].

SPRUCE HILL. A hill overgrown with spruce trees.

1773 MS. 272, 287 In low pine Land. Spruce Hill ¼ m. runs North . . . A hill of spr. [spruce] Tr. [trees] S.W. off . . . On hilly Pe. [pine] Ld. [land] . . . above spr: [spruce] Hill.

SPRUCE-PINE RIDGE. A ridge on which the predominating growth is spruce pine.

1773 MS. 278, 285, 287 On Do. [the Ridge of sandy mountains] Spruce Pine Ridge . . . A spruce pine ridge S.E. off . . . Savh. [savannah] runs far South and the Ridge of Spruce pine.
1825 GADSDEN 120 The last 9½ miles to Tomoka, sandy, blackjack, scrub, and spruce pine ridge, occasionally diversified with pine flats.

SPRUCE RIDGE. A ridge on which spruce trees grow.

1773 MS. 286, 287 In high Pe. [pine] Ld. [land] . . . sp: [spruce] ridge & Ham: [hammock] 1 mile off . . . Above Savh. [savannah] end of Spr: [spruce] ridge.

SPUR. A range, ridge, hill, or part of this, projecting for some distance from the main system; an offshoot. OED. Spec., a bluff (1818 p. 34).

1818 Y 23, 34 Some of their [i.e., oak hills] spurs, with broad gentle slopes extend down the Okalokina for several miles . . . At its southern extremity, a Bluff comes in on the east side—a barren spur from the sand-hills.
1823 V 73 One spur [of the dividing ridge] leading from the old Suwanee town . . . runs parallel to the coast on the west of the great Alachua savanna.
1837 W 130 Hickory hill . . . throws off a spur or ridge, which extends about six miles to the S.W.
1829 USCHED vol. 187 #147.11 The mass of rotten limestone . . . [forms] the rich and extensive spur on which lies Tallahassee.

STRAIT. (1a) Also, STREIT (a form unrecorded in the OED). A comparatively narrow water-way or passage connecting two large bodies of water. When used as a geographical proper name, the word is usually pl. with

sing. sense. OED. (b) With reference to the Straits of Florida.

(1a) 1771 VIAUD 71 We could see another [island], that was separated from ours by a strait, about half a quarter of a league over.
1817 ASPPL IV. 178 Deer Point, or the west cape of the small point formed by the bay of Pensacola and the straits of St. Rosa.
1823 V 36 After passing the straits, Nassau river discharges itself between Amelia and Talbot islands.
(b) 1652 HEYLIN 117 Sea faring men . . . know by leaving these Rocks [sc., Martyrs] or Ilands on the left hand of them, that they are already entred in the Streits.
1769 STORK vi, 1 This confined strait . . . is about 60 miles wide, and somewhat more than 200 miles long . . . The peninsula terminates in the gulph of Mexico, by which it is also bounded on the west, and by the atlantick ocean, and the strait of Florida on the east.
1848 USCSD vol. 531 #30.13 The streams which enter into the straits of Florida are navigable.
1869 BRINTON 41 This ocean-river rushes eastward through the Straits of Florida.

STRAND. The land bordering the sea. OED. The NID does not agree with the OED that this term is "now poet., arch. or dial." "Specif.: The beach of the ocean, a sea"—NID (here, 1776). Spec., the sea-shore (1791).

1771 VIAUD 82 Quite overpowered by fatigue, we sunk down on the strand.
1775 R Apx. lxix [This] land has a woody flat appearance, with an even white beach, and a bold shore, so as to have 10 or 11 fathom water within a mile, or a mile and a half from the strand.
1776 NAWIG under Florida, West The Strand takes up a great depth, it is a white and dry sand.
1791 B 157 I at length by dusk made

a safe harbour, in a little lagoon, on the sea shore or strand of a bold sandy point.
1821 F 110   Trunks of the largest trees are often found lying upon the strand.
1823 V 46   The adjoining strand [is] ... called the money bank.

STREAM. (1a) A course of water flowing continuously along a bed on the earth, forming a river, rivulet, or brook. OED. (b) Appended to a river-name. Now only *poet.* OED. (c) Preceded by a qualifying term. (2a) The flow or current of a river. OED. (b) Extended to apply to the well-known current usually called the Gulf Stream, but referred to here as (ellipt.) the Stream (1774; 1803), the stream of the Gulf of Florida (1769), or the Florida stream.

(1a) 1563 RIBAULD 30   [We] found ... as large a deuiding it selfe into many great streames, great and broade stretchinges towards the high land.
1635 Hondy's Mercator's Atlas 900   All the country is watered with divers Rivers and Streames.
1763 ROBERTS 13   This river is joined by a great stream.
1772 WALKER Apx. No. 5   [The estate] ... is comprehended from the stream called *El Caño de Palica.*
1800 ASPPL I. 99   By the most southern stream of the river St. Mary.
1827 W 9   The springs and streams in this part of the country ... sink beneath the limestone rock, where, having united their currents and become highly impregnated with lime, they rise at once navigable rivers; such are the St. Marks, the Wakulla, and Oscilla rivers.
1842 letter in SPRAGUE 385   This stream [Fish-eating Creek] is very tortuous, and sometimes swells into a river, and then dwindles to a brook.
(b) 1773 MS. 175   The Kofasiki Nation ... was settled on the west Side of Apalachicola Stream, discharging itself into the Gulf of Mexico to the East of

Cape Escondido, at that time bearing the Name of St. Helena.
(c) 1837 W 290   We now returned to the fork ... and proceeded up the main stream [of the Caloosahatche].
1823 STCW 18   The waters ... sink through the sands and, forming these subterannean [*sic*] streams, emerge from the great spring of the Wakully.
1766 B 19   The surrounding sand [slipping] ... into the cavity ... presses down the spring until the water below is collected from the back under-ground stream so strong as to force the sand and water above the common surface, so that there is a continual periodical motion.
1821 F 178   Six mile Brook ... is a pretty little winding stream.
(2a) 1837 W 51   St. Lucia enters Indian River near the south end, with a broad bold stream.
(b) 1769 STORK vi   When they have got round the capes, and fall into the stream of the gulph of Florida, they are carried forcibly to the northwards by the strength of that ... current.
1774 Barton in G 27   From Cape Canaveral to this river the Stream runs from 4 to 5 leagues from the shore.
1796 G 17   You will then often find the vessel gliding smoothly along in the direction of the Florida stream, till you come to the parallel of 28°.
1803 E 260-61   In sailing south into the Gulf of Mexico, the stream should be avoided with as much care as it is sought for in the other case ... In latitude 26° 30′ N. the stream passes near the land, and sometimes touches it.
1822 ASPNA IV. 964   It will ensure the undisturbed navigation of the northwest side of the Florida stream (or Gulf of Florida) to our merchant vessels.
1826 ASPMA III. 295   It is, however, far from certain that the Florida stream is always to be the channel of communication from the gulf to the Atlantic.

See also GULF STREAM; HEADSTREAM; STREAMLET; TRIBUTARY STREAM (attrib.); WATER-STREAM.

STREAMLET. A small stream; a brook, rill, or rivulet. OED.

1842 PREBLE 40 After dining hauled the canoes through a narrow streamlet.
1870 BILL 117 Again the river seems lost in a bewildering perspective of silver streamlets.

SUGAR-CANE LAND. Sugar land.

1871 H 63 The hammocks [of Manatee county] are from a light to a dark gray color, and naturally rich; they constitute our sugar-cane land, principally.

SUGAR LAND. Land suitable for growing sugar cane. DA 1692. Prob. Southern.

1823 V 48 This lake is thirty-five or forty miles in length, with marshes at its south end, which contains a body of such fine sugar land.
1836 SSW 175 The sugar lands were extensive and fine, being what is called "high hammock."
1837 W 11 The Big swamp, Long swamp and Wahoo swamp, present large bodies of first rate sugar lands.
1851 BYRNE v Within a few miles of Cedar Keys, on the banks of the Suwannee, the Wacasassa, and the Withlacochee rivers, are some of the largest and richest bodies of sugar land in the State.
1869 FICSP 34 There are in Levy County alone, not less than one hundred thousand acres of the very best description of sugar lands.
1874 SAR 147 [The] rolling lands ... in connection with the river swamps constitute some of the most desirable sugar lands in the State.

SULPHUR SPRING. A spring of water containing sulphurous compounds, or impregnated with sulphurous gases. DAE 1807.

1837 W 55 This stream rises about a mile from the lake in several large sulphur springs.
1856 LANMAN 138 [The Suwanee river] boasts of two large white sulphur springs, which are twelve miles apart, and pour their medicated treasures immediately into the river.

Attrib. with *run.*
1874 S 19 "I remember one mornin' we went down to the big sulphur spring run—you've bin thar yourself."

SUMMIT. The topmost point or ridge of a hill. OED. Also applied to the upper part of a bank (1837), or submerged cliff (1856).

1791 B 179-80 Now the sand ridges become higher ... the summit of the ridges more gravelly.
1823 V 40 Turtle Mount or Mount Tucker, the summit of which is about 80 feet above the level of Hillsborough river.
1829 USCHED vol. 187 #147.37 This point can be considered as the summit of the Florida ridge in that direction.
1837 ASPMA VII. 376 I likewise placed myself behind a large cypress that stood on the summit of the bank.
1856 FHQ I. 35 From one side of [the portal of Wakulla Springs] ... looms up a limestone cliff, the summit of which is itself nearly fifty feet beneath the spectator in a boat.

Attrib. with *ground, pass.*
1829 USCHED vol. 187 #147.8 The summit ground between Barbour's plantation and the upper fork, has been found to be 100 feet above low tide in St. Mary's harbor.
1832 USCHED vol. 219 #185.7 [The route] pursues the valley to the western termination of the Summit pass.

SWALE. Here, SWAIL. A marshy or moist depression in a level or rolling area. DAE 1667.

1870 BILL 133 One [road] is by the beach, where little swails and sluices, emptying into the lake, have to be leaped in wet weather.

SWAMMOCK. Land resembling both swamp land and hammock land; a swampy hammock. DAE 1863 (both DAE quotations pertain to Florida). A blend-word formed by the contamination of *swamp* and *hammock*. Prob. local in Florida.

1851 BYRNE 13 Low hammocks (which, from the fact of their participating of the nature both of hammocks and swamps, have been very graphically termed *swammocks,*) are not inferior to swamp lands in fertility, but perhaps are not so durable.—They are always level, or nearly so, and have a soil of greater tenacity than that of the high hammocks.

Ibid., 14 Red cedar and cypress of immense growth abound in most of the "swammocks."

SWAMP. (1a) A tract or area of low-lying ground, usually along streams or near lakes or lagoons, often marshy or overflowed in wet seasons, and supporting many trees or bushes. DAE 1624. The DAE editors acknowledge "the difficulty of defining the word in precise terms." No doubt the primary reason for this confusion is the fact that there are several types of swamps. Williams divides swamps into three principal categories: (A) river swamps (*v.* 1827 below); (B) pine-barren swamps, or cypress swamps (*q.v.*—1827); and (C) galls (*q.v.*). Specifically referred to as *low hammock* (1823; 1869); *morass* (1818); a *thicket* (1837 p. 197). Used synonymously with *marsh* (1766 p. 12) and *woods* (1817; 1828). Also, once with reference to a *mangrove swamp* (1837 p. 98). It is possible that the 1766 (p. 29) quotation belongs under (3). With regard to (b) below, it must be pointed out that "bare swamp" is difficult to explain. Since swamps are distinguished from marshes in being timbered, a bare

swamp can hardly be one which lacks vegetation. However, one possibility is that the author is attempting to describe swamp land which has been cleared, but which is still referred to as *swamp.* One other example in this section should be noted: The "isolated swamps" which are the sources of small streams are specified by the 1871 writer as "cypress swamps, cypress ponds, and bay galls." (2) Swamp land. DAE 1671 (last date: 1784). (3) A boggy or marshland stream; a slough, or slue. *Local, U.S.* NID. Spec., a branch (1823); a drain (1803); a lake (1821). Poss. Southern.

(1a) 1765 B 5 We crossed . . . many narrow moist swamps.

1766 B 12 On the other side of the river, is a large swamp or reedy marsh.

1766 B 28, 29 Here was also a rich swamp of ash and maple . . . Adjacent to which is a shallow but good swamp with some cypress-trees.

1769 STORK ftn., 5 All the forest trees (pine excepted) thrive best in the swamps, where the soil is always rich; and when cleared and drained, is proper for the growth of rice, hemp, and indigo.

1786 in SIEBERT II. 58 The Rice Swamp which was cultivated and planted in 1779 . . . was a fresh water Marsh & Mr. Oswald & he (the Witness) were the only persons that raised Rice upon that kind of Swamp.

1817 ASPMA I. 687 The number [of Indians] was very considerable, extending about one hundred and fifty yards along the shore, in the edge of a swamp or thick woods.

1818 Y 47 The soil of this morass is similar to that in the larger Bay-Galls . . . The growth, both of timber and thicket is uncommonly impervious and it would be difficult to conceive a prospect of greater gloom and horror than it contributes in the interior of the [Eokafanoke] swamp.

1823 V 87 *Graham's swamp,* between Matanzas and Tomoco, is chiefly low hammock.

1825 ASPPL IV. 617 As far as the swamp called White Oak.

1827 W 52 First, those formed on the borders of rivers, by inundation; these are the richest swamps, and most extensive. They are usually separated from the stream by a ridge of dry land, formed by the heaviest parts of the alluvial matter, which is deposited immediately after leaving the current; this ridge, or natural embankment, prevents the waters from draining off, as the surface of the rivers subside. They are, usually, densely covered with heavy timber, and this tangled with innumerable vines, which renders them almost impenetrable.

c. 1828 ASPPL VI. 121 The four remaining parts in the wood or swamp in the southeast part of Lake George.

1837 W 98 The White Mangrove ... grows in profound swamps, unmixed with any other timber.

1837 W 197 [A company of negroes] were sent to form an ambuscade in an impervious thicket, called Twelve Mile Swamp.

1869 FICSP 53 The larger proportion of what has loosely been called swamp in Florida, is simply low hammock, with a soil of inexhaustible fertility, and covered with a dense growth of mainly Cypress, Magnolia and Sweet Bay.

(b) Preceded by a specifying term.

1853 FHQ VIII. 17 The water was up to foot [*sic*] of the Noble field and all over the bare swamp up to Murans at Mill place.

1823 ASPPL III. 791 Two thousand five hundred and sixty acres of land, lying between the creeks called Boggy swamp and Clapboard creek.

1765 B 9 The river ... is lined on both sides with very rich hard swamps.

1823 V 65 After passing the head swamps of Nassau river.

1871 H 27 Isolated swamps from which the branches and creeks have their starting point, are called "cypress swamps," "cypress ponds," or "bay galls," according to the growth of the trees they sustain.

1821 F 177 On the east, a wet, rushy swamp, bordering northerly with forests, having small underwood.

1766 B 10 The woody swamps are chiefly black and white ash, with red maple next the river.

(2) 1743 C II iii The Scituation of this Land [Rice Land] is various, but always low, and usually at the Head of Creeks and Rivers, and before they are cleared of Wood are called *Swamps* ... [and] are thick, overgrown with Underwood and lofty Trees of mighty Bulk, which by excluding the Sun's Beams, and preventing the Exhalation of these stagnating Waters, occasions the Land to be always wet.

1765 letter in STORK Apx. 35 Above Piccolata, for 40 miles along the river is as good swamp, or rice land, as any in Carolina.

1778 in SIEBERT II. 42 There were 905 Acres of Swamp, Marsh & Oak Land.

1823 V 70 The lands on the margin of St. John's river below lake George, are hammock and swamp of all qualities.

1871 H 49 The arable lands ... are classed as swamp, hammock and pine ... The swamp is wet, and subject, to some extent, to overflow—soil alluvial, heavy [*sic*] timbered with gum, oak, magnolia, beech, and bay.

(3) 1803 E Apx. 139-40 The principal, or largest of those swamps, or drains, is the most easterly one.

1821 F 72 [The river St. Mary's] takes its rise in a large swamp, or lake, called Quakaphanake.

1823 ASPPL III. 798 Three hundred acres of land, lying on Spell swamp, a branch of the Nassau river.

Attrib. with *branch, island, run.*

1823 ASPPL III. 801 Twenty-five acres of land lying on Secret Swamp branch, to the southwardly of the city of St. Augustine.

1823 V 68   Passing Buffalo bluff . . . its [*i.e.*, the St. Johns] character is slightly varied by a chain of swamp islands.

1773 MS. 220   To Swamp run to pine land.

See also ASH SWAMP; BACK-WATER SWAMP; BAY-GALL SWAMP (attrib.); BAY SWAMP; CABBAGE SWAMP; CANE SWAMP; CEDAR SWAMP; COVE SWAMP (attrib.); CREEK SWAMP (attrib.); CYPRESS SWAMP; DISMAL SWAMP; FRESH-WATER SWAMP; FRESH-WATER TIDE-SWAMP; GUM SWAMP; HIGH SWAMP; INLAND SWAMP; ISLAND SWAMP; LILY SWAMP; LIVE-OAK SWAMP; LOBLOLLY-BAY SWAMP; MAGNOLIA SWAMP; MANGROVE SWAMP; MAPLE SWAMP; MYRTLE SWAMP; OAK SWAMP; PALMETTO SWAMP; PINE-BARREN SWAMP (attrib.); RICE SWAMP; RIVER SWAMP; SAVANNA SWAMP; (attrib.); SEDGE SWAMP; TIDE-RIVER SWAMP; TUPELO SWAMP; WATER-OAK SWAMP; WET SWAMP.

SWAMP LAND.   Land, usually cultivable and fertile, in a swamp. DAE 1663. (A.) According to the 1851 author, this type of land was originally a basin, which became filled up by deposits washed in from the adjacent higher land.

1778 in SIEBERT II. 42   He cleared 20 Acres of Swamp Land.

1821 F 147   *Swamp lands* are distinguished by the growth of the cypress and other large trees in forests.

1837 W 139   The expense of draining [marshes] is less, than that of clearing the heavy timber from our swamp lands.

1851 BYRNE 12   The swamp lands are unquestionably the most *durably* rich lands in the country. They are the most recently formed lands, and are still annually receiving additions to their surface. They are intrinsically the most valuable lands in Florida, being as fertile in the beginning as the hammocks, and more durable. They are evidently

alluvial, and of recent formation. They occupy natural depressions or basins, which have been gradually filled up by deposites [*sic*] of vegetable *debris*, etc., washed in from the adjacent and higher lands.

See also MANGROVE-SWAMP LAND; RIVER-SWAMP LAND.

SWASH.   A channel or inlet between sand banks or between a sand bank and the shore. DAE 1681. (A.) (Corresponds to British *swatch*.)

1742 RCBH Apx. 43   It was agreed, *That the Galleys should be attacked provided there was water eno' upon the Swash, opposite to the Castle, for our Boats to go round.*

1829 USCHED vol. 187 #147.12   The swash, or northeast channel . . . comes into the main channel [of the Appalachicola river] 3 miles from the bar, and presents a depth of five feet through.

SWEET-WATER COUNTRY.   A region abounding in streams of fresh water.

1784 GME 97   The Indians with much propriety, call this *the sweet water country*, on account of the fine streams of water every where to be met with.

SWELL.   (1) An area or extent of rising land. "The absol. use [1827 below] is specially American (OED)." DAE 1808 (absol.—[A.]; with qualifying phrase, in OED: 1764).

(1)   1818 Y 161-62   In the fourteenth mile there is a swell of ground forming a low ridge which nearly encircles the Barancas on the land side.

1823 V 47   One swell of high ground [on Jupiter sound] rising above the rest is called on marine charts the Bleachyard, from the large spots of land uncovered by vegetation, presenting . . . the appearance of linen spread out on the hills upon the side next the beach.

1827 W 88   From the level tract of pine land, above described, the country

rises over gentle swells of red and white clay ... Between these swells, abundant streams of pure water enliven every valley.
1837 W 11 [The land] towards the sea coast, falls off in gentle swells of pine land.
See also PINELAND SWELL (attrib.).

SWIMMING CREEK. A creek which is too deep to be crossed on foot.

1823 FHQ XIV. 92 From Pensacola to the Choctawhatchie, the country is very broken and intersected with a great number of small branches and swimming creeks, which caused great delay.

SWORD-GRASS POND. A pond covered with sword-grass.

1773 MS. 219, 220 Gall near a Sword grass pond ... Near a Sword grass pd. [pond] in pine ld. [land].

T

TABLE-LAND. An elevated region of more or less flat land usually free of tree growth; a plateau. DAE 1826.

1775 R Apx. lvii The *Table Land* [called *Mesa Maria*] and the *Saddle Hill* over ... [the entrance] shew as i have delineated them.
1823 V 67 Kingsley's bluff ... is about twenty-five feet high, with a table land of some extent, presenting an eligible scite for a town.
1871 H 93 The interior of the county ... is mostly a table land of flat woods, from which the rains drain off slowly.

TANK. A natural pond. "Chiefly W." DAE 1869.

1796 G 18 Just within the sandy beach ... you will often find fresh water ponds or natural tanks, which receive and retain the rain water.

TERRACE. (a) A table-land; (b) a horizontal shelf or bench on the side of a hill, or sloping ground. OED. It

is not clear to which of the definitions given above the dividing platform referred to below should be assigned; however, it appears more likely that the second interpretation is the one intended.

1791 B 199 We turned to the right hand, riding over the charming green terrace dividing the forests from the plains.

THICKET. A dense growth of shrubs, bushes, or small trees. DAE 1612.

1743 CADOGAN 20 The Road by Fort *Diego* is a very good one ... [a] great part of which is broad hard Beach, and the rest open Land, except two small Thickets.
1744 KIMBER 23 His Excellency taking up his Quarters in a hollow Thicket.
1791 B 75 An Indian stepped out of a thicket.
1818 Y 24 The thickets in this part prevent the luxuriant growth of grass.
1827 W 83-84 A narrow swamp ... entirely surrounds this hammock, with a thicket so impervious, that until the surveyors were obliged to push a line through it, no one had suspected any thing but swamp existed there.
1874 S 23 The entrance to the glades was a thicket of custard-apple trees.
See also LIVE-OAK THICKET; MYRTLE THICKET; OAK THICKET; THICKET-WOOD(S); TITI THICKET.

THICKET-WOOD(S). A thicket.

1836 ASPMA VII. 418 The only sure means of terminating [the difficulties with these savages will be to scour] ... the tangled thicket-woods and deep swamps into which the enemy would escape.

TIDELAND. Land that is covered and uncovered by the flow and ebb of the tide. DAE 1802.

1787 in SIEBERT II. 239 200 acres of rich tide land well dam'd.

TIDE-RIVER SWAMP. A swamp adjacent to, or partially surrounding, a tidal river. *Cf.* FRESH-WATER TIDE-SWAMP.

1787 in SIEBERT II. 168 At length having found an excellent tide river swamp, on St. Mary's river.

TIDEWATER. (1a) Water brought into a given area by the action of the rising tide. DAE 1785. (b) Water, as of a given area or in specified streams, which is affected by the tide; a region or area in which water is affected by the tide. DAE 1772. Poss. Southern.

(1a) 1827 W 28 A water moccasin, that covers the old logs, in the rivers near tide water, is a large dreadful looking snake.

1869 FICSP 138 These Keys are only a few feet above tide water.

(b) 1823 V 36 The St. Sebastian river ... owes its size chiefly to the influence of tide water.

1829 USCHED vol. 187 #147.39 In order to descend from Okefenoke swamp to tide-water.

1852 WFH 31 Palatka is a small settlement on the tide waters of the St. John's.

TIDEWATER CHANNEL. A channel affected by the tides.

1871 H 70 Amelia Island ... is separated from the mainland by a tide-water channel, called Amelia river.

TIMBERED COUNTRY. A timbered or wooded region. DAE 1807. (A.)

1818 Y 36 On the west side of the Main pass the timbered country extends to the mouth [of the Apalachicola river].

TIMBERED LAND. Land covered with timber. DAE 1722. (A.)

1818 Y 42 One mile from the fort, the timbered land both on the Wakully

and St. Mark, recedes from the banks diverging towards the gulf.

1836 SSW 75-76 It is the general opinion that the rich, timbered lands, such as those on the St. John's ... are sickly in the summer and autumn.

1837 W 9 Black Water River descends through a valley of fine timbered land.

TIMBERLAND. Land that is well wooded. DAE 1654. (A.)

1827 W 19 The centre of the island is usually covered with pine forests, among which there are some hammocks of good hard timber land.

1829 ASPPL V. 692 tr. Matters ... ought to be in conformity to the general ordinance respecting timber lands [montes] of the year 1748.

1874 SAR 130 Timber lands along the line of railroad and rivers can be bought in large tracts.

TITI THICKET. A thicket consisting of titi trees.

1837 W 128 The streams [on the east side of Aliqua river] ... pass into brakes of reed cane, and then titi thickets succeed.

TONGUE. (1a) A narrow strip of land, running into the sea or other body of water, or between two branches of a river (1827). OED. Spec., a point or narrow cape (1874). (b) With reference to the East Florida peninsula.

(1a) 1827 USCHED vol. 217 #43.41 The western point is the junction of the waters of two rivers, by which is plainly meant the extremity of the tongue of land between them, or that spot upon which, when you stand, one of your arms is extended over the water of one river, and the other over those of the other river.

1832 USCSD vol. 214 #136.16 The tongue of land between the northern and ... arms of the bay, furnishes a most excellent position for a town site.

1870 BILL 81 Fifteen miles away is Mandarin, a projecting tongue of land, which, from where we stand, seems to sever the river.

1874 S 22 An osprey had built its nest in a cypress tree upon this cape ... The tongue of land was called Osprey Point.

(b) 1660 LE BLANC 352 Towards this point or tongue of land, in form of an *Isthmus,* 'tis dangerous sayling.

1773 MS. 191 East Florida is an irregular Figure representing a Tongue or Peninsula containing near 62718 square miles.

1831 ASPNA IV. 121 Having the ocean on each side of it, that tongue of land was peculiarly adapted to the growth of the [live oak] tree.

TORRENT. A stream of water flowing with great swiftness and impetuosity, whether from the steepness of its course (1827), or from being temporarily flooded. OED.

1771 VIAUD 207 I thought it impossible to be able to stem the torrent, till it had delivered us into the sea.

1827 W 84 In the western part [of Walton county], the streams burst in large torrents from the ridges, and pursue their course to the bay, in deep ravines.

TRIBUTARY. A stream that contributes to or flows into a larger stream or lake. DAE 1831.

1822 SIMMONS 29 [The appearance of bonnet leaf] indicates from a distance, the influx of some tributary of the main stream.

1825 GADSDEN 120 These are the sources of Indian river ... communicating with the savannahs and tributaries of the St. John's river.

1837 W 145 Smith's Creek, a tributary of Halifax River.

1874 SAR 118 Thomas, Boggy, Funks, Mills, and Lofton, tributaries of the Nassau river, and of the little St. Mary's river.

Attrib. with *stream, water.*

1823 V 56 The Choctawhatchie river, and all its tributary streams discharge into the eastern end of this bay.

1827 W 34 The bank ... commands a beautiful and extensive wild prospect of the Appalachicola, and its tributary streams.

1823 V 39 Haul-over Creek ... receives Ormond's creek, and another tributary water.

TUPELOW SWAMP. A swamp overgrown with tupelo trees (*i.e.,* black or sour gum trees, or any one of the various trees of the genus *Nyssa*). DAE 1765 under *tupelo* (no def.). (*Tupelo* is originally a Creek Indian word.) Probably the same thing as *back swamp* (*q.v.*). Cf. GUM SWAMP. Prob. local in Florida.

1787 in SIEBERT II. 255 The soil of both tracts [is] ... of the richest quality of Tupelo swamp. It had a rise and fall of Tide of about 5 feet; and was regularly over flowed every Springtide.

TURN. A place or point at which a river or stream turns. OED.

1821 F 121 Although the bar of Apalachicola River is a plain one, yet the navigation up is difficult ... owing to ... the great number of turns.

1874 S 28 The turns in the ditches [of the Everglades] were so short that it frequently took several minutes to push the boat around them.

TURNING. A change in the direction of the course—here—of a river. OED.

1773 MS. 247 [There] is a Reserve of 10000 acres for a Town and Township 13 miles, according to the Turnings of the [St. Mary's] River, distant from the Bar of the Inlet.

1791 B 228 It is in the eddy coves, under the points and turnings of the river, where the surface of the waters

... is covered with the leaves of the Nymphea.

TURPENTINE LAND. Land sufficiently overgrown with pine trees to be suitable for the production of turpentine. DAE 1848 under *turpentine* (no def.). (Not in OED.) Poss. (A.).
1874 SAR 130 Turpentine and timber lands along the line of railroad and rivers can be bought in large tracts.

TURPENTINE TRACT. A tract of turpentine land; spec., pine barren land.
1786 in SIEBERT II. 43, 44 He likewise lost by the Cession a Turpentine Tract of 300 Acres ... This Tract ... was all Pine barren Land Except 20 or 30 Acres which were Cypres & Oak Swamps ... [The claimant got] 8 *s* or pound 10 by Tar made on this Tract.

TURTLE HOLE. A nest constructed on the beach in which a turtle lays its eggs.
1874 S 26 Nothing but a rifle-ball will keep a bear from a turtle hole.

U

UNDERGROWTH. Shrubs and small trees growing under and about tall trees; brushwood, underwood. DAE 1666.
1823 STCW 22 We were unable to find where the waters emerged ... on account of canebrakes and undergrowth.
1836 ASPMA VI. 997 The banks boggy, and covered with a dense undergrowth.

UPLAND. (a) High ground; an area or piece of high ground. (b) An area or stretch of high ground rising from low land near a body of water. "Chiefly *local* and *U.S.*" (OED)–DAE 1635. It is probable, though not certain, that all of the quotations (ex-

cepting perhaps the 1791) belong in the (a) category. Spec., hammock land (1818). According to Williams (1827), the uplands in West Florida are clay formations.
1791 B 144 These rich lands are neglected, and the upland only is under culture.
1803 E 279 The upland is generally of an inferior quality, producing little besides wire-grass, pitch-pine, (pinus) and broom pine.
1818 Y 31 The fertile upland is called *hammock land.*
1827 W 45-46, 47 Uplands are formations of clay, which arise gradually on the subtending limestone; they usually commence about twenty miles from the coast. The first stratum of clay is usually white; red clay succeeds; while the surface is covered with a mulatto or chocolate colored loam. The trees, on this soil, are abundant, and form the pleasantest groves imaginable ... The uplands produce few shrubs.
Ibid., 66, 68 The red clay uplands suit this vegetable [Irish potato] better than any of our soils ... Apple trees ... might perhaps succeed better on the clay upland, at a distance from the coast.
1871 H 136 The saw palmetto ... makes a dense border of evergreen along the edge of the upland.
Attrib. with *hill.*
1827 W 24 This spring is on the south-east side of the Suwannee river, below the Santaffee, at the foot of the Upland hills.

See also OAK UPLAND.

V

VALE. A valley. DAE 1666.
1587 L 24L Then we discovered a little hil adioyning vnto a great vale very greene and in forme flat.
1791 B 203 We continued down the great vale, along its banks, quite to

the savanna and lake where it vented itself.

1827 W 84 North and east of the Alaqua, the streams head in gentle vales, like grass savannas in the outward circle.

1871 H 32 The surface of the whole county [sc., Gadsden] is somewhat undulating and broken, exhibiting frequent hills and vales, and running streams.

VALLEY. (1a) A long depression between hills or stretches of high ground. DAE 1612. (b) With reference to specific rivers. DAE 1831. (A.)

(1a) 1708 OLDMIXON I. 375 There's a pleasant Lake and Valley in [the country upon the River May].

1743 C II. iv Many of these Vallies are ... bounded by steep Rocks.

1784 HUTCHINS 81 The vallies [between Escambia river and Pensacola] are covered with grass or canes.

1829 USCHED vol. 187 #147.9 The valley of the stream is about one mile wide at this place.

1832 USCHED vol. 219 #185.6 This route would continue in the valley of the pond.

1837 W 128 Holmes Valley on the east side of the Chactawhatche River, extends eastward ten or twelve miles.

1874 SAR 159 The lands [along the Halifax river] ... drop off into valleys.

(b) 1855 USCSED vol. 756 #76.5 The divide between New and Sampson rivers ... continues to the valley of the Santa Fe river.

See also MEADOW VALLEY (attrib.).

W

WARM SPRING. A spring containing or producing warm water. Also pl. as proper name. DAE 1748.

1765 B 5 At the foot of the last issued out another warm spring of clear water.

1766 B 19 One of these springs was so warm, that although I was in a sweat, yet it seemed warm to my hand; they are all of them warm, and of a loathsome taste, their sediment is white, and one may smell them at many yards distance.

1851 BYRNE 14 A tract extending from above Newnansville to the Warm Springs.

WASTE. Uninhabited and uncultivated country; a wild and desolate region, a desert, a wilderness (1871). OED. Spec., a savanna (1822).

1771 VIAUD 161 We ... could see nothing to rest our wearied sight upon, but a boundless and barren waste, extending on all sides.

1791 B 204 The view Southerly seemed endless wastes, presenting rocky, gravelly and sandy barren plains.

1822 SIMMONS 24 The river ... terminated in this savanna. This immense waste is mostly inundated.

1871 H 102 Several citizens of the county, meeting by accident in the middle of this dreary wilderness, named it Walton Waste.

1874 SAR 145 Nothing is seen in this section but scrub and barren wastes.

Attrib. with *plain, pond.*

1874 SAR 96 A little shrubbing and refencing are all the preparation necessary for plowing and planting those waste plains.

1836 SSW 145 Passed several dried up ponds with tall broomlike dried grass, and a squalid cypress or two, or pine growing in them ... Nothing was to be seen like water, but these waste ponds which deceived us from a distance, proving always dry or nearly so, when we got up to them.

See also DESERT WASTE (attrib.); WASTE LAND.

WASTE LAND. Uncultivated or uninhabited land. DAE 1640.

c. 1821 ASPPL V. 724-25 tr. The Brigadier Count of Punonrostro ...

humbly requests . . . all the waste lands
[tierras incultas], not heretofore ceded,
in Florida, lying between the river Perdido, westward of the Gulf of Mexico,
and the rivers Amaruja and St. John's
. . . And also all the waste land [el ter-
reno baldio] not ceded to any other
individual, which is between the river
Hijuelos, in East Florida . . . to the point
of Tancha.

WATER. A body or collection of (a)
flowing or (b) standing water. OED.
(c) Preceded by a qualifying term.
The 1773 classification of running
waters under (a) is no doubt largely,
if not entirely, arbitrary. (The EDD
gives the following senses for this
term as dialectal: a river, stream,
or brook; also, a lake.)

(a) 1773 MS. 308 I distinguish the
runing [sic] Waters in Streams, Rivers
& Rivulets; the last as not navigable
Branches of Rivers or Streams. The
Rivers as Navigable Waters emptying
into Streams, & the Streams as navigable
Waters disemboguing into the Ocean.
1803 E 234 The up-land on the Chattahocha, and Flint Rivers, from the
boundary southward is . . . much better
than on some of the waters already
mentioned.
1818 Y 29 All the branches of New
river and many of the Okalokina waters
rise in these thickets.
1823 ASPPL III. 808 One hundred
acres of land, situated on Front Creek,
a water of St. John's river.
1823 V 41 The main stream of the
last water [Indian river] has one of its
sources in this swamp.
1823 STCW 24 It was plain to dis-
cern the general course of the water [of
the subterranean river] by a succession
of sink holes.
1827 W 84 At the south-west side of
the hammock, the waters [of Shoal river]
again collect, and run off in a fine current.
1837 W 49 From the Silver Spring, a

navigable water of the Ocklawaha, to
this place, is seventeen miles.
Ibid., 127 A high ridge divides the
waters that descend easterly into the
Uche Creek, and Aliqua River, south
into the Chactawhatche Bay, west into
Pensacola Bay, and north into Shoal
River.
(b) 1821 F 101 The savages add,
that in going far south, they go round
a large water [Lake Okeechobee] emptying itself into the Gulf of Mexico.
1837 W 56 Spring Garden Lake, is a
shallow water, extending from near the
spring, nearly a mile south.
(c) 1775 R Apx. lxii The violence of
the easterly gales beats the gulph water
over the reef, so as to destroy the effects of the flood tides.
1831 USCSD vol. 214 #136.16 The
survey was . . . commenced . . . at a point
where the bluff land makes down to the
edge of the open water.
1837 W 57 Seven miles of bold and
open water brings us to Little Lake.
1812 FHQ IX. 67 We camped about
8 miles beyond the Saw Mill on a bottom where we found good running water.
1744 KIMBER 10 Eight Feet the most
shoal Water, on the Bar, at half Flood.
1839 *Winter in the West Indies* 129
The great extent of shoal water . . .
make the atmosphere moist.
1837 W 67 The Moccassin . . . inhabits
still waters.
1791 B 89 In great storms of wind and
rain, when the river is suddenly raised,
large masses of these floating plains are
broken loose, and driven from the
shores, into the wide water, where they
have the appearance of islets.
    Attrib. with *passage.*
1776 FHQ IX. 28 I was . . . employ-
ing the Sloop Rebeca Captain Mowbray
for three months certain to secure the
inland water passage to Saint John River
from Georgia.
    See also BACK WATER; BACK-WATER
SWAMP; DEAD WATER; EDDY WATER;

FRESH WATER; FRESH-WATER BASIN; FRESH-WATER BROOK; FRESH-WATER CREEK; FRESH-WATER KEY; FRESH-WATER LAKE; FRESH-WATER MARSH; GULF WATER (attrib.); HEADWATER(S); LAKE WATER (attrib.); MARSH WATER (attrib.); POND WATER (attrib.); RIVER WATER (attrib.); SALT WATER; SALT-WATER MARSH; SALT-WATER RIVER; SEA-WATER; SWEET-WATER COUNTRY; TIDEWATER; TIDEWATER CHANNEL; TRIBUTARY WATER (attrib.); WATERCOURSE; WATERING-PLACE; WATER RUN; WATER-STREAM.

WATERCOURSE. A stream of water, a river or brook. OED. Note that the 1827 and second 1837 examples refer to underground streams.

1775 R 31   The bay galls are properly water courses.

1792 POPE 73   The Soil, from *Pensacola* to *Augusta*, except upon the Water Courses where it is very fertile wears the gloomy Face of uniform Sterility.

1823 V 37   The marshes here are wide, but the water course very narrow.

1827 W 146-47   This general character is demonstrated ... by the infinite number and variety of subterranean watercourses that penetrate and pervade the bowels of the earth.

1837 W 146, 150   Indeed, the whole of our extensive sea coast is lined by inland water courses ... These [avenues] were bounded by water courses at the time we visited the cave in 1825.

WATERING-PLACE. A place where a supply of water can be obtained. OED 1621.

c. 1565 Hawkins voyage, in HAKLUYT (1589) 539   Our captaine sending [to Laudonnière] to understand of a watering place.

1742 RCBH 79   [They] halted at the second Watering Place.

1775 R Apx. xxxiv   Next is *Old Matacombe*, remarkable for being the most handy and best watering place on all this coast.

1796 G 18   The principal watering place is at the North end of Old Matacumbe.

1822 ASPNA IV. 963   The watering place is two miles from the anchorage ground, situated on the south side of the island.

WATER-OAK SWAMP. A swamp in which the predominating growth is water oak.

1773 MS. 282   In cyp. & water Oak Swamp.

WATER RUN. A small stream; a run.

1812 FHQ IX. 68   At 9 arrived at a reedy branch in a deep hollowlike channel where the water runs is so boggy that we were obliged to unpack everything in order that the horses may cross unencumbered.

WATER-STREAM. A stream or current of water; a river or brook. Now *rare*. OED (last date: 1862).

1823 ASPPL III. 784   Nine hundred and twenty acres of land, lying at the Matanzas, on the head of the last water stream, ten miles south of the fort at Matanzas.

1830 ASPPL VI. 76   One-half of the quantity of acres of land ... upon the head of the East Water stream, ten miles south of he [sic] Fort Matanzas.

WATERSHED. The whole gathering ground of a river system. OED. 1874. Spec., a drain. Since there are no British examples listed, the probability is that the usage is American, and constitutes an extension of meaning (from the interpretation of the term as a slope down which water flows from a water parting). DA 1874.

1871 H 49   This [sic] the main drain or water shed of the county.

WAVING COUNTRY. Undulating country. DAE under *waving* 1817.

1818 Y 25   The waving country, forming the first stage of descent from the hills, has none or very little of this limestone.

WELL. A spring of water rising to the surface of the earth and forming a small pool or flowing in a stream. "Now *arch.* or *dial.*" OED. Spec., a chasm (1823); a bowl (1869).

1773 MS. 307 On some of these Islands are Ponds, and Wells in Rocks, of exceeding good fresh Water.

1791 B 207 These rocks are perforated by perpendicular wells or tubes, four, five, and six feet in diameter, exactly circular as the tube of a cannon or walled well; many of these are broken into one another, forming a great ragged orifice, appearing fluted by alternate jambs and semicircular perpendicular niches or excavations.

1796 G 18 Five natural wells are found in the rock about 4 feet deep, and constantly full of excellent water.

1803 E 246 Old Matacombe ... is noted for affording a greater quantity of good water than any other of the Keys ... The water is found in natural wells about four feet deep, which are no more than cracks or cavities in the rock, and not the effect of art as some have imagined.

1823 V 120 On its east end are fine wells in the solid rock, said to have been cut by the Indians, but which appear to be natural chasms.

1851 BYRNE 26 That bad water may be found in the rotten limestone wells ... of the peninsula, will not be denied.

1869 BRINTON 104 The *Punch bowl* is the name given by the sailors to a curious natural well about one mile south of the mouth of the Miami and close to the shore. It is always filled with good sweet water.

1873 FHQ XIV. 258 [Green Cove] spring ... is ... a natural well of twenty feet in diameter.

See also FRESH-WATER WELL (attrib.).

WET GLADE. A glade which is wet as opposed to one which is dry; an

everglade. Used synonymously here with *savanna* and (grassy) *pond*. Note that this author apparently refers only to the West Florida terrain. According to the OED citation of Bartlett (1859) under *glade*, glades are "so called in Maryland, where they are divided into wet and dry glades." Poss. Southern.

1818 Y 27-28 On the route to Sahwanne from St. Marks ... these dreary flats [are] only diversified by the intervention of wet glades.

Ibid., 144, 147 The path crosses Savannas or wet glades ... The country becomes still lower and the wet glades more frequent. In the seventh and eighth miles these ponds [west of Athena] assume the appearance of large prairies.

1823 FHQ XIV. 94 In this part of the route there is not more than twelve miles of the low wet glades.

See also EVERGLADE(S); GLADE; PINE GLADE.

WET LAND. Land which remains too wet or is covered by water part of the year. DAE 1804.

1743 C II. iv On this wet Land grows a variety of Evergreen Trees and Shrubs.

WET PRAIRIE. A prairie on which water stands at least part of the year. DAE 1819. (A.) DA 1817.

1869 FICSP 115 [Ocklawaha swamp consists] of a commingling of swamp and wet prairie, interspersed with the richest quality of hammock.

WET SAVANNA. Saturated savanna land as opposed to savanna woodland.

1791 B 222 We next crossed a wet savanna.

1836 ASPMA VII. 147 Our dependence for water was on the wet savannahs ... all of them grown up with vegetation and teeming with insects.

1837 W 126 The peninsula between Pensacola Bay and St. Rosa Sound, is a mixture of pine and black jack ridges ... with strips of wet savanna.

1837 ASPMA VII. 161 The island being surrounded by very broad and wet savannahs, and so boggy that it was with difficulty the men could struggle through it.

WET SWAMP. A swamp, perhaps one that is wetter than most. DAE 1654 under *wet*. (A.)

1743 C II. 52 This Shrub ... grows in wet Swamps.

1837 W 222 The south bank was a wet swamp, for two hundred yards.

WHARF. "A rocky or gravelly concretion ... where the tides throw up dangerous ripples and overfalls." OED, citing SMYTH, *Sailor's Wordbook*, 1867. Note the British plural form, which Pickering observed in Massachusetts no later than 1735, but which is here preserved by a Loyalist residing in East Florida. Spec., a rocky reef.

1773 MS. 335 The rocky Reefs ... remain awfull and dangerous Wharfs in that Sea.

WILD. An unsettled, uncultivated, or uncivilized region. Often pl. "Now mostly *rhet.* or *poet.*" DAE 1785. (A weald. EDD.)

1825 FHQ III. 38 Tallahassee, Sept. 10 (1825). It was in the month of April, 1824, that the first wagon was seen wending its devious way through that part of the wilds of Florida which now constitutes the Middle Judicial District.

WILD COUNTRY. An uncultivated, uninhabited or sparsely settled region. DAE 1775 under *wild*.

1827 W 21 The Alaqua ... runs through one of the pleasantest wild countries in Florida.

WILDERNESS. An area of uncleared, uncultivated, unsettled, or sparsely settled land. DAE 1638. With reference to the Okefenokee swamp (1822).

1609 VRV 177 Through the wildernesse great Riuers doe passe.

1775 R 278 Thus we have a melancholy instance ... of the depredations of time, and a country onċe nobly and extensively settled, through the inroads of the savages reduced again to a wilderness.

1791 B 158 I find myself alone in the wilderness of Florida, on the shores of Lake George.

1822 SIMMONS 56 [There is a tradition] that a beautiful race of Indians ... resided amidst the recesses of the great Oakefanokee wilderness.

1827 W 109 The grant to general Lafayette, containing 23,000 acres of the best land, adjoining the town, remains a wilderness.

1836 SSW 170 This dead wilderness had something frightful about it.

Attrib. with *country*.

1826 FHQ XIV. 188 Yet notwithstanding these difficulties, a road of more than four hundred miles has been constructed in a wilderness country.

See also OAK WILDERNESS.

WILD LAND. Land either uncultivated or uncultivable; unsettled or unoccupied land; forest. DAE 1813. (A.)

1870 BILL 212 The State owns a large portion of the wild lands.

WILD-ORANGE GROVE. A grove of wild-orange trees.

1874 SAR 148 There is no place in the State where the wild orange groves are so extensive as on this lake. Groves of two or three hundred acres in extent are often found in solid bodies, and many of them are being rapidly converted into sweet trees.

Attrib. with *land*.

1874 SAR 146 Wild-orange grove lands ... abound on all of our lakes and rivers.

WINDING(S). The meanderings, twists and turns, of a stream. OED.

1791 B 226 Even subterraneous rivers ... wander in darkness beneath the surface of the earth, by innumerable doublings, windings, and secret labyrinths.

1823 V 36-37 The head of navigation, including all the windings of the stream [*sc.*, St. Sebastian], is scarcely ten miles from its mouth.

WOOD. A forest or portion of forest; land overgrown by trees, shrubs, etc. Usually pl. DAE 1608. Spec., a swamp (1824).

1563 RIBAULD 12-13 We did beholde to and fro the goodly order of the Woods wherewith God hath decked euery way the sayde lande.

c. 1565 Hawkins voyage, in HAKLUYT (1589) 541 The land ... floresheth with ... woods of Cedar and Cypres.

1587 L 63 They knewe none other meane to saue their liues, but by fleeing into the Wooddes adioyning.

1609 VRV 17 The countrie is cumbersome with woods and bogs.

1652 HEYLIN 115 The Woods ... full of the largest Okes.

1742 RCBH Apx. 16 The Enemy *Indians* from a Wood near the Fort fired upon, and killed a Servant.

1765 B 3 I and my son walked in the woods.

1775 R 4 The fatal hurricane ... destroyed the woods for about 30 miles from the sea coast.

1812 FHQ IX. 69 The woods however were a tiresome sameness.

1824 ASPPL IV. 398 The four remaining parts in the wood or swamp in the southeast part of Lake George.

1869 FICSP 47 A correspondent of the New York World, writing from the Indian River says: "The primeval woods

on the banks are vast gardens of the sour wild Orange."

1873 BRYANT in FHQ XIV. 259 At times you come upon groups of the palmettos, towering to a height which they do not attain further north, and giving a tropical aspect to the woods.

See also FLATWOOD(S); OPEN WOOD(S); PINE WOOD; THICKET-WOOD(S).

WOODLAND. Land covered with trees; a wooded region. DAE 1638.

1775 R Apx. lxxii The wood-land ... is of a middling stout growth.

1786 in SIEBERT II. 7 General Robert Cunningham [says that he] ... went to settle ... on *a plantation* on St: Mary's river of fifty acres of woodland.

1823 ASPPL IV. 323 Your memorialist claims ... eight hundred acres ... bounded ... on the east by the border of wood lands and the river Matanzas.

1873 BRYANT in FHQ XIV. 258 In another [spot], named Magnolia, is an excellent hotel, with a row of cottages for guests, and all around them the solitary woodland.

WRECKING GROUND. The region of the Florida Reef, where countless ships were wrecked because of the treacherous currents and dangerous rocks and shoals.

1823 V 125-26 Since the termination of the late war, the town of Nassau has been almost supported by the wreckers, who are so sensible of the advantages derived from their employment, that they have openly declared they will never leave the reef, until driven off by armed force, and seem to consider themselves possessed of a right in the *wrecking ground* as their own individual property, independent of any change of government.

1826 FHQ XXII. 183 Employment for the wreckers diminishes daily, and some of them have left the wrecking ground.

BIBLIOGRAPHY

Adair, James, *The History of the American Indians*. London, 1775.

Adams, J. S., *Florida: Its Climate, Soil, and Productions*. Jacksonville: Edwd. M. Cheney, 1869. (Issued by the Florida Lands and Immigration Commissioner.)

Allen, Sarah, *A Narrative of the Shipwreck . . . of Mrs. Sarah Allen . . . on her passage . . . from New York to New Orleans*. Boston: Printed for M. Brewster, 1816.

The American Gazetteer. London, 1762. [Entries under *Florida* and *Georgia*.]

American Speech. Vols. X (February, 1935) and XXIV (December, 1949). New York: Columbia University Press.

Archdale, John, *A New Description of That Fertile and Pleasant Province of Carolina*. London, 1707. (In Carroll, Vol. II.)

(Ash, Thomas), *Carolina; or a Description of the Present State of That Country, etc.* London: T. A. Gent, 1682. (In Carroll, Vol. II.)

Audubon, John James, "Three Floridian Episodes." *Tequesta*, No. 5 (January, 1946), pp. 52-68.

An Authentic Narrative of the Seminole War. Providence, 1836. (Imperfections supplied in photostat.)

Barr, Capt. James, *A Correct and Authentic Narrative of the Indian War in Florida*. New York: J. Narine, 1836.

Bartram, John, *Journal* (1765-1766), in Stork.

Bartram, William, *Travels through North and South Carolina, Georgia, East and West Florida*. Philadelphia, 1791.

(Bigges, Walter), *A Summarie and True Discorse of Sir Frances Drakes West Indian Voage*. London: Richard Field, 1589. (Photostated at the Massachusetts Historical Society.)

Bill, Ledyard, *A Winter in Florida*. New York: Wood & Holbrook, 1870.

A Brief Description of the Province of Carolina on the Coasts of Floreda. London, 1666.

Brinton, Daniel Garrison, *A Guide-Book of Florida and the South*. Philadelphia: George MacLean, 1869.

———————, *Notes on the Floridian Peninsula*. Philadelphia: Joseph Sabin, 1859.

Bryant, William Cullen, *Letters of a Traveller*. New York: George P. Putnam, 1850.

Byrne, Bernard M., *Letters on the Climate, Soils, and Productions of Florida*. Jacksonville, 1851.

Cadogan, George, *The Spanish Hireling Detected*. London, 1743.

Carroll, B. R., *Historical Collections of South Carolina*, Vol. II. New York: Harper & Brothers, 1836.

Catesby, Mark, *The Natural History of Carolina, Florida, and the Bahama Islands*. London, 1731 (Vol. I), and 1743 (Vol. II).

The Century Dictionary: An Encyclopedic Lexicon of the English Language. New York: The Century Co., 1889-91. Suppl. 1909.

Cohen, Myer M., *Notices of Florida and the Campaigns*. Charleston: Burges & Honour, 1836.

Craigie, Sir William A., and Hulbert, James R., editors, *A Dictionary of American English on Historical Principles*. Chicago: University of Chicago Press, 1938-1944.

Criswell, E. H., *Lewis and Clark: Linguistic Pioneers*, University of Missouri Studies, XV, No. 2 (Columbia, Mo., April, 1940).

Darby, William, *Memoir on the geography, and Natural and Civil History of Florida, . . .* Philadelphia: T. H. Palmer, 1821.

De Brahm, John Gerard William, "History of the Three Provinces, South Carolina,

Georgia, and East Florida." Unpublished manuscript in the Harvard University Library, Vol. 1, pp. 171-342 (microfilmed). 1773.

Eagan, Dennis, *Sixth Annual Report of the Commissioner of Lands and Immigration of the State of Florida for the Year Ending Dec. 31, 1874.* Tallahassee: Charles H. Walton, 1874.

Ellicott, Andrew, *The Journal of Andrew Ellicott.* Philadelphia: Budd & Bartram, 1803.

Emerson, Ralph Waldo, "Little Journal at St. Augustine," 1827, in *The Florida Historical Quarterly,* XVII (October, 1939).

The Encyclopaedia Britannica. Chicago: Encyclopaedia Brittanica, Inc., 1946.

Fairbanks, George R., *The History and Antiquities of the City of St. Augustine, Florida.* New York: Charles B. Norton, 1858.

Federal Writers' Project of the Work Projects Administration for the State of Florida, *Florida: A Guide to the Southernmost State.* New York: Oxford University Press, 1939.

The Florida Historical Quarterly, Published by the Florida Historical Society, St. Augustine, Fla. Vols. I, II, III, IV, VII, VIII, IX, XI, XII, XIII, XIV, XV, XVII, XVIII, XIX, XX, XXI, XXII, XXIII.

The Florida Pirate, or An Account of a Cruise in the Schooner Esperanza. New York: W. Borradaile, 1823.

Florida Road Department Research and Records Division, Prepared by the Florida State Road Department in Cooperation with the Federal Works Agency Public Roads Administration, *Map of Alachua County.* 1936; revised, January, 1948.

Forbes, James Grant, *Sketches, Historical and Topographical, of the Floridas; More Particularly of East Florida.* New York: C. S. Van Winkle, 1821.

A Full Reply to Lt. Cadogan's Spanish Hireling. London, 1743.

Gauld, George, *Observations on the Florida Kays, Reef and Gulf.* London, 1796. (Includes Capt. Barton's "General Directions for Sailing from Cape Canaveral to Kay Biscaino . . . into the Gulf of Mexico," which was communicated to Gauld on October 24, 1774, and appears on pp. 27-28.)

A Geographical and Historical Description of the Principal Objects of the Present War in the West-Indies . . . and San Augustin. London, 1741.

Gibson, Martha Jane, " 'Swamp' in Early American Usage," *American Speech,* X (February, 1935), 30-35.

Guthrie, William, *A New System of Modern Geography.* London, 1795.

Hakluyt, Richard, *Diuers voyages touching the discouerie of America.* London, 1582.

————————, *The Principall Navigations.* London, 1589.

————————, *The Principal Navigations.* Vol. III. London: George Bishop, *et al.,* 1600.

————————, *Virginia Richly Valued, by the Description of the Maine Land of Florida, her next Neighbour.* London, Printed by Felix Kyngston for Matthew Lownes, 1609.

Hawkins, Sir John, *A true declaration of the troublesome voyadge of M. John Haukins to the . . . west Indies. . . .* London: Thomas Purfoo, 1569. (Photostatic reproduction by the Massachusetts Historical Society.)

Hawks, J. M., ed., *The Florida Gazetteer.* New Orleans: Bronze Pen Steam Office, 1871.

Hewatt, Alexander, *An Historical Account of the Rise and Progress of the Colonies of South Carolina and Georgia.* Vol. II. London, 1779.

Heylin, Peter, *Cosmographie. . . .* (Book 4, Part 2.) *Containing the Chorography & History of America.* London, 1652.

Heylin, Peter, *Microcosmos*. Oxford: Iohn Lichfield, & Iames Short, 1621.

Hilton, William, *A Relation of a Discovery lately made on the Coast of Florida*. London, 1664.

Hondy, Ivdocvs, *Historia Mundi: or Mercator's Atlas ... Englished by W. S.* London: T. Cotes, etc., 1635.

Hutchins, Thomas, *An Historical Narrative and Topographical Description of Louisiana, and West-Florida*. Philadelphia, 1784.

An Impartial Account of the Late Expedition against St. Augustine. London, 1742.

Incidents of a Journey from Abbeville, S.C., to Ocala, Fla. Edgefield, S.C.: Printed at the Advertiser Office, 1852.

Jefferys, Thomas, *A Description of the Spanish Islands....* London, 1762.

Keasbey, Anthony Quinton, *From the Hudson to the St. Johns*. Newark: *Newark Daily Advertiser*, 1874.

Kimber, Edward, *A Relation, or Journal of a Late Expedition to the Gates of St. Augustine....* London, 1744. (Photostatic reproduction of the original in the John Carter Brown Library.)

Kurath, Hans, *A Word Geography of the Eastern United States*. Ann Arbor: University of Michigan Press, 1949.

Lanman, Charles, *Adventures in the Wilds of the United States*. Vol. II. Philadelphia: John W. Moore, 1856.

Laudonnière, René, *A Notable Historie containing foure voyages made by certayne French Captaynes Vnto Florida ... Newly translated ... by R. H.* London, 1587.

Le Blanc, Vincent, *The World Surveyed: Or, the Famous Voyages & Travailes of Vincent Le Blanc*. (Tr. from the French by F[rancis] B[rooke].) London, 1660.

Lederer, John, *The Discoveries of John Lederer*. ("Tr. out of Latine ... By Sir William Talbot.") London, 1672.

Mathews, M. M., ed., *A Dictionary of Americanisms on Historical Principles*. 2 vols. Chicago: University of Chicago Press, 1951.

McJimsey, George Davis, *Topographic Terms in Virginia*, in *American Speech*. Reprints and Monographs No. 3. New York: Columbia University Press, 1940.

McKnight, G. H., *English Words and Their Background*. New York: D. Appleton Co., 1923.

McMillan, James B., "Observations on American Place-name Grammar," in *American Speech*, XXIV (December, 1949), pp. 241-248.

Melish, John, *A Military and Topographical Atlas of the United States; Including the British Possessions & Florida*. Philadelphia: G. Palmer, 1813.

Mencken, H. L., *The American Language*, fourth edition, revised. New York: Alfred A. Knopf, 1937.

——————, *Supplement II*. New York: Knopf, 1948.

Moore, W. G., *A Dictionary of Geography*. Harmondsworth, Middlesex: Penguin Books, 1949.

Morse, Jedidiah, *The American Gazetteer*. Boston: S. Hall and Thomas & Andrews, 1797.

——————, *The American Geography*. Elizabeth Town: Printed by Shepard Kollock, 1789.

——————, *The American Universal Geography*. Vol. 2. Boston: Isaiah Thomas and Ebenezer T. Andrews, 1793.

——————, *Geography Made Easy*. New-Haven: Printed by Meigs, Bowen & Dana, 1784.

The Narrative of a Voyage to the Spanish Main. London, 1819.

Niles Weekly Register, 1813 (Vol. III); 1815 (Vol. VIII, Suppl.).

226 ENGLISH TOPOGRAPHIC TERMS

The North-American and the West-Indian Gazetteer. London, 1776.

Oldmixon, John, *The British Empire in America.* Vol. I. London, 1708.

——————, *The History of Carolina.* London, 1708. (In Carroll, Vol. II.)

Osborne, Thomas, *A Collection of Voyages and Travels.* . . . London: Printed by Thomas Osborne, 1745.

Oxford English Dictionary, ed. by James A. H. Murray and others. Oxford: Clarendon Press, 1933.

Pope, John, *A Tour through the Southern and Western Territories of the United States . . . and the Floridas.* Richmond: Printed by John Dixon, 1792. Reprinted for Charles L. Woodward, New York, 1888.

The Present State of Carolina, by R. F. London, 1682. (Photostat ed. by Massachusetts Historical Society.)

The Present State of the West-Indies, . . . London, 1778.

Purchas, Samuel, *Purchas his Pilgrimage.* London: Printed by Wm. Stansby, 1613.

——————, *Purchas his Pilgrimes.* Vol. III. London: Printed by Wm. Stansby, 1625.

Read, William Alexander, *Florida Place-Names of Indian Origin.* Baton Rouge, La.: Louisiana State University Press, 1934.

The Report of the Committee of both Houses . . . in the late expedition against St. Augustine. South-Carolina, Charles-Town: Printed by Peter Timothy, 1742.

Ribaut, Jean, *The VVhole and true discouerye of Terra Florida . . . Written in French by Captaine Ribauld . . .* "And nowe newly set forthe in Englishe the xxx. of May. 1563." London: Rouland Hall, for Thomas Hacket. (Photostated from the original by Massachusetts Historical Society.)

Roberts, William, *An Account of the First Discovery and Natural History of Florida.* London, 1763.

Romans, Capt. Bernard, *A Concise Natural History of East and West Florida.* New York, 1775.

Rude, Gilbert Thomas, "St. Augustine and Its Oceanic Spring," *Bulletin of the Geographical Society of Philadephia,* XXIII (July, 1925), 85-91.

The East Florida Herald, published in St. Augustine, Florida. (April 23 and June 21, 1823, issues.)

A Scrapbook of Newspaper Clippings Relating to Florida, 1851-1894. (Bound as a notebook by the New York Public Library.)

Siebert, Wilbur Henry, *Loyalists in East Florida, 1774 to 1785.* DeLand: The Florida State Historical Society, 1929. (Vol. II contains *Records of Their Claims for Losses of Property in the Province.*)

Simmons, William Hayne, *Notices of East Florida.* A. E. Miller, 1822. (See also John Lee Williams, *Journals* in *FHQ*).

A Sketch of the Seminole War and Sketches during a Campaign. By a Lieutenant. . . . Charleston: Dan. J. Dowling, 1836.

Smith, Buckingham, *Espiritu Santo Bay,* in *Memoir of Hernando de Escalante Fontaneda.* (Not a tr.) 1854.

——————, *Letter from Hernando de Soto.* 1539. Tr. by B. Smith. Washington: 1854.

——————, *Memoir of Hernando de Escalante Fontaneda, Respecting Florida.* 1575. Tr. by B. Smith. Washington: 1854.

——————, *Notes by the translator,* in *Memoir of Hernando de Escalante Fontaneda,* 1854.

Sprague, John T., *The Origin, Progress, and Conclusion of the Florida War.* New York: D. Appleton & Co., 1848.

Stork, William, *A Description of East Florida*. London, 1769. (Includes Bartram, John, *Journal* [1765-1766].)

Tailfer, Pat., *et al.*, *A True and Historical Narrative of the Colony of Georgia*. Charles-Town: Printed by P. Timothy, 1741.

Tanner, H. S., *New American Atlas* (5 parts, 1818-23, including the 1823 *Map of Florida*).

Tequesta, published by the Historical Association of Southern Florida and the University of Miami as a Bulletin of the University of Miami, Coral Gables, Fla. Numbers 1; 4; 5. (No. 5 contains Rear Admiral George Henry Preble's "A Canoe Expedition into the Everglades in 1842," pp. 30-51.)

U.S. Congress, *American State Papers, Class II, Indian Affairs*, Vols. I & II. (1789-1827.)

————————, *Class V, Military Affairs*, Vols. I, III, IV, V, VI, VII. (1789-1837.)

————————, *Class IX, Miscellaneous*, Vols. I & II. (1789-1823.)

————————, *Class VI, Naval Affairs*, Vols. I, III, IV. (1794-1836.)

————————, *Class VIII, Public Lands*, Vols. I, III, IV, V, VI, VIII. (1789-1837.)

————————, *House Documents*, Vol. 255 # 61 (1833.)

————————, *House Executive Documents*, Vols. 172 #166 (1827); 187 #147 (1829); 217 #43 (1828); 219 #185 (1832); 893 Pt. 1, pp. 550-553 (1856).

————————, *House Miscellaneous Documents*, Vols. 523 #79 (1845) and #77 (1846).

————————, *Senate Documents*, Vols. 214 #136 (1832); 531 #30 (1848).

————————, *Senate Executive Documents*, Vol. 756 #76 (1855).

U.S. Continental Congress, *Secret Journals*. Vol. I. Boston: Thomas B. Wait, 1821.

Viaud, Pierre, *The Shipwreck and Adventures of Monsieur Pierre Viaud*. Tr. from the French by Mrs. Elizabeth Griffith. London, 1771.

Vignoles, Charles Blacker, *Observations Upon the Floridas*. New York: Bliss and White, 1823. Separate *Map of Florida* to accompany this work "by Charles Vignoles . . . 1823. Engraved by H. S. Tanner. . . ."

Walker, Fowler, *The Case of Mr. John Gordon*. London, 1772. (All Apx. appears to be a translation except Exhibit 27.)

Webster's Dictionary of Synonyms, Springfield, Mass.: G. & C. Merriam Co., 1942.

Webster's Geographical Dictionary. Springfield, Mass.: G. & C. Merriam Co., 1949.

Webster's New International Dictionary of the English Language, second edition, unabridged, ed. William Allan Neilson and others. Springfield, Mass.: G. & C. Merriam Co., 1945.

Williams, John Lee, *The Territory of Florida*. New York: A. T. Goodrich, 1837.

————————, *A View of West Florida*. Philadelphia, 1827.

————————, and Simmons, W. H., *Journals* (1823), in "The Selection of Tallahassee as the Capital," *The Florida Historical Quarterly*. I, No. 1, pp. 26-44, and No. 2, pp. 18-29.

A Winter from Home, anon. New York: John F. Trow, 1852.

A Winter in the West Indies and Florida, by an invalid. New York: Wiley & Putnam, 1839.

Wright, Joseph, ed., *The English Dialect Dictionary*. London: Henry Frowde, 1898.

Wynne, John Huddlestone, *A General History of the British Empire in America*. Vol. II. London, 1770.

Young, Capt. Hugh, "A Topographical Memoir on East and West Florida with Itineraries of General Jackson's Army" (1818), *The Florida Historical Quarterly*, XIII, No. 1, pp. 20-50; No. 2, pp. 82-104; No. 3, pp. 129-164.